THE
PHYSIOLOGY OF SYNAPSES

By JOHN CAREW ECCLES

Professor of Physiology
The Australian National University
Canberra

With 101 Figures

1964

NEW YORK

ACADEMIC PRESS INC., PUBLISHERS

BERLIN · GÖTTINGEN · HEIDELBERG
SPRINGER-VERLAG

SPRINGER-VERLAG

BERLIN · GÖTTINGEN · HEIDELBERG

Published in U.S.A. and Canada by

ACADEMIC PRESS INC., PUBLISHERS

111 Fifth Avenue, New York 3, New York

Library of Congress Catalog Card Number 63–22376

Printed in Germany

For Irene Frances

PREFACE

I must thank my friend, Professor HANS WEBER, for being, as it were, the prime mover in causing this book to be written. He persuaded me in 1960 to contribute a review to the Ergebnisse der Physiologie. As originally planned, it was to be relatively short. However, the interest and scope of the whole subject of synapses stimulated me to write a much more comprehensive and extensive account. I was not even then satisfied, particularly as so many new and attractive investigations and ideas were being evolved during and after the writing of this review; and during the writing of this book most interesting developments are occurring in so many centres of research. Through the kind cooperation of my friends I have been given the opportunity to quote and even to illustrate from these new and fascinating developments before their final publication.

There would be some justification if the author were to make the claim that this book is the fruit of a life-time of enquiry into the physiology of synapses. In 1927 the subject of Excitatory and Inhibitory Synapses was chosen for investigation in the course leading to the Oxford D. Phil. But there have been such remarkable developments during the last 12 years that in this book very little reference will be made to work earlier than 1951 except in the historical introductions. Yet the influence of three great scientists has been with me as I have striven to give a coherent account of synapses, which we may regard as the key structures of the nervous system. There is firstly RAMON Y CAJAL whose achievement was to show that the nervous system was made up of independent structures, the neurones, cells of the utmost diversity, yet amazingly organized in their relationship to each other. Secondly is SHERRINGTON who linked this structural separateness with neuronal integration by the concept of the synapse and who defined the essential properties of the synapse with great insight. Thirdly is DALE who was the leader in developing the theory of chemical transmission across synapses, which has been so fruitful in all recent developments, structural, physiological, pharmacological and neurochemical.

The enormous advances in knowledge and understanding have been brought about largely as a result of the microtechniques: electron-microscopy; electrical investigations by microelectrodes, particularly by intracellular electrodes; and microinjection procedures both intracellular and extracellular. Relatively few types of synaptic actions have yet been subjected to intensive investigation by these new procedures; nevertheless we can have confidence that general principles of synaptic action are being established because there has been a remarkable uniformity of the essential features of synaptic actions for a wide variety of synapses in invertebrates as well as vertebrates.

It is noteworthy that the same general principles of synaptic action have been expressed in a book "Synaptic Transmission" by Dr. H. McLENNAN (1963) that was published after the manuscript of this book had been sent to press. Though there is an essential similarity in the two accounts of synaptic transmission, Dr. McLENNAN's book is also in part complementary to the present book. This is especially so in his extensive and very well documented accounts of neuropharmacology and neurochemistry.

We may provisionally define a synapse as a structure that is formed by the close apposition of neurone either with neurone or with effector cell and that is specialized for the transmission of excitation or inhibition. Presumably this definition will have to be extended to include transmission from some receptor cells to afferent terminals, but it seems best to defer this development until there is more precise information on the nature of this transmission (cf. DAVIS 1961; GRAY 1959). It may be objected that the word, ephapse, has commonly been used for many electrically transmitting junctions that would come within this broad definition of the synapse, as has been done for example by GRUNDFEST (1959) in his valuable review. However ARVANITAKI (1942) first introduced "ephapse" for a quite different situation in which under certain conditions of spatial arrangement the electrical currents generated by an impulse in a giant axon excited another axon. The requisite spatial arrangement of the ephapse could be that naturally occurring or it could be artificial, but the distinction was made by ARVANITAKI that the synapse "designates surfaces of contact (whether axo-somatic, axo-dendritic or axo-muscular) anatomically differentiated and functionally specialized for the transmission." The further distinction was made that at the synapse transmission is irreciprocal, but this irreciprocity of transmission is now known to occur for junctional transmissions indubitably ephaptic, such as the electrical excitation of intramuscular nerve fibres by the muscle spike potential (LLOYD 1942; LEKSELL 1945; BROWN and MATTHEWS 1960), or even between two giant axons when specially treated. On the other hand reversibility of transmission is very well developed at junctional regions that because of the criteria of design and of function will be classed as synapses (Chapter IX)—for example the septa of some giant axons and the electrically transmitting bridges between nerve cells or between giant axons, and with the large synapses of avian ciliary ganglia.

It is assumed that the reader of this book already will be informed about the general physiological properties of nerve fibres, nerve cells and muscle fibres. In particular it is assumed that the reader has a knowledge of the electrical properties of excitable cells that is at a level equivalent to that given in the initial chapters of my previous books "The Neurophysiological Basis of Mind" and "The Physiology of Nerve Cells." Though the symbols used as abbreviations are defined at the time of their introduction, a list is given immediately after the Table of Contents.

The stories and ideas that are expressed in this book have derived in large part from the numerous discussions and symposia that have been such a feature of these recent years. It has been a singular advantage to meet and to know personally almost all of the scientists whose work forms the basis of this book. I am particularly indebted to my colleagues in Canberra. They have come from all parts of the world and have given me and each other conditions in the laboratory that have been both happy and fruitful. During the actual labour of writing this book I was helped particularly by my colleagues: D. R. CURTIS, J. S. COOMBS; J. I. HUBBARD; P. ANDERSEN; M. ITO; J. C. WATKINS; and ROSAMOND ECCLES who read chapters and made most valuable suggestions. I wish also to thank Mr. L. M. DAVIES for his expert technical assistance; V. PARAL, R. WESTON, A. CHAPMAN, Miss C. MACPHERSON and Miss S. WILLIAMSON for their expert assistance with all the illustrations; and Miss I. SHEAFFE and Miss R. MACDONALD for all their work in preparation of the manuscript.

Dr. R. F. SCHMIDT has given most valuable help in the indexing. My special thanks go to the publishers for their unfailing courtesy and for their extraordinary efficiency in producing this volume in such a short time. As a consequence, in a book published in 1963, there are nearly 100 references to papers published in this same year.

Canberra, 1963   JOHN CAREW ECCLES

ACKNOWLEDGEMENTS

Grateful thanks are due to following publishers and editors for their generosity in giving permission for reproduction of figures: International Review of Neurobiology; "Nature"; Journal of Physiology; Journal of Neurophysiology; Journal of General Physiology; Pergamon Press, Inc.; Rockefeller Institute Press; The Wistar Institute of Anatomy and Biology; Canadian Journal of Biochemistry and Physiology; British Medical Bulletin; Journal of Pharmacology and Experimental Therapeutics; Japanese Journal of Physiology; Cambridge University Press; Acta Physiologica Scandinavica.

CONTENTS

SYMBOLS AND ABBREVIATIONS

Physical and Chemical

mm	= millimetre	mM	= 10^{-3} M	
μ	= 10^{-3} mm	V	= volt	
Å	= Ångstrom = 10^{-7} mm	mV	= 10^{-3} volt	
min	= minute	μV	= 10^{-6} volt	
sec	= second	Ω	= ohm	
msec	= 10^{-3} second	MΩ	= 10^{6} ohm	
c/sec	= frequency	A or amp	= ampere	
g	= gram	mA	= 10^{-3} ampere	
mg	= 10^{-3} gram	μA	= 10^{-6} ampere	
μg	= 10^{-6} gram	mμA	= 10^{-9} ampere	
mμg	= 10^{-9} gram	mho	= reciprocal ohm	
M	= mole (one gram molecule) per litre	F	= farad	

Physiological

EPP	= endplate potential (intracellular)
min. EPP	= miniature endplate potential
EPC	= endplate current
EPSP	= excitatory postsynaptic potential (intracellular)
IPSP	= inhibitory postsynaptic potential (intracellular)
DRP	= dorsal root potential
PAD	= primary afferent depolarization (intracellular)
EHP	= extracellular hyperpolarizing potential
E_R	= resting membrane potential
E_{Cl}	= equilibrium potential for chloride ions
E_K	= equilibrium potential for potassium ions
E_{IPSP}	= equilibrium potential for IPSP
$(K^+)_i$	= intracellular concentration of K^+ ions
$(Cl^-)_i$	= intracellular concentration of Cl^- ions

Anatomical

IS	= initial segment at axonal origin from neurone
SD	= soma plus dendrites of neurone
Group Ia	= afferent fibres from annulospiral endings of muscle spindles
Group Ib	= afferent fibres from Golgi tendon organs of muscle

Group I   = Group I a + I b
Group II = afferent fibres from secondary endings of muscle spindles
Group III = small medullated afferent fibres from muscle
DSCT   = dorsal spinocerebellar tract
VSCT   = ventral spinocerebellar tract
L_7VR = ventral root of lumbar seven segment
S_1VR = ventral root of sacral one segment
PBST   = posterior biceps-semitendinosus
SMAB   = semimembranosus-anterior biceps

Pharmacological

ACh   = acetylcholine
AChE = acetylcholine esterase
dTC   = d-tubocurarine
DFP   = di-isopropyl fluorophosphate

TEPP = tetraethylpyrophosphate
GABA = γ-amino butyric acid
TMA   = tetramethyl ammonium

CHAPTER I

THE DEVELOPMENT OF IDEAS ON THE SYNAPSE

A. The conflict between the neurone theory and the reticular theory

When neurohistologists began to study the nervous system in detail, the complexity of the interlacing fibre structure led them to postulate that the nervous system was a complex net-like structure, which is the reticular theory of GERLACH (1871). The nerve cells were believed to be at the nodes of this reticular structure, and the nerve fibres originating from them branched profusely and anastomosed, so forming the fibre meshwork characteristic of grey matter (GOLGI 1885).

This interpretation was first challenged by HIS (1886, 1889) and FOREL (1887) who proposed instead that each nerve cell was an independent unit and that their branches did not anastomose, but merely entered into close contacts. His arrived at this conclusion from a study of the development of the nervous system from the individual neuroblasts, while FOREL was impressed by the selectivity of the atrophy of nerve cells after nerve fibres had been destroyed. Independently, RAMÓN Y CAJAL (1888, 1890a, 1890b, 1890c) had reached the same conclusions as a result of his investigations of embryonic material and of the intensive application of the Golgi technique, which stained specifically a very few nerve cells, that were thus revealed in their entirety and in isolation from all others. Other neurohistologists such as KÖLLIKER (1890), VAN GEHUCHTEN (1891) and v. LENHOSSÉK (1892, 1893) also strongly supported the theory of the independence of the nerve cells, which, following the suggestion of WALDEYER (1891), came to be known as the neurone theory, in contrast to the reticular theory.

Implicit in the neurone theory was the assumption that nerve cells must enter into functional connection with one another by contiguity, not continuity. As originally described by the neurohistologists this contiguity was achieved by the profusely branching nerve terminals which embraced nerve cells to form the baskets (corbeilles) and terminal brushes of RAMÓN Y CAJAL (1890a) and the "Fasernkörbe" that HELD (1891) first described in the trapezoid body. Fibres were also described interlacing with dendritic processes, such as for example the climbing fibres around the dendrites of the Purkinje cells (RAMÓN Y CAJAL 1890a) and in sympathetic ganglia (RAMÓN Y CAJAL 1909; DE CASTRO 1922, 1932). At first no differentiated terminals were distinguishable, probably because they were not developed in the very young animals that were investigated, and also because of the ineffectiveness of the Golgi technique in displaying the ultimate terminals. It remained for HELD (1897), AUERBACH (1898), RAMÓN Y CAJAL (1903), and WOLFF (1905) to demonstrate the characteristic "Endkörbe," "Endfüße," or "boutons" by which actual functional contact is achieved. It is convenient to use the term "synaptic knob" for the differentiated terminals of all kinds. Subsequently there was an intensive investigation of synaptic knobs with st udies of the details of morphology and distribution on a wide variety of neurones (cf. WINDLE and CLARK 1928; BARTELMEZ and HOERR 1933; BARR 1939; BODIAN 1937, 1940, 1942).

Nevertheless, despite the wealth of evidence against it (cf. RAMÓN Y CAJAL 1909), the reticular theory lingered on with the support of GOLGI (1890, 1891) and later of HELD (1905, 1909), who wrote in defence of it as recently as 1929. For example HELD (1905) believed that continuity between neurones was established by the fine neurofibrils that were described as passing from the synaptic knob to the underlying nerve cell. At that time neurofibrils were often believed to form the structural basis for transmission of impulses. Much detailed histological evidence was also adduced (cf. BIELSCHOWSKY 1928) that the synaptic knobs gave origin to a fine pericellular network of fibres, which established continuity with fine fibrils in the underlying nerve cell. This interpretation closely paralleled the periterminal reticulum which BOEKE (1911, 1932, 1940) described as subserving continuity across the neuromuscular junction. It is now recognized that these fine pericellular networks are non-nervous, and consequently they do not provide evidence for continuity between nerve cells (HINSEY 1934; NONIDEZ 1944).

In view of this continued support for the reticular theory, RAMÓN Y CAJAL (1934) was constrained to write his memorable last work in which he examined critically the whole controversy between the exponents of the neuronal and reticular theories. So effectively did he do this that the neuronal theory has not been seriously challenged since that time, though many of the old reticularists continued in their beliefs, or at least continued to claim that the neuronal theory was dead (cf. BOEKE 1940). The subsequent unassailable position of the neurone theory has been well described by BODIAN (1942, 1952) and NONIDEZ (1944). It has received strong support from degeneration experiments which showed that after section of a presynaptic pathway there was degeneration of the synaptic knobs, but not of the postsynaptic structure (HOFF 1932; FOERSTER, GAGEL and SHEEHAN 1933; SCHIMERT 1939), and that after axon section the retrograde degeneration did not involve the synaptic knobs in contact with the degenerated neurone (BARR 1940; SCHADEWALD 1941, 1942).

The resolving power of conventional light microscopy was inadequate to reveal the fine structure of the synapse at a level that was required to explain the physiological mechanism. As techniques improved, the synaptic knobs appeared to be more closely attached to the postsynaptic membrane (cf. WYCKOFF and YOUNG 1956); so much so that there was thought to be just one membrane shared by the pre- and post-synaptic structures (BODIAN 1952). Such an arrangement was not acceptable as an efficient device for chemical transmission.

However, as described in Chapter II, the higher magnification given by electron microscopy has revealed that the presynaptic and postsynaptic membranes are two separate membranes about 70 Å thick, and that they are separated by a cleft about 200 Å in width which may be termed the synaptic cleft. This cleft is in direct communication with the interstitial spaces between the neurones (PALADE and PALAY 1954; PALAY 1956; DE ROBERTIS 1956; DE ROBERTIS and FRANCHI 1956). Similar features are also displayed at the vertebrate neuromuscular junction (ROBERTSON 1956). An important consequence of this pioneer electron-microscopy was that the neurone theory was definitively established for the vertebrate central nervous system.

B. Early developments in the functional concept of the synapse

Meanwhile the physiological implications of the neurone theory were being realized, as has been so well described by LIDDELL (1960) in "The Discovery of Reflexes." SHERRINGTON in particular suggested that the characteristic features of the reflex arc may be satisfactorily explained by the special properties of the transverse membranes that separate two neurones in regions of close juxtaposition, and consequently in 1897 he introduced for this junctional region the term "synapse," which is derived from the Greek word σύνάπτω, to clasp. For example the one-way conduction in the reflex arc was attributed by SHERRINGTON (1900, p. 798) to the valve-like behaviour of the synapse and not to a one-way conduction within a nerve cell, from dendrite to axon, such as was postulated by RAMÓN Y CAJAL (1895, 1909) and VAN GEHUCHTEN (1892) in their concept of dynamical polarization. Another important property of the reflex arc was the delay additional to that attributable to conduction time in the nerve pathway (SHERRINGTON, 1906, p. 22). Values as brief as 2 msec were assumed for the delay in traversing one synapse (cf. SCHÄFER 1900, p. 609). However, it was not until 1922 that HOFFMANN described the monosynaptic reflex and was thus able to derive from experimental data (cf. JOLLY 1911) the first reliable estimate (about 1 msec) for transmission time across a single synapse. Subsequent investigations (LORENTE DE NÓ 1935, 1938a; ECCLES and PRITCHARD 1937; RENSHAW 1940; LLOYD 1943) have given values ranging from 0.5 to 1.3 msec for the delay in transmission of an impulse across a synapse.

SHERRINGTON (1906, p. 141—142) also pointed out that interaction would be likely between the many synapses situated on the surface of a single moto-neurone. Activated excitatory synapses would give mutual reinforcement, while inhibitory synapses would antagonize the excitatory. He also listed many other differences between conduction in nerve-trunks and in reflex arcs and suggested that these differences were attributable to the synapses across which reflex transmission must pass. For example, reflexes are cha-racterized by such features as fatigability, after-discharge, and greater sensi-tivity to oxygen lack and to anaesthetics.

Though having a structural basis, SHERRINGTON always used "synapse" in its functional sense, restricting it to those areas of close contact that were specialized for effective transmission from one neurone to another. Until the advent of electronmicroscopy there was much uncertainty about the specificity of the areas of close contact. For example it was widely held that any areas of sufficiently close contact between neurones would act effectively as synapses. There was also much speculation on the nature of the synaptic membrane, and neurohistologists as recently as 1952 referred to it as a single membrane, the "synaptolemma," which was composed by fusion of the juxtaposed membranes of the two neurones. In almost every respect SHER-RINGTON'S conceptual developments with regard to the synapse during the early decades of this century were on the direct path to the present position. So much so that the significant development of ideas can be very effectively illustrated from his writings on excitatory and inhibitory actions on reflexes. For example in 1908 he wrote:

> From the observations it seems clear that the reflex effect of concurrent stimulation of excitatory afferent nerve with inhibitory afferent nerve on the vastocrureus nerve-muscle preparation is an algebraic summation of the effects obtainable from the two nerves singly, as v. CYON has maintained for the heart... One inference allowable from this is that in the case before us the two afferent arcs employed act in opposite direction at one and the same point of application in the excitable apparatus... As to the common locus of operation, the point of collision of the antagonistic influences, it seems permissible to suppose either that it lies at a synapse ... or that it lies in the substance of the "central" portion of a neurone. The net change which results there when the two areas are stimu-lated concurrently is an algebraic sum of the *plus* and *minus* effects producible separately by stimulating singly the two antagonistic nerves.

Here we have a clear statement of the algebraic summation of central excitatory and inhibitory actions, but still vagueness about the location and nature of these antagonistic actions.

In 1925 SHERRINGTON wrote a theoretical paper on central excitation and inhibition from which we may extract the following key statements.

Following the view that with the nervous impulse a short-lived local change ... is propagated along the course of the nerve-fibre, it may be supposed that the arrival of that change at the central terminals of the afferent fibre is an essential element in the central excitation process... There the nervous impulse resulting directly from the external stimulus may be regarded as ending, for there through an intermediary process and mechanism it generates, not inevitably though commonly, a new impulse.

SHERRINGTON then goes on to state that in order to account for summation of repetitive stimulations we must postulate that:

at some central situation there be a structure which is something other than a nerve-fibre, and has, unlike nerve-fibre, no absolute refractory phase. In such a structure the production of an exciting agent, in response to a previous stimulus, would on receipt of a second stimulus before subsidence of it be augmented by further production, so that its amount would be increased. In this way the central exciting state might by repetition of successive stimuli to the afferent nerve-fibre rise from below liminal amount or concentration to above liminal value.

Here we have the first clear statement of the concept of the central excitatory state. And later the locus of the state was defined as post-synaptic:

Of the terminals themselves histological evidence (CAJAL and others) shows them as severally discrete. But those convergent upon the same perikaryon and dendrites, although themselves discrete, reach a surface or synaptic membrane which, since it is that of one and the same cell, is in so far a single entity and is at the same time an arrival place common to the several terminals.

There is no conflict between these statements and the contemporary views on excitatory synaptic action, though on account of technical advances more precise statements are now possible.

SHERRINGTON was fascinated by the problem of central synaptic inhibition right to the end of his scientific life. So much so that his Nobel Oration in 1932 was entitled "Inhibition as a Coordinative Factor." Therein he ventured still further in his attempt to explain inhibition.

It is still early to venture any definite view of the intimate nature of "central inhibition." ... the suggestion is made that it consists in the temporary stabilization of the surface-membrane which excitation would break down. As tested against a standard excitation the inhibitory stabilization is found to present various degrees of stability. The inhibitory stabilization of the membrane might be pictured as a heightening of the "resting" polarization, somewhat on the lines of an electrotonus. Unlike the excitation-depolarization it would not travel; and, in fact, the inhibitory state does not travel.

The recently developed technique of intracellular recording from neurones has shown that inhibition is indeed due to a "heightening of the resting polarization."

However, concurrently with these theoretical developments in which reflex inhibition was explained in accordance with the neurone theory of the structure of the nervous system, there was an alternative view that was based on the reticular theory. It was tentatively proposed first by LUCAS (1917) and later by FORBES (1922) and ADRIAN (1924) that central inhibition might be similar to Wedensky inhibition, and that it could be brought about by the interference of high frequency discharges in the fine anastomosing fibres of the reticulum. This suggestion had the merit of relating the blockage of excitatory pathways to factors that were known to operate in the peripheral nervous system, i.e. to refractory states, but it required many subsidiary postulates in order both to convert single afferent inhibitory volleys into high frequency discharges and to ensure that these discharges were effectively fed into the reflex excitatory pathways. Moreover, it was inseparably linked with the reticular theory, and interest in it declined as evidence accumulated against the reticular theory.

When it had been shown that a nerve impulse was followed by a prolonged state of hyperpolarization and an accompanying depression of excitability, it was proposed by GASSER (1937) that inhibition was due to depression of interneurones that were common to the central inhibitory and excitatory pathways. Prior activation of some of these interneurones by the inhibitory volley would be followed by the prolonged depression during which they could not be activated by the excitatory volley, and hence the excitatory volley would be less effective in evoking the discharge of motoneurones, i.e. there would be inhibition of its reflex response. This postulated mechanism failed, however, to account for the inhibition of monosynaptic reflexes, which have been employed in investigating many different types of inhibition (RENSHAW 1941, 1942, 1946b; LLOYD 1941, 1946a; LAPORTE and LLOYD 1952; BRADLEY, EASTON and ECCLES 1953). Nevertheless it still could be a contributory factor in the inhibition of polysynaptic reflexes.

Meanwhile evidence had been accumulating that synaptic excitatory action on a neurone caused primarily a depolarization, which if sufficiently intense evoked the discharge of an impulse. Initially this depolarizing potential was recorded after electrotonic transmission from motoneurones along their axons to the ventral root (BARRON and MATTHEWS 1936, 1938; ECCLES and PRITCHARD 1937; BREMER, BONNET and MOLDAVER 1942; BONNET and BREMER 1948; ECCLES 1946a; BERNHARD 1947), but later it was recorded as an extracellular field potential by a microelectrode in close proximity to the motoneurones (BROOKS and ECCLES 1947b; BROOKS, DOWNMAN and ECCLES 1950). It was generally agreed that this synaptically evoked potential of neurones in the central nervous system was analogous to the endplate potential of muscle and the synaptically evoked potential of ganglion cells. However some experimental evidence was interpreted as indicating that, both in ganglion cells and the central nervous system, synaptic excitation could directly evoke the discharge of impulses by a brief early action (called originally "detonator action" [ECCLES 1936] and more recently "transmitter potentiality" [LLOYD and McINTYRE 1955; HUNT 1955]) in addition to a secondary action via the more prolonged synaptic potential. More precise investigations with intracellular recording (Chapter IV) have shown that this additional postulate is no longer required, because the synaptically evoked depolarization, i.e. the excitatory postsynaptic potential, provides a sufficient explanation of the generation of impulses by synaptic excitatory action (BROCK, COOMBS and ECCLES 1952; FRANK and FUORTES 1956b, 1961; ECCLES 1957, 1958a; COOMBS, CURTIS and ECCLES 1957b). The spatial and temporal summations of the excitatory actions on a motoneurone can both be accounted for by summation of the individual depolarizations.

C. Transmission across the synapse, chemical or electrical ?

The experimental investigation of the mechanism by which synaptic excitatory action evokes the discharge of impulses is linked inseparably with the problem of the means by which a presynaptic nerve impulse evokes a postsynaptic depolarization. The first speculations on the nature of transmission across junctional regions had long preceded the period of controversy in the 1930's between the exponents of the chemical and electrical hypotheses. DuBois-REYMOND (1877) was the first to suggest that junctional transmission could be either chemical or electrical, more probably the former, while KÜHNE (1888) thought it more probable that the action current of the nerve impulse excited the muscle fibre at the motor endplate. The next significant development occurred in 1904 when ELLIOTT suggested that sympathetic nerve impulses acted by liberating adrenaline at the junctional regions on smooth muscles, and a little later DIXON (1906) proposed that parasympathetic nerve impulses acted by liberating a muscarine-like substance. At the close of that early era of speculation that fore-shadowed the development of the chemical transmitter hypothesis, DALE (1914) wrote:

The question of a possible physiological significance, in the resemblance between the action of choline esters and the effects of certain divisions of the involuntary nervous system, is one of great interest, but one for the discussion of which little evidence is available. Acetylcholine is, of all the substances examined, the one whose action is most suggestive in this direction. The fact that its action surpasses even that of adrenine, both in intensity and evanescence, when considered in conjunction with the fact that each of these two bases reproduces those effects of involuntary nerves which are absent from the action of the other, so that the two actions are in many directions at once complementary and antagonistic, gives plenty of scope for speculation.

Later DALE (1938) was to refer to this preliminary stage of the chemical transmitter hypothesis in the following dramatic manner:

Such was the position in 1914. Two substances were known, with actions very suggestively reproducing those of the two main divisions of the autonomic system; both, for different reasons, were very unstable in the body, and their actions were in consequence of a fleeting character; and one of them was already known to occur as a natural hormone. These properties would fit them very precisely to act as mediators of the effects of autonomic impulses to effector cells, if there were any acceptable evidence of their liberation at the nerve endings. The actors were named, and the parts allotted; a preliminary hint of the plot had, indeed, been given ten years earlier, and almost forgotten; but only direct and unequivocal evidence could ring up the curtain, and this was not to come till 1921.

The pioneer investigations of LOEWI (1921) and LOEWI and NAVRATIL (1926), as summarized by LOEWI (1933, 1945 a, b), showed that the vagus inhibited the heart by means of the chemical transmitter, acetylcholine. Later, stimulation of the orthosympathetic was shown to release an adrenaline-like substance and thus to cause acceleration of the heart (CANNON and BACQ 1931; CANNON and ROSENBLUETH 1933). A particularly fine series of experimental investigations (FELDBERG and GADDUM 1934; FELDBERG and VARTIAINEN 1934; DALE, FELDBERG and VOGT 1936; BROWN, DALE and FELDBERG 1936) led to the extension of the chemical transmitter hypothesis to sympathetic ganglia and neuromuscular junctions with acetylcholine as the transmitter (DALE 1935, 1937, 1938). However, the short latency and brevity of these postulated transmitter actions (measured at most by a few milliseconds) contrasted with the long latency (greater than 100 msec) and a duration of seconds for the transmitter actions at many post-ganglionic junctions, e.g. the vagus and nervi accelerantes on the heart (BROWN and ECCLES 1934). This discrepancy gave rise to the postulate that the presynaptic action current was responsible for the initial brief excitatory action at the neuromuscular junction and sympathetic ganglion and that the transmitter substance, acetylcholine, was responsible for the prolonged residual depolarization (ECCLES 1936, 1937, 1944). A similar postulate was made for transmission to smooth muscle, which also exhibited an initial fast and a later slow phase (MONNIER and BACQ 1935; ECCLES and MAGLADERY 1937).

In retrospect it can be seen that the conflict between these two hypotheses of synaptic transmissions in sympathetic ganglia and neuromuscular junctions served as a potent stimulus to investigation and also caused the rival hypotheses to be defined more precisely. For example the chemical transmitter hypothesis led to very thorough pharmacological investigations, as reviewed for example by BACQ (1935, 1937), BROWN (1937 b), DALE (1937, 1938), KOELLE and GILMAN (1949), HUNT and KUFFLER (1950), ROSENBLUETH (1950), RIKER (1953) and MINZ (1955), while the electrical hypothesis necessitated a more precise study of the presynaptic and postsynaptic electrical events (KUFFLER 1949, 1952) and of the electrical events occurring across synaptic models (ephapses) that were formed by the close apposition of nerve fibres (KATZ and SCHMITT 1939; ARVANITAKI 1942; MARRAZZI and LORENTE DE NÓ 1944; GRANIT and SKOGLUND 1945 a, b).

It was first proposed by ADRIAN (1924) that inhibitory synaptic action in the central nervous system might be caused by a chemical transmitter on analogy with the "vagus substance" that LOEWI had shown to be responsible for the vagal inhibition of the heart. Shortly afterwards SHERRINGTON (1925) developed the same idea in connection with central excitatory and inhibitory states:

It may further be objected to the scheme that it reduces the afferent neurone fibre... to somewhat the character of secretory nerves. This, however, would be but in accord with recent evidence in favour of a so-called humoral view of the nervous production of peripheral excitation and inhibition. It appears unlikely that in their essential nature all forms of inhibition can be anything but one and the same process.

DALE (1935) reiterated this last statement in suggesting the extension of the chemical transmitter hypothesis to the synapses of the central nervous system.

Nevertheless the electrical hypothesis of synaptic transmission in the central nervous system continued to have a large measure of support until it was rendered untenable by experimental investigations from 1951 onwards employing intracellular recording. The review of FELDBERG (1945) reveals that the attempts to establish the chemical transmitter hypothesis failed to be as convincing as those applied to peripheral junctions, partly because they were related to the postulate that acetylcholine was the central transmitter substance and partly because there were much greater technical difficulties. It was eventually realized that it was most improbable that acetylcholine would be the transmitter liberated by primary afferent impulses because the dorsal root fibres were singularly deficient both in acetylcholine and cholineacetylase (MACINTOSH 1941; FELDBERG and VOGT 1948) (cf. Chapter V).

Stages in the relatively long period of conflict between the electrical and chemical hypotheses of central synaptic action are well illustrated by the symposia which were held in 1939, 1949 and 1951. In 1939 ERLANGER, GASSER and LORENTE DE Nó strongly advocated the electrical hypothesis, while BRONK and FORBES were relatively non-committal. In the Paris Symposium of 1949 there was fairly general agreement that both neuro-muscular and ganglionic transmission were mediated by acetylcholine, particularly as KUFFLER (1949) reported most convincing experiments against the electrical hypothesis. However, there was still fairly general agreement that central synaptic transmission was likely to be electrical. The detailed hypotheses of excitatory and inhibitory synaptic action (ECCLES 1946b; BROOKS and ECCLES 1947a) were restated with slight modifications and shown to be successful in accounting for the various experimental findings (ECCLES 1949). ARVANITAKI and CHALANOZITIS (1949) showed how the electrical events in ephaptic transmission could account for synaptic transmission. BONNET and BREMER (1948) thought that there was insufficient evidence to decide between the two hypotheses. In the Brussels conference (1951) FESSARD gave a brilliant discussion of the application of the rival hypotheses to central synaptic action and gave strong support to the electrical hypothesis, which he regarded as the principal mechanism, with chemical transmission as a subsidiary. On the other hand FELDBERG (1951) was content with a discussion of the role of acetylcholine as a central transmitter as revealed by pharmacological experiments. Only general conclusions could be drawn, because no central cholinergic synapses had yet been identified. BREMER (1951) argued convincingly that acetylcholine was not a mediator for the action of dorsal root volleys in the frog's spinal cord. At about this same time FESSARD and POSTERNAK (1950) published an excellent critical evaluation of the various hypotheses relating to the mode of operation of synapses. This can be regarded as a definitive statement of the position obtaining before the investigation of synaptic action was revolutionized by intracellular recording (Chapters IV, X).

However, just when it appeared that electrical synaptic transmission was finally to be eliminated, a new development in the synaptic drama reinstated it firstly for a special type of synapse in crustacea (FURSHPAN and POTTER 1957, 1959a); and now electrical synaptic transmission has reappeared in many guises and for inhibitory as well as excitatory synapses, as will be described in Chapters IX and XV.

CHAPTER II

STRUCTURAL FEATURES OF CHEMICALLY TRANSMITTING SYNAPSES

Examination by light-microscopy discloses very great diversity in the various types of chemically transmitting synaptic contacts, e.g. the neuromuscular junctions of vertebrates, the various types of synapses in different regions of the central nervous system of vertebrates, the synapses in sympathetic ganglia, the giant synapses in the squid stellate ganglion, the synapses in neuropiles of invertebrates, the synapses of electric organs. The higher order of magnification given by electron-microscopy reveals that in these diverse types of synapse there is a remarkable uniformity in the structures which are believed to be essentially concerned in their functional operation. The review by COUTEAUX (1961) gives a particularly valuable correlation between structural features and physiological events. It will be convenient firstly to illustrate these features by an account of the vertebrate neuromuscular junction, which has been more thoroughly investigated than any other synapse.

A. The vertebrate neuromuscular junction

Fig. 1 A shows diagrammatically the ultimate achievement of light microscopy (COUTEAUX 1958). The motor axon loses its myelin sheath quite close to the branching of the terminal by which it expands to make a series of discrete contacts (3 in Fig. 1 A) with a specialized region of the muscle fibre, the motor endplate. These terminal axonal branches have a much denser mitochondrial content than the axon and lie partly embedded in shallow troughs on the surface of the motor endplate. The motor endplate is characterized by an accumulation of sarcoplasm in which are embedded many nuclei and mitochondria. By differential staining it has been established that a continuous membrane is interposed between the axoplasm and the sarcoplasm, and on the deep surface of this membrane there is a regular structure appearing in Fig. 1A as small rods arranged perpendicularly, the subneural apparatus. Also shown in Fig. 1 A is a teloglial or Schwann cell (tel.) with its prominent nucleus on the upper surface of the nerve terminal. An important additional observation is that by histochemical identification the acetylcholine-esterase (AChE) is associated with the subneural apparatus and remains after degeneration of the nerve terminal (KOELLE and FRIEDENWALD 1949; COUTEAUX and TAXI 1952; DENZ 1953; COUTEAUX 1958). The conclusion that the location of AChE is on the muscle fibre and not on the nerve terminal is fully substantiated by electron-microscopy, which identifies the subneural apparatus with the junctional folds of the muscle surface membrane (Fig. 1 B).

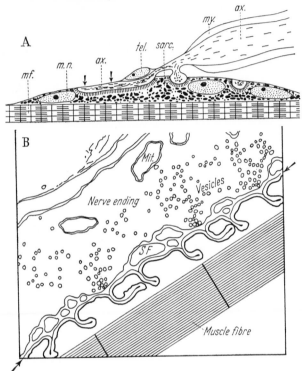

Fig. 1 A and B. A. Schematic drawing of a motor endplate. *ax.*, axoplasm with its mitochondria; *my.*, myelin sheath; *tel.*, teloglia (terminal Schwann cells); *sarc.*, sarcoplasm with its mitochondria; *m.n.*, muscle nuclei; *mf.*, myofibrils. The terminal nerve branches lie in "synaptic gutters" or "troughs". Immediately under the interface axoplasm-sarcoplasm, the ribbon-shaped subneural lamellae, transversely cut, may be seen as rodlets (COUTEAUX 1958). B. Tracing of a longitudinal section of a frog neuro-muscular junction, × 19,000. The line of the synaptic cleft between the nerve ending and the muscle is indicated by the arrows. Note the junctional folds of the synaptic cleft extending into the muscle. Four mitochondria (*Mit.*) are shown surrounded by double lines. *SF* denotes one of the "Schwann finger" extensions of the Schwann cell (seen above the nerve ending) into the synaptic cleft (BIRKS, HUXLEY and KATZ 1960)

There have been several very thorough electron-microscopic studies of neuromuscular junctions of amphibia, reptiles and mammals (PALADE and PALAY 1954; ROBERTSON 1956, 1960; REGER 1958; ANDERSON-CEDERGREN 1959; BIRKS, HUXLEY and KATZ 1960), and it is now well established that all have the essential structure which is illustrated in Fig. 1 B from a longitudinal section of an amphibian neuro-muscular junction. We may regard this as a higher magnification of the element in Fig. 1 A between the arrows. Correspondingly, there are the Schwann cell on the upper surface of the nerve terminal, the mitochondria in the nerve terminal and the subneural apparatus or junctional folds projecting into the sarcoplasm from the junctional region. But the much higher resolution reveals in addition two structural features which are of great functional importance and which characterize all chemically transmitting synapses.

Firstly, as indicated by the arrows in Fig. 1 B, there is a cleft of about 500 Å width completely separating the surface membranes of the nerve terminal and the motor endplate. In Fig. 1B an unusual number of fine teloglial processes (Schwann fingers, SF) have intruded into the synaptic cleft, but otherwise the nerve membrane is freely exposed to the muscle membrane across the cleft, being separated only by the contents of the cleft which is thought to have a fluid or thin gel consistency (PALAY 1958), and which is seen to contain in Fig. 1B an opaque central band that extends down into the junctional folds. At the edge of the neural contact the synaptic cleft opens into the extracellular space.

Secondly, there are numerous vesicles about 500 Å in diameter in the pre-synaptic terminal, and they tend to collect in groups at sites on the presynaptic membrane fronting the cleft, particularly in proximity to the junctional folds. There is much indirect evidence to suggest that these synaptic vesicles repre-sent packets of the transmitter substance (Chapter III). Consequently several functional problems can be formulated, though as yet none is satisfactorily answered: the mode of production of vesicles; the control of their movement up to the synaptic cleft; the way in which a nerve impulse effects a release of their contents into the cleft; their subsequent fate after extrusion of contents.

Additional features revealed by electron-microscopy are the coverage of the nerve terminal by the Schwann cell except where it is embedded in the troughs of the motor endplate (cf. Fig. 1B), and the fact that the junctional folds are formed by folding of the surface membrane of the muscle fibre, so including, as noted above, a space communicating with the synaptic cleft and apparently filled by the same material.

Thus in summary the structure of the neuromuscular junction has a struc-tural design that is very efficient for the operation of a chemically transmitting synapse. The synaptic vesicles tend to be aggregated close to the synaptic cleft so that they are readily available for releasing their contents into the cleft. Once released into the cleft the transmitter substance should rapidly diffuse to and act on the subjacent muscle membrane. The ionic fluxes so generated could cause a flow of electrical current from the adjacent surface of the muscle fibre through the extracellular spaces and in through the cleft to the subsynaptic membrane of the muscle fibre. The junctional folds increase the effective area of this membrane, and hence its electrical conductance, by a factor of about three. The location of AChE on the cleft side of the junctional folds ensures that it is optimally sited for hydrolysing the transmitter, acetyl-choline, and so for terminating its action.

B. Synapses of the mammalian central nervous system

In less than a decade electron-microscopy has enormously advanced our knowledge of synapses in the central nervous system. There is a remarkable degree of agreement in the essential features of synapses as described by the

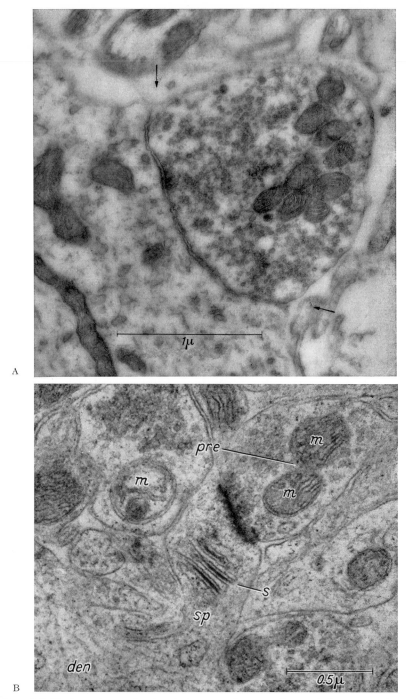

Fig. 2 A and B. Electron-micrographs of central synapses in mammalian central nervous system. A shows synaptic knob separated from subsynaptic membrane by a synaptic cleft (marked by arrows) about 200 Å wide. Synaptic vesicles are seen to be concentrated close to the cleft in one "active zone", where there is also thickening of the membranes on either side of the cleft (PALAY 1958). B shows synaptic knob making a Type 1 synaptic contact with the spine (sp) of an apical dendrite of a cortical pyramidal cell the synaptic cleft being the darkest zone. The spine apparatus (s) is well seen in the spine (GRAY 1963)

three principal groups of investigators under the leaderships of DE ROBERTIS, PALAY and GRAY, as may be seen by reference to their review articles (DE ROBERTIS 1958, 1959a; PALAY 1958; WHITTAKER and GRAY 1962). Thus, as illustrated in the microphotographs and in the drawings of various types of synapses (Figs. 2 and 3), the presynaptic fibre ends in an expanded terminal, the synaptic knob, which makes an intimate contact with a portion of the membrane of the postsynaptic neurone, the subsynaptic membrane, being separated from it by a very narrow and remarkably uniform space, the synaptic cleft.

This structure is thus not unlike the neuromuscular junction, but is usually very much smaller because there are multiple endings on any one nerve cell, even many hundreds. A considerable proportion of the surface of the soma and large dendrites may be covered with synaptic knobs (WYCKOFF and YOUNG 1956; PALAY 1958, Fig. 1; PALAY, McGEE-RUSSELL, GORDON and GRILLO 1962, Fig. 11).

In electron-microscopic examination the very thin section usually does not display the fine presynaptic fibre expanding to form the synaptic knob as in Fig. 3 C. Rarely the terminal myelinated segment of the axon is seen narrowing down and at the same time shedding its myelin, layer by layer, just as at a node of RANVIER (GRAY 1959, 1963), before expanding to the synaptic knob. The myelin sheath may approach to within one micron of the actual synaptic contact, but probably the great majority of synapses are formed by unmyelinated presynaptic fibres that may be no more than 0.1 μ across before expanding to the synaptic knob, and so often would not be recognized by light microscopy. The extension of the myelin sheath almost to the synaptic terminal had earlier been observed by light microscopy for large synapses (BODIAN 1952).

Just as with the nerve terminal at the neuromuscular junction, the synaptic knob contains several mitochondria, and, most characteristically, large numbers of synaptic vesicles 300 to 600 Å in diameter. It is now generally agreed that these round profiles are not sections of tubules, but are spherical objects (PALAY 1956). As shown in a typical synaptic knob (Fig. 2A), the vesicles tend to be concentrated at one or more sites fronting the synaptic cleft, and at such sites both the presynaptic and postsynaptic membranes are more opaque. Synaptic vesicles are not seen in the postsynaptic cytoplasm of Fig. 2A, B, which is a characteristic of all synapses except those responsible for presynaptic inhibition, where the postsynaptic structure is in fact a synaptic knob (Fig. 5). Synaptic vesicles were independently recognized by the earliest investigations employing electron-microscopy (DE ROBERTIS and BENNETT 1954, 1955; PALADE and PALAY 1954; PALAY and PALADE 1955), and have particular significance because there is much circumstantial evidence that they contain preformed packets of the transmitter substance (Chapters III,

VI). With the highest resolution of electron-microscopy some vesicles can be seen apparently discharging their contents into the synaptic cleft (DE ROBERTIS and BENNETT 1955; DE ROBERTIS 1958, 1959; PALAY 1956).

The patches of increased density and thickening of the membranes on either side of the synaptic cleft were first reported by DE ROBERTIS (1956)

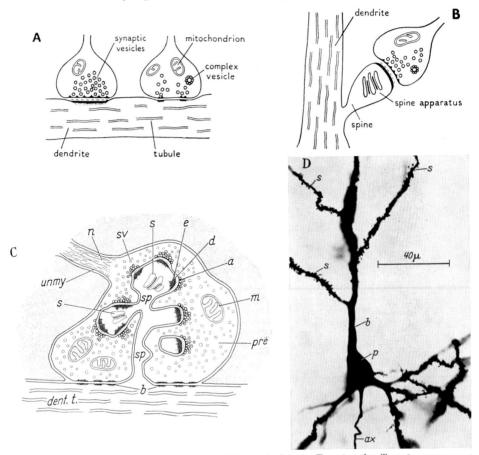

Fig. 3A—D. Some variations in synaptic morphology. A shows a Type 1 and a Type 2 synapse on a dendrite with the characteristic features described in the text. In B there is a dendritic spine of a neocortical pyramidal cell with its spine apparatus and an associated Type 1 synapse. C is a complex synapse on the spine (sp) of a dendrite of a hippocampal pyramidal cell (HAMLYN 1962). D is a Golgi preparation of a neurone from cat cerebral cortex with spines (s) shown on apical and basal dendrites, but not on the soma (p), axon (ax) or dendritic stumps (b) (WHITTAKER and GRAY 1962)

and later by PALAY (1956, 1958) and by HORSTMANN and MEEVES (1959), who noticed that synaptic vesicles were often concentrated at such sites. However these patches of membrane density also resemble the attachment zones or desmosomes connecting adjacent epithelial cells, so two possible functions have been proposed: sites for extrusion of the transmitter material in the vesicles; and sites for adhesion between presynaptic and postsynaptic membranes. Further investigations by GRAY (1959, 1961a, 1963), DE LORENZO (1961) and HAMLYN (1962) have indicated that there are three types of these dense patches of which only two are functional synapses. These two are illustrated in Fig. 3 A, being designated as Type 1 and Type 2. Since there always are associated concentrations of vesicles at the dense patches, the whole assemblage probably is a zone for the extrusion of the transmitter substance and for its action on the subsynaptic membrane, so forming what COUTEAUX (1961) appropriately calls "active zones" of the synapse. GRAY (1961 a, 1963) and HAMLYN (1962) give four criteria for distinguishing Type 1 from Type 2: the synaptic cleft is wider (300 Å) as against 200 Å for Type 2; the postsynaptic membrane is more thick and dense; the dense patch is much more extensive, occupying the greater part of the opposing synaptic membranes; and in the cleft there is a plaque of extracellular material nearer to the postsynaptic membrane. The third type of membrane thickening is not associated with any accumulation of vesicles, there being merely a symmetrical thickening of both membranes on either side of an unchanged synaptic cleft (b in Fig. 3 C). Similar patches devoid of vesicles also occur between adjacent dendrites, where presumably they are simply attachment plaques (GRAY 1961 a, 1963); this may be the function of all symmetrical plaques devoid of vesicle accumulation.

It is of particular interest that there is selectivity in the distribution of the two types of synapses (GRAY 1961 a; WHITTAKER and GRAY 1962; DE LORENZO 1961; HAMLYN 1962; BLACKSTAD 1963). In pyramidal cells of the cerebral cortex a very important synaptic contact occurs on the spines (S) that can be seen in Fig. 3 D to project from both the apical and basal dendrites, but not from the soma or adjacent dendritic stumps and the axon. The synapses on these spines are always Type I, as in Figs. 2 B, 3 B, and many also are characterized by staining for AChE (DE LORENZO 1961). On the other hand the synapses on the somas of pyramidal cells of the neocortex are always of Type 2 and do not stain for AChE (GRAY 1959, Fig. 11; DE LORENZO 1961). Type 1 synapses also exclusively occur on the spines of hippocampal pyramidal cells (Figs. 3 C), while Type 2 synapses occur on the somas of the hippocampal pyramids (Fig. 4 A; HAMLYN 1962; BLACKSTAD 1963; BLACKSTAD and FLOOD 1963) and of the cerebellar Purkinje cells (Fig. 4 B; PALAY, McGEE-RUSSELL, GORDON and GRILLO 1962). On the dendritic surface between the spines both types occur, as in Fig. 3 A.

The synaptic endings on the somas of the Purkinje cells of the cerebellum (Fig. 4 B) are from the basket cells (RAMÓN Y CAJAL 1911; ESTABLE 1923; PALAY, McGEE-RUSSELL, GORDON and GRILLO 1962), and likewise the synapses on the somas of hippocampal pyramidal cells are from the hippocampal basket cells (RAMÓN Y CAJAL 1911; LORENTE DE NÓ 1934). There is now evidence suggesting that these latter cells exert a powerful postsynaptic inhibition on the pyramidal cells (ANDERSEN, ECCLES and LØYNING 1963, Chapter XIII); hence Type 2 synapses here (Fig. 4 A) would be inhibitory in function. The structural similarity with the cerebellar basket cells (RAMÓN Y CAJAL 1911) suggests that these, too, are inhibitory, and in Fig. 4 B, this synapse also appears to be Type 2. The inhibitory action of basket cells on Purkinje cells has now been demonstrated (ANDERSEN, ECCLES and VOORHOEVE 1963).

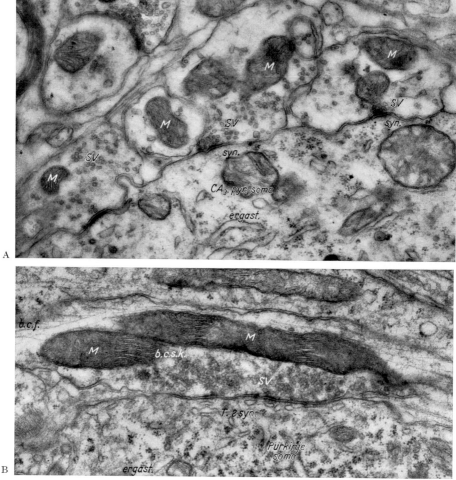

Fig. 4 A and B. Electron-micrographs of synapses formed by basket cell axonal terminals. In A part of the soma of a hippocampal pyramidal cell of CA3 area is seen below with ergastoplasm: × 28,000. Two of the three synaptic knobs of basket cells with their contained mitochondria (M) and synaptic vesicles (SV) are seen making Type 2 synapses with the pyramidal cell (BLACKSTAD 1963). In B part of the soma of a Purkinje cell of the cerebellum is seen to receive Type 2 synaptic contacts from an expanded synaptic knob (b.c.s.k.) that is *en passage*, as shown by the axon (b.c.f.) of the basket cell on each side of it (PALAY, unpublished electron-micrograph, about 25,000 ×)

The synapses on apical dendrites of pyramidal cells remote from the axon-soma region presumably must be excitatory (ANDERSEN 1960; cf. LI 1961), for it would be very bad functional design if inhibitory synapses were located so far from the effective site of their action in suppressing the generation of impulses (Chapters VII and XIII). It thus seems probable that the Type 1 synapses are excitatory—at least on the dendritic spines, where they are invariably present; and not only on the spines of neo-cortical pyramidal cells (Fig. 3 B), but also on the spines of the hippocampal pyramids, there being for example 8 Type 1 synapses in Fig. 3 C. The dendritic spines of Purkinje cells of the cerebellum also have Type 1 synapses (GRAY 1961 b), the presynaptic components being the parallel fibres formed by the axons of granule cells.

The functional distinction between Types 1 and 2 is further indicated by the fact that, on every occasion where a single presynaptic ending enters into synaptic relationship with two different postsynaptic structures, the synapses are either both Type 1 or both Type 2 (GRAY 1961a). At least it can be concluded that this speculation gives hope that it may be possible to distinguish between excitatory and inhibitory synapses on morphological grounds. By means of ingenious degeneration experiments SZENTÁGOTHAI (1958, 1961) obtained evidence that, with motoneurones, oculomotor neurones and dorsal spinocerebellar tract cells, inhibitory synaptic action is exerted by an extremely fine meshwork of fibres ramifying over the cell body. WHITTAKER and GRAY (1962) suggest that the associated inhibitory synaptic knobs would not be stained by the silver techniques because they have no ring of neurofibrils, and hence would be undetectable by light microscopy.

Staining by phosphotungstic acid reveals complex structures or organelles projecting into the presynaptic cytoplasm from the dense membrane zones (GRAY 1959, 1963). These structures are shown in transverse section in Figs. 2 B, 3 A, B and 5 A, B, and on tangential section have a hexagonal pattern with about 1000 Å between centres. It seems likely that they are concerned in the release of transmitter substances, either being attachment sites for synaptic vesicles or perhaps accumulations of vesicles that have discharged their contents and are awaiting recharge.

Figs. 2 B, 3 B, C illustrate a unique type of organelle deep to the postsynaptic membrane, the spine apparatus (GRAY 1959, 1961 a; WHITTAKER and GRAY 1962; HAMLYN 1962). This structure of alternating bands and sacs has been seen only in the spines of pyramidal cells in the neocortex and hippocampus of mammals (GRAY 1961a), and does not occur for example in the spines of Purkinje cells (GRAY 1961 b) or in the spinal cord (GRAY 1963). Because of this very selective location it has been suggested that it may be concerned in the processes of learning and memory (HAMLYN 1962).

Even in the densely tangled structure of the central nervous system synaptic knobs may be identified with assurance by their contained vesicles. Such synaptic knobs are frequently in close contact, being separated only by a 200 Å cleft, which presumably does not allow significant interaction so long as there is no specialization indicative of the active zones of chemical synaptic action, namely the membrane thickenings and vesicle accumulations characteristic of Types 1 or 2 synapse and also the associated organelles. Hitherto these active zones were restricted to axo-somatic and axo-dendritic contacts.

2*

However in the spinal cord GRAY (1962, 1963, and personal communication) has now discovered numerous examples of presumed functional contacts

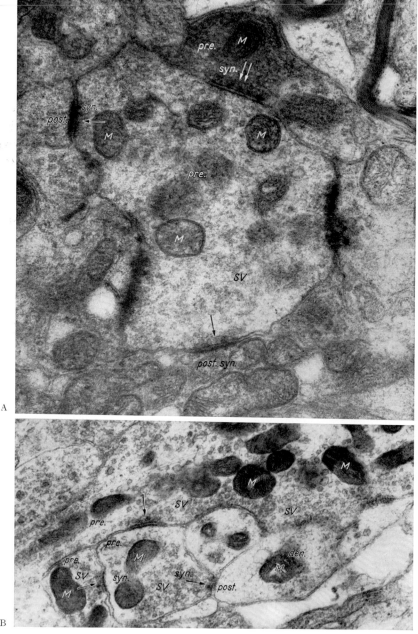

Fig. 5A and B. Electron-micrographs of presumed presynaptic inhibitory synapses, ×31,000. In A a large synaptic knob (*pre*) in the upper lumbar spinal cord of a cat is seen in synaptic relationship at five sites. The arrows indicate the presumed direction of synaptic transmission in three. Evidently the synaptic terminal are presynaptic at two sites to postsynaptic structures (*post*), but is itself postsynaptic at one (indicated by double arrows), which is the required structural relationship for presynaptic inhibition (GRAY 1962). B gives another example of a presynaptic inhibitory relationship as shown by the arrows, there being in this case two synapses onto a synaptic knob that itself enters into a very small synaptic relationship to a dendrite (*den*) (GRAY, unpublished electron-micrograph)

between two synaptic knobs, that is of an axo-axonic synapse. For example in Fig. 5 A the large central structure with mitochondria and vesicles has five areas indicative of active zones. As shown by the arrows, in two the organelle structure and the relative thickenings of the membranes of the synaptic cleft indicate that the central synaptic knob is presynaptic, with a Type 1 synapse, to structures that appear to be dendrites, and in two the relationship is obscured by the obliquity of the section. However in the remaining contact a small presynaptic knob with vesicles and one mitochondrion is seen to be presynaptic (note direction of the double arrow) to the large central knob, the organelle on the presynaptic side being particularly convincing. A second example of synaptic relationship between two vesicle-containing synaptic knobs is shown in Fig. 5 B, where the same identification as in Fig. 5 A indicates transmission as shown by the arrows, the small central structure being post-synaptic to both a large and a small vesicle-containing presynaptic terminal, and being itself presynaptic to a small dendrite. Comparable structures have been observed by KIDD (1962) in the vertebrate retina and by SZENTÁGOTHAI in the lateral geniculate body (1963 a and personal communication). These axo-axonic synapses are of great functional interest because the existence of synapses between axon terminals was postulated to account for the depolarization of presynaptic terminals that is responsible for presynaptic inhibition (Chapter XV; ECCLES 1961 c, 1961 d).

The discovery that synapses are superimposed on presynaptic terminals in order to depress their output of synaptic transmitter gives new insight into the significance of the various complex synaptic structures that have long been recognized in several regions of the central nervous system. With this end in view SZENTÁGOTHAI (1963 a) has reconsidered two of these synaptic structures. In the granule layer of the cerebellum, branches of the mossy fibres form islets or glomeruli by intertwining with the dendrites of the surrounding granule cells. Electron-microscopy shows that the ramifying terminal branches of the mossy fibre form numerous synapses with the granule cell dendrites with the zones of thickened membranes and vesicle accumulations characteristic of Type 1 synapses (GRAY 1961 b; PALAY, McGEE-RUSSELL GORDON and GRILLO 1962; SZENTÁGOTHAI 1963 a). However this glomerular structure is not simply a rather complex synaptic arrangement of mossy fibre axons to granule cell dendrites, because axons of the Golgi cells also enter the glomerulus. By means of degeneration procedures SZENTÁGOTHAI (1963 a) has shown that branches of the Golgi cell axons actually penetrate between the terminals of the mossy fibres and the granule cell dendrites, making what he calls "sand-wich type" synapses. Evidently such an arrangement is likely to be some feed-back device onto this main synaptic relay to the Purkinje cells of the cere-bellum. SZENTÁGOTHAI (1963 a) also describes a somewhat similar structural relationship in the glomeruli in the lateral geniculate body. There appear here to be synapses upon presynaptic terminals such as in Fig. 5, so that possibly there is a presynaptic inhibitory control of transmission through the lateral geniculate nucleus. Another example of complex synaptic structures is exhibited by the inferior olivary nucleus (SCHEIBEL and SCHEIBEL 1955), but further investigation is required before its significance can be appreciated. SZENTÁGOTHAI suggests that we have to envisage these complex synaptic apparatuses as having special physiological significance. For example they could act as a first stage of integration and of feed-back control. It can be predicted that many more varieties of these synaptic apparatuses await recognition.

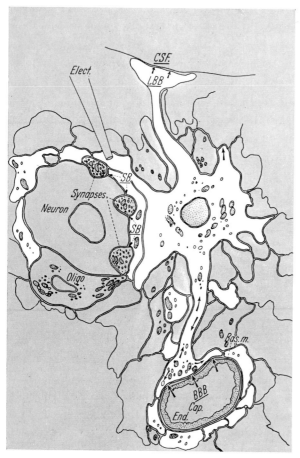

Fig. 6. Diagram showing the different topographical relationships of an astrocyte of the gray matter. Processes adjacent to a capillary (*Cap*) or vascular foot, to the pia-glial membrane, and surrounding a nerve cell are shown. The position of the so-called blood-brain barrier (*BBB*), liquor-brain barrier (*LBB*) and synaptic barrier (*SB*) are indicated. The thick arrows represent the possible movements of fluids and solutes within the astrocytic cytoplasm. A perineuronal oligodendrocyte is also indicated. The drawing emphasizes the clear cytoplasm of the astrocyte and astrocytic processes and the lack of true cellular space. An extraneuronal recording microelectrode with its implantation into the glia is shown (*End.*, endothelium; *Bas.m.*, basement membrane) (DE ROBERTIS and GERSCHENFELD 1961)

Since there is now conclusive evidence that glial cells are not directly concerned in synaptic transmission (DE ROBERTIS and GERSCHENFELD 1961; GRAY 1961a; HILD and TASAKI 1962; KUFFLER and POTTER 1963), it will be sufficient here to refer quite briefly to the relationship of glial cells to neurones and synapses as revealed by electron microscopy. No attempt will be made at classification, which is still controversial.

Of present interest is the revolution that electron-microscopy has effected in our concept of extracellular space. This is now recognized as being little more than a three dimensional reticulum of narrow (200 Å) clefts between glial cells and neurones (Fig. 6; PALAY 1958; HORSTMANN and MEEVES 1959; DE ROBERTIS and GERSHENFELD 1961;

LUSE 1960; GRAY 1961a; BLACKSTAD and DAHL 1962). With synaptic contacts of large area there are sometimes glial processes breaking the continuity of the presynaptic-postsynaptic contacts just as occurs with Schwann fingers in Fig. 1B. There are never any signs of membrane thickenings and vesicle accumulations on the enormous areas of close apposition with only a 200 Å cleft between the glial and neuronal membranes. However, just below areas of close glial contact, special structures do occur in the neuronal cytoplasm, which apparently are concerned in fluid and electrolyte transfer (GRAY 1961a; DE ROBERTIS and GERSCHENFELD 1961). Fig. 6 illustrates the presumed function of astrocytes in this fluid movement between capillaries, neurones and the cerebrospinal fluid. It also indicates two important barriers to the movement of solutes: The blood-brain barrier (BBB) due to the surface membrane of the astrocyte; and the perisynaptic barrier (SB) limiting the diffusion both of transmitter substance out of the synaptic cleft and of pharmacological agents into it (Chapters V and XII).

C. Synapses of sympathetic ganglia

The synapses of frog sympathetic ganglia were amongst the first to be studied by electron-microscopy (DE ROBERTIS and BENNETT 1954, 1955) with recognition of the accumulation of vesicles and the associated membrane thickenings on either side of the synaptic cleft. TAXI (1961, 1962) has produced beautiful pictures of these specialized synaptic areas (Fig. 7A, B), which have the following characteristics in sequential order: accumulation of synaptic vesicles; thick and dense presynaptic membrane; well defined synaptic cleft; subsynaptic membrane more thick and dense than the presynaptic; about 500 Å below the subsynaptic membrane there is usually a dense band about 500 Å across and considerably less extensive than the membrane thickenings, and this band may be double. Because of its appearance and location deep to the subsynaptic membrane, a relationship to the spine apparatus of the cortical pyramidal cells (Figs. 2B and 3B, C) has been suggested (TAXI 1961; COUTEAUX 1961). This subsynaptic band has not been seen in sympathetic ganglia of reptiles, birds and mammals (TAXI 1962), but in other respects a wide variety of sympathetic ganglia (SZENTÁGOTHAI 1963c) exhibit the same essential characters of synaptic structure, with the special areas of vesicle accumulation and membrane thickening that are assumed to be the functionally "active zones."

In the ciliary ganglion of the chick and pigeon the synapses usually have a remarkable caliciform structure, whereby, as illustrated diagrammatically in Fig. 7C, a single presynaptic terminal forms a calix embracing a considerable fraction of the surface of an approximately spherical ganglion cell. Nevertheless, as DE LORENZO (1960) and SZENTÁGOTHAI (1963c) have shown, this very

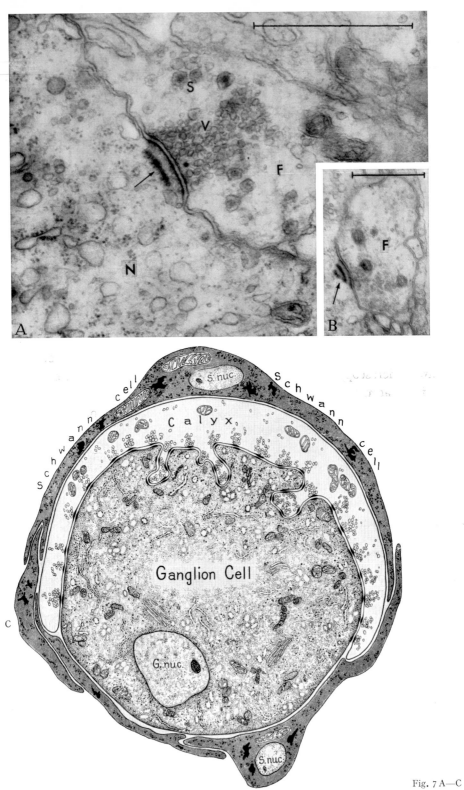

Fig. 7 A—C

atypical structure exhibits the characteristic features of a chemically transmitting synapse: accumulations of vesicles and the associated zones of specially thick and dense presynaptic and subsynaptic membranes. Fig. 7C also shows that Schwann cells cover both the presynaptic terminal and that part of the ganglion cell not covered by the calix. With other ganglion cells the presynaptic coverage is in the form of a basket of fibres with synaptic knobs, as originally described by v. LENHOSSÉK (1911). However, here also there are the characteristic "active zones" with vesicle accumulations and membrane thickenings. The special physiological features of this remarkable synapse (MARTIN and PILAR 1963 a, 1963 b) will be discussed in Chapter IX.

D. Other types of chemically transmitting synapses

Since other chemically transmitting synapses have the same essential characteristics as those illustrated and described above (COUTEAUX 1961), only very brief reference need be made to them. The synapse from nerve to electroplaque has presynaptic accumulations of vesicles and a synaptic cleft of about the same width as at the neuromuscular junction (MATHEWSON, WACHTEL and GRUNDFEST 1961; COUTEAUX 1961). The sympathetic nerve terminals make typical synapses on the chromaffin cells of the adrenal medulla, with accumulations of synaptic vesicles and associated membrane thickenings (DE ROBERTIS 1958; COUTEAUX 1961). Invertebrate synapses also have essentially the same structure, as was initially shown by DE ROBERTIS and BENNETT (1955) for synapses in the neuropil of the earthworm and recently by GERSCHENFELD (1962) for the molluscs, *Aplysia* and *Helix*. So far as they have been investigated invertebrate neuromuscular junctions also are essentially similar to vertebrate (COUTEAUX 1961).

E. Discussion

It will be sufficiently evident that in less than a decade electron-microscopy has provided a clear picture of the main structures that are required for physiological explanations of chemical transmission at synapses. There are firstly the synaptic vesicles that correspond to the packets in which the chemical transmitter is released. These vesicles accumulate on special zones of the presynaptic membrane fronting the synaptic cleft, which is an essential

Fig. 7A—C. A, B. Electron-micrographs of a synapse in lumbar sympathetic ganglion of the frog, scales, 1 μ. F is the presynaptic nerve terminal and N the ganglion cell. The arrow indicates an active zone with the accumulation of synaptic vesicles (V), thickened membranes on each side of the synaptic cleft and a dense organelle deep on the postsynaptic side. In B this organelle is double (TAXI 1962). C is schematic drawing incorporating the principal fine structure details of caliciform endings in the ciliary ganglion of the chick. The calix is shown in contiguity with a considerable area of ganglion cell surface, and many active zones are shown with clusters of synaptic vesicles and thickened membranes: Schwann cells invest both the calix and the ganglion cell (DE LORENZO 1960) location, because release into the synaptic cleft is triggered by a nerve impulse in a fraction of a millisecond. Secondly, the increased thickening and density of such zones of the presynaptic membrane correspond to the postulate that a special physiological mechanism is concerned in the release (Chapter VI). It also can be correlated with the special physiological and pharmacological properties that are exhibited by some presynaptic terminals (Chapter VIII). Thirdly, the synaptic cleft is an essential requirement of a chemical synapse, because the postsynaptic reaction is always an ionic flux across the subsynaptic membrane that generates the flow of current through the synaptic cleft and so to the extrasynaptic regions of the postsynaptic membrane (Chapters IV and X). Fourthly, the very thick and dense subsynaptic membrane corresponds to the essential physiological postulate of specific chemical receptor sites and the associated channels for ionic fluxes (Chapters IV, V, X, XI and XII).

However these structural and functional correlations are still of a rudimentary nature, as will be appreciated as soon as enquiry is pursued at a deeper level. For example there is as yet no clear morphological evidence relating to the mode of production of vesicles (GRAY 1961 b; WHITTAKER and GRAY 1962). At the motor nerve terminal a series of structures can be seen showing apparently all stages of transition from mitochondria to clumps of vesicles escaping from a membrane resembling the outer sheath of a mitochondrion (ANDERSON-CEDERGREN 1959; BIRKS, HUXLEY and KATZ 1960). However there is no evidence of such mitochondrial origin for synaptic vesicles in the central nervous system (WHITTAKER and GRAY 1962), where the complex vesicles shown in Fig. 3 A, B might be a stage in vesicle manufacture. The evidence for depletion, replenishment and mobilization of vesicles of several types of synapse under conditions of high levels of activity or of disuse (DE ROBERTIS 1956, 1958, 1959a, 1959b; DE ROBERTIS and FRANCHI 1956; BIRKS, HUXLEY and KATZ 1960) will be discussed in relationship to the physiological investigations. Very little is known about the way in which vesicles are caused to release their contents into the synaptic cleft. Finally, virtually nothing is known about the nature of the receptor sites of the subsynaptic membrane and their controlling influence on the channels for ion fluxes; all of which requires a refinement of the structural concepts down to the level of molecular configuration.

Another direction of enquiry leads to questions relating to the development and organization of the structural complex that COUTEAUX (1961) refers to as the "active zone" of the synapse. These zones are restricted to only a fraction of the total contact area between the presynaptic and subsynaptic membranes. Once developed, these zones appear to have a remarkable stability, as may be seen in the survival of their postsynaptic components for some time after presynaptic degeneration (BIRKS, KATZ and MILEDI 1960; COUTEAUX 1961; TAXI 1962). Such problems of development, degeneration and regeneration will be considered in Chapter XVI.

CHAPTER III

PHYSIOLOGICAL PROPERTIES OF CHEMICALLY TRANSMITTING SYNAPSES IN THE RESTING STATE

A. The electrical coupling across the synapse

Only with one type of chemically transmitting synapse, the giant synapses of the squid stellate ganglion, has it been possible to insert electrodes simultaneously

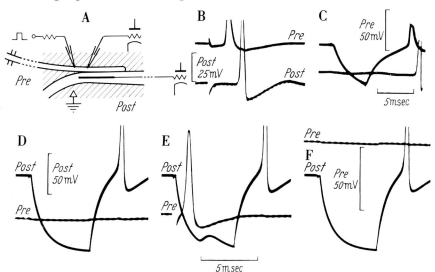

Fig. 8A—F. A. Diagram of giant synapse of squid stellate ganglion showing two electrodes in the pre-synaptic giant fibre and one in the postsynaptic giant fibre. B. Simultaneous recording of the presynaptic spike potential (upper trace) and of the postsynaptic spike potential (lower trace) generated by synaptic transmission. C. Presynaptic hyperpolarizing pulse causes no appreciable postsynaptic potential, but at end of trace the presynaptic spike that is generated as an off-response evokes a postsynaptic response as in B. D. Reverse of B, with postsynaptic hyperpolarizing pulse, the spike generated as an off-response giving no presynaptic potential. E. As in D, but a presynaptic spike was set up to show that electrodes were in place and the excitatory postsynaptic potential was superimposed on the postsynaptic hyper-polarization. F. Same as in D, but the presynaptic recording electrode was withdrawn in order to record extracellular potential. Potential scales and time scales are indicated for B, C and for D—F. Temperature, 21—22⁰ C (HAGIWARA and TASAKI 1958)

into both presynaptic and postsynaptic elements (Fig. 8A), and so to investigate the electrical interaction between these two elements (BULLOCK and HAGIWARA

27

1957; HAGIWARA and TASAKI 1958). The negligible level of the electrical coupling between the presynaptic and postsynaptic components of the synapse is shown in Fig. 8 D, F, where on hyperpolarizing the postsynaptic membrane there is no detectable change in presynaptic membrane potential, the small potential shift in D, being exactly duplicated in the extracellular record, F. Likewise, on hyperpolarizing the presynaptic membrane (Fig. 8 C), there is no detectable potential change in the postsynaptic membrane. However, before these definitive investigations were made, it was recognized that there was a high degree of electrical uncoupling across chemically transmitting synapses. With intracellular recording there is no detectable potential change across the postsynaptic membrane when the presynaptic impulse propagates into the presynaptic terminals (FATT and KATZ 1951; BROCK, COOMBS and ECCLES 1952). This is also convincingly demonstrated in the squid giant synapse (Figs. 8 B; 12 A—D; BULLOCK and HAGIWARA 1957; HAGIWARA and TASAKI 1958).

In contrast there are two examples of chemically transmitting synapses that may display effective electrical coupling (see Chapter IX). This coupling is particularly well developed in the chick ciliary ganglion, where in about half of the synapses electrical transmission of the impulse forestalls the chemical transmission (MARTIN and PILAR 1963a).

Since there is such very close juxtaposition of the membranes fronting each other across the 200 Å gap of the synaptic cleft, electric coupling might be expected to be a prominent feature with chemical synapses. However, if the synaptic cleft freely opens into the extracellular space around the borders of the synaptic contact, and if the specific resistances of the synaptic cleft and of the surface membranes fronting it have conventional values (of the order of 100 Ω cm and 500 Ω cm^2 respectively), it has been calculated that the current generated by the membrane on either side of the synaptic cleft would almost entirely flow through the cleft and out to the extracellular space; for example, with a synaptic contact 2 μ across, very much less than one thousandth would flow through the membrane on the other side of the cleft (ECCLES and JAEGER 1958). This calculation applies of course only to relatively prolonged currents, such as are applied in Fig. 8. With the much briefer currents that flow for example during a presynaptic spike potential, the capacity of the postsynaptic membrane would lower the impedance by several times, but even so the coupling across the synaptic cleft would be likely to be less than one percent, which is in accord with observations on the great majority of synapses. The synaptic cleft can thus be regarded as a very effective shunt preventing electrical interaction between the presynaptic and postsynaptic components of a chemically transmitting synapse. It provides a complete break between the cable-like transmissions of impulses in the presynaptic nerve fibre and in the postsynaptic element.

The exceptional chemical synapses with large coupling potentials (Chapter IX) have such large surfaces of contact across a 200 Å cleft that a very considerable fraction of the current generated by the presynaptic spike potential would be expected to flow across the subsynaptic membrane. There is thus a direct continuity of cable transmission across the synapse, though the attenuation factor may be too high for impulse transmission. The various types of electrical synaptic transmission will be considered in Chapter IX.

Even with the giant synapse of the squid stellate ganglion it has not been possible to determine if special electrical properties distinguish the subsynaptic membrane from the remainder of the postsynaptic membrane. With other synapses also any investigations performed with a microelectrode in the postsynaptic cell necessarily have a very large area of ordinary postsynaptic membrane in parallel with the areas of subsynaptic membrane, so the properties of the latter have been indeterminate. There are, however, certain types of chemically transmitting synapse where the subsynaptic area is relatively very extensive, for example the tonic muscles of amphibia (KUFFLER and VAUGHAN WILLIAMS 1953; BURKE and GINSBORG 1956a, b) and the innervated faces of some types of electric organ: *Raja, Torpedo, Atroscopus* and *Narcine* (ALBE-FESSARD 1951; FESSARD and POSTERNAK 1950; BROCK, R. M. ECCLES and KEYNES 1953; BROCK and R. M. ECCLES 1958; GRUNDFEST 1957b; BENNETT and GRUNDFEST 1961; BENNETT 1961). There is general agreement that these postsynaptic membranes are electrically inexcitable according to the criteria defined in Chapter VII. No selective sodium conductance develops at any level of depolarization; hence there is no trace of the membrane property responsible for impulses. The general postulate (GRUNDFEST 1957a, b, 1959) that all chemically excited membrane is electrically inexcitable will be discussed in Chapter VII.

B. Spontaneous miniature postsynaptic potentials

With many synapses in the resting state small depolarizations of the postsynaptic membrane occur in a temporal sequence that accurately conforms to a random process. For example at the neuromuscular synapses of amphibians and mammals the so-called miniature endplate potentials (min. EPPs) are readily detected either with an intracellular or an extracellular microelectrode close to the synaptic region (Fig. 9A, B; FATT and KATZ 1952b; DEL CASTILLO and KATZ 1954a, b, 1956a, b; LILEY 1956a, b, c; BURKE 1957; HUBBARD and SCHMIDT 1963); and have recently been observed in excised human intercostal muscle (ELMQVIST, JOHNS and THESLEFF 1960). These min. EPPs resemble the endplate potentials (EPPs) produced by the action of presynaptic impulses in every respect except size, being little more than 1 % of the EPP (FATT and KATZ 1952b; TAKEUCHI and TAKEUCHI 1960a). For example, pharmacological agents exhibit identical action, anticholinesterases increasing and prolonging both types of potential, while curarizing agents similarly depress both types (FATT and KATZ 1952b; DEL CASTILLO and KATZ 1956b; LILEY 1956a), and botulinum toxin similarly blocks both (BROOKS 1956; THESLEFF 1960a).

There is conclusive evidence, fully reviewed by DEL CASTILLO and KATZ (1956b) and by KATZ (1958a, 1962), that the min. EPPs are produced by acetylcholine that is liberated from the presynaptic terminals in packets or quanta of remarkably uniform size, each comprising several thousand molecules. Thus the frequency of min. EPPs (but not their quantal size) is greatly

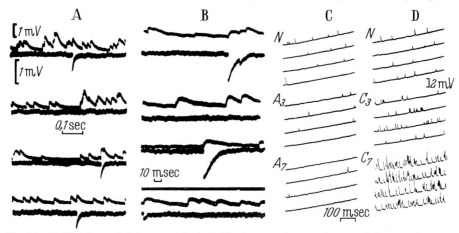

Fig. 9 A—D. Miniature endplate potentials. A, B. Simultaneous intra- and extracellular recording of spontaneous miniature EPPs of frog muscle fibre. The upper trace of each record shows the miniature EPPs recorded with an intracellular electrode. In both traces an upward deflexion signals a positive-going potential change at the tip of the microelectrode. Series at B is recorded at faster sweep speed. Note the potential scales for the two traces (DEL CASTILLO and KATZ 1956a). C and D. min. EPPs recorded intracellularly from a muscle fibre of a rat diaphragm. In each, upper four traces give control level of discharge. A_3 and A_7 show effect of hyperpolarizing currents of strengths 3 and 7 in an arbitrary scale applied to the nerve fibre and electrotonically conducted to the nerve terminal. Similarly C_3 and C_7 show effect of depolarizing current in increasing the frequency (LILEY 1956c)

increased by the application of depolarizing currents to the presynaptic terminals and is decreased by hyperpolarizing currents (Figs. 9C, D; 10A; DEL CASTILLO and KATZ 1954d; LILEY 1956c), whereas it has not been appreciably changed by polarizing the postsynaptic membrane (DEL CASTILLO and KATZ 1955b; TAKEUCHI and TAKEUCHI 1960a, 1961). Thus KATZ (1962) summarizes all the results by saying that "the *frequency* of the miniature potentials is controlled entirely by the conditions of the *pre*synaptic membrane, while their *amplitude* is controlled by the properties of the *post*synaptic membrane."

When isolated muscles are soaked in Ringer solutions containing excess potassium, there is a large increase in the frequency of the min. EPPs, which is attributable to depolarization of the presynaptic terminals (LILEY 1956c; FURUKAWA, FURUKAWA and TAKAGI 1957; BIRKS, HUXLEY and KATZ 1960; TAKEUCHI and TAKEUCHI 1961); and in fact has been used by LILEY in his attempt to discover the relationship between depolarization of the presynaptic terminals and min. EPP frequency. Thus, with external potassium concentrations above 10 mM, the membrane potential falls by approximately 26 mV for every 2.7 fold rise in concentration; and such a depolarization increases the frequency of the min. EPPs by $(2.7)^4$ or about 55 times, as is illustrated in Fig. 10B, which is a recalculation and a replot by KATZ (1962) of measurements given by LILEY (1956c, Fig. 6). It will be seen that in both Fig. 10A and B the logarithm of the frequency is linearly related to the presynaptic membrane potential, but the potassium results in B have the advantage of providing a voltage scale for the membrane potential, which is not possible with electrical polarization in Figs. 9C, D and 10A.

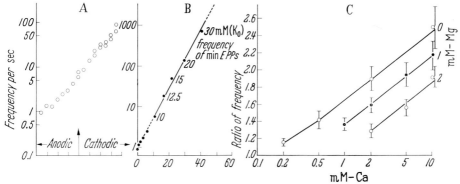

Fig. 10A—C. Frequencies of intracellularly recorded min. EPPs. A. Muscle fibre of rat diaphragm with polarizing currents applied to the nerve and electrotonically spreading to the terminals as in Fig. 9C and D, the abscissae being current strengths in arbitrary units (LILEY 1956c). B. Relation between frequencies of min. EPPs and calculated values in mV of nerve terminal depolarization due to increase in external potassium to the levels indicated for the points (plotted by KATZ 1962) from data of LILEY 1956c). C. Influence of calcium concentration upon min. EPP frequency. Ordinate. Ratio of frequency of min. EPPs in calcium-containing solution to frequency in solution without calcium. Abscissa. Calcium concentration. Upper points obtained in absence of $MgCl_2$, middle in 1 mM-$MgCl_2$, lower in 2 mM-$MgCl_2$. Bars indicate $\pm$ S.E. of mean ratio of frequencies (HUBBARD 1961)

When min. EPP frequencies are increased by excess potassium, TAKEUCHI and TAKEUCHI (1961) find that the application of hyperpolarizing currents through a microelectrode in the muscle at the endplate zone decreases the min. EPP frequency. However, this observation does not refute the above generalization that frequency is entirely dependent on presynaptic conditions; TAKEUCHI and TAKEUCHI show that probably the frequency is diminished because the current from the synaptic cleft into the muscle is largely carried by potassium ions, the synaptic cleft being consequently depleted of the excess potassium and the presynaptic depolarization diminished. As would be expected, the diminution of frequency is larger the greater the excess of extracellular potassium; and at normal levels of potassium the application of hyperpolarizing currents to the muscle fibre does not change the min. EPP frequency. The very large increase in min. EPP frequency when ammonium is substituted for sodium (FURUKAWA, FURUKAWA and TAKAGI 1957) is apparently due to the depolarization of the presynaptic terminals. At the same time there is an increase in size of the min. EPPs because ammonium ions penetrate the activated endplate membrane more readily than sodium (Chapter IV).

The role of presynaptic terminals in generating min. EPPs is well shown by investigations during nerve degeneration (BIRKS, KATZ and MILEDI 1960). All min. EPPs cease after several days, and then, after an intermission of several days, min. EPPs reappear but at a much lower frequency and with a much larger dispersion of amplitude. Though abnormal in many respects, pharmacological testing indicates that these min. EPPs are due to the quantal release of ACh; yet the presynaptic terminal has degenerated and a Schwann cell has entered into close contact with the muscle endplate membrane. BIRKS, KATZ and MILEDI suggest that the quanta are now released by this Schwann cell; and correspondingly they find in it sparsely distributed vesicles of various sizes that may have origin from ingested fragments of the presynaptic terminal.

Many procedures influence the frequency of the random production of min. EPPs; but, as indicated by their size, only one special pharmacological procedure (ELMQVIST, QUASTEL and THESLEFF 1963) modifies the amount of ACh in the packets. This exception will be shown later (Chapter V) not to conflict with the supposition here made that the packets of ACh are preformed in the presynaptic terminals and that the liberation of each packet is an independent event. Though there is no direct evidence that the synaptic vesicles of the presynaptic endings do contain acetylcholine, there is very convincing circumstantial evidence that these vesicles are in fact the preformed packets of transmitter.

Firstly, in the motor nerve terminals the vesicles are concentrated in that part of the presynaptic terminal that fronts the synaptic cleft (Fig. 1 B), some being in close apposition with the surface membrane (BIRKS, HUXLEY and KATZ 1960).

Secondly, the uniform size of the vesicles corresponds with the uniformity that is indicated for the packets of transmitter responsible for the miniature EPPs, and for the failure to modify the size of these packets by experimental means (DEL CASTILLO and KATZ 1956b). Furthermore, as measured by the size of the postsynaptic current flow, the packets have the same size for muscle fibres of very different diameters, the miniature EPPs being consequently even more than ten times larger in the smaller fibres than in the larger (KATZ and THESLEFF 1957a). However, there is evidence that occasionally the packets may be several times above the standard size (LILEY 1957), but there seem to be a few correspondingly large elongated vesicles (ROBERTSON 1956). If the transmitter is contained in the vesicles as an isotonic solution of an acetylcholine salt (0.15 M), there would be about 6,000 molecules in a spherical vesicle 500 Å in diameter, which is in good agreement with estimates of the packet size (DEL CASTILLO and KATZ 1956b; KATZ 1958a), though

MacIntosh (1959) gives a much lower figure. Recently there have been higher estimates (Straughan 1960; Krnjević and Mitchell 1961), which would require hypertonicity of the ACh in the vesicles; however the very large value given by the latter authors appears to be an over-estimate (Mitchell and Silver 1963).

Thirdly, the quantal liberation occurs at a multitude of foci distributed over the whole area of the synaptic contact (del Castillo and Katz 1956a), which corresponds with the distribution of the vesicles. The spatial distribution of the min. EPPs is particularly well illustrated in Fig. 9, because extracellular recording can only detect min. EPPs in close proximity to the electrode, while with intracellular recording the space constant is sufficiently long to allow all the min. EPPs at an amphibian endplate to be recorded. With the slow muscle fibres of amphibia the distribution of the min. EPPs along the muscle fibre corresponds with the wide distribution of the nerve terminals (Burke 1957).

It is well established that, when the presynaptic terminal of a motor nerve fibre is depolarized by a nerve impulse, there is momentarily an enormous acceleration in release of the packets of ACh; and that normally the EPP is composed of more than a hundred superimposed min. EPPs (Katz 1958a, 1962). However the actions of calcium and magnesium have appeared to be at variance with this concept. In both amphibia and mammals the size of the EPP is approximately proportional to the external calcium concentration (del Castillo and Katz 1954b; Liley 1956c), and magnesium acts as an antagonist to calcium (del Castillo and Engbaek 1954; Jenkinson 1957), being apparently a competitor for the active sites available for calcium occupation (Katz 1962). Yet only in the action of calcium on mammalian preparations is there any parallel between the frequency of min. EPPs and the size of the EPP (Boyd and Martin 1956a; Liley 1956c). Hubbard (1961) has suggested that this discrepancy arises because min. EPPs are of two types, one being calcium-independent and unrelated to the EPP, the other calcium-dependent and constituting the component units of the EPP. Fig. 10C shows that the frequency bears a linear relationship to the logarithm of the calcium concentration over the range 0.5 to 10 mM, and that magnesium antagonizes calcium, just as would be expected if it were a competitor for the sites of calcium action on the presynaptic terminals. The proportionality factor appears much lower than for the EPPs evoked by nerve impulses under these conditions; but, after allowance for the calcium-independent fraction, the proportionality factor corresponds to that for the EPP (del Castillo and Stark 1952). Depolarization of the nerve terminals by immersion in a bathing fluid in which the concentration of K^+ ions is raised to 10 or 20 mM confirms that the presence of calcium is essential for the acceleration of the min. EPP frequency by depolarization.

The postulate of a calcium-independent fraction of min. EPPs is based on the observation that min. EPPs continue indefinitely in the absence of calcium in the bathing solution, and even in the presence of a chelating agent and high magnesium (HUBBARD 1961). The frequency of this fraction is not affected by presynaptic depolarization by potassium, and therefore is assumed not to contribute to the EPP; but, in contrast to the calcium-dependent fraction, its frequency is raised by the stresses of stretching and of increased osmotic pressure. It appears that in the frog under resting conditions almost all of the min. EPPs are of the calcium-independent type; hence there arise

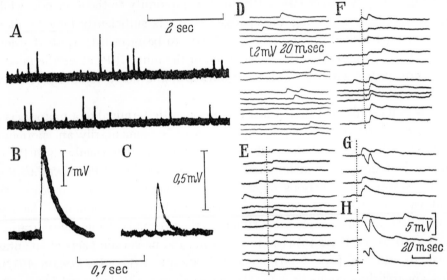

Fig. 11 A—H. Intracellularly recorded miniature postsynaptic potentials. A—C from a crayfish muscle fibre with a resting potential of −75 mV, A and C being spontaneous min. EPPs on same voltage scale, but with much faster sweep for C. B is an EPP set up by a single motor nerve impulse recorded at a lower amplification, but same speed as C (DUDEL and KUFFLER 1961a). D—H show miniature EPSPs and EPSPs from a motoneurone of an isolated frog spinal cord in which reflex responses were abolished by high magnesium. In E—H in addition a volley was set up with progressively stronger stimulation from E to H at the dotted line. Note that the minimum EPSP resembles the spontaneous miniature EPSP (KATZ and MILEDI 1963)

the discrepancies between observations on the min. EPP frequency and the size of the EPP.

Besides the amphibian and mammalian neuromuscular synapses that have been so intensively investigated, min. EPPs occur also at the neuromuscular synapses of fish (TAKEUCHI 1959) and of birds (GINSBORG 1960).

In crustacea (Fig. 11 A; DUDEL and ORKAND 1960; DUDEL and KUFFLER 1961a; GRUNDFEST and REUBEN 1961) the distribution of the min. EPPs corresponds to the numerous synaptic areas along the muscle fibres. In such respects as the random release of standard packets of transmitter these min. EPPs correspond to those of vertebrate muscle, which is of particular interest because quantal release is thus shown to occur for transmitters other than acetylcholine. Similarly the frequency is accelerated by increasing the osmotic pressure or the potassium of the external medium; for example it is accelerated by a factor of two by doubling the concentration of potassium from its initial level of 5.4 mM.

Min. EPPs also are regularly found at the adrenergic neuromuscular synapses on a mammalian smooth muscle, the guinea pig vas deferens (BURNSTOCK and HOLMAN 1961, 1962a). There is a very wide range in size distribution, and all have a slow time course, with a total duration over 100 msec. Presumably, when the quantal liberation occurs close to the recording site, the min. EPP is large on account of the small size of the muscle fibre (KATZ and THESLEFF 1957a), and the smaller and slower min. EPPs are produced by the more distant action of quanta. The min. EPPs are reduced in frequency, but otherwise are not changed by partial denervation and by chronic reserpinization. This latter observation is of special interest because it relates the min. EPP frequency to the catecholamine metabolism, both the noradrenaline content and the miniature frequency being reduced by the reserpinization to about 10% (BURN and RAND 1959; BURNSTOCK and HOLMAN 1962b).

With intracellular recording from neurones in the central nervous system spontaneous small excitatory postsynaptic potentials (EPSPs) have been frequently observed (BROCK, COOMBS and ECCLES 1952; ARAKI, OTANI and FURUKAWA 1953; GRANIT and PHILLIPS 1956; KUNO 1957; KOLMODIN and SKOGLUND 1958; LI 1959, 1961; ECCLES, ECCLES, IGGO and LUNDBERG 1961); but at least in large part this synaptic noise, as it has been called, is probably attributable to random synaptic bombardment. Certainly it is necessary to exclude production in this way before these random EPSPs can be regarded as true min. EPSPs analogous to min. EPPs.

KATZ and MILEDI (1963) have shown that the spontaneous EPSPs of frog motoneurones persist without obvious diminution (Fig. 11D) when the reflex activity of the isolated cord is reversibly abolished by soaking in high magnesium solutions (up to 40 mM) or when impulse conduction in the cord is suppressed by soaking in 60 mM potassium. Many of these EPSPs must therefore be analogous to the min. EPPs of the neuromuscular synapse and be due to the release of quanta of transmitter spontaneously from the nerve terminals. Spontaneous IPSPs are also observed, and likewise have a very wide dispersion in amplitude. However it must not therefore be concluded that, in contradistinction to EPPs, the individual quanta vary greatly in size, because the min. EPSP amplitude would be greatly reduced if the quanta were released at a dendritic site remote from the soma where the intracellular electrode presumably is located.

Intracellular recording from frog sympathetic ganglion cells discloses small spontaneous EPSPs that qualify as true min. EPSPs because random synaptic bombardment can be excluded in the isolated preparation (NISHI and KOKET-

SU 1960; BLACKMAN, GINSBORG and RAY 1961). TAUC (1958) has recorded random EPSPs and IPSPs from the giant ganglion cells of *Aplysia*, but concluded that they are probably due to random synaptic bombardment. In some synapses where such random bombardment can be excluded, miniature EPSPs are not observed; as for example with the giant synapse of the stellate ganglion of *Loligo* (BULLOCK and HAGIWARA 1957; TAKEUCHI and TAKEUCHI 1962). However the latter authors point out that, if a quantum of transmitter effected the same conductance change as on the frog endplate membrane, miniature EPSPs would be only about 5 μV in size and so not detectable above the noise level; hence the spontaneous release of packets of transmitter cannot be excluded.

At all synapses that have properties indicating chemical transmission synaptic vesicles are concentrated in the presynaptic terminals; so it can be presumed that quantal liberation of transmitter substance is a general phenomenon during synaptic activation, and it is not restricted to those synapses that give true miniature potentials. There is of course no necessity that there should be a background liberation of transmitter in the resting state. An absence of miniature postsynaptic potentials thus can be taken to indicate that the quantal emission does not occur until a threshold level of presynaptic depolarization has been attained. The relationship of presynaptic impulses to quantal emission will be discussed later.

CHAPTER IV

EXCITATORY POSTSYNAPTIC RESPONSES TO PRESYNAPTIC IMPULSES

With excitatory synapses it has been an invariable finding that presynaptic impulses evoke a localized depolarization of the postsynaptic membrane. With neuronal synapses this response has been termed the excitatory post-synaptic potential (EPSP), and, with neuromuscular synapses, the endplate potential (EPP). In the earlier investigations the EPSP and EPP were observed by extracellular recording (GÖPFERT and SCHAEFER 1938; SCHAEFER and HAASS 1939; ECCLES and O'CONNOR 1938, 1939; FENG 1940; ECCLES and KUFFLER 1941; ECCLES, KATZ and KUFFLER 1941; KUFFLER 1942a, b; BROOKS and ECCLES 1947b; BULLOCK 1948; BISHOP 1953), or by recording the potential electrotonically propagated along the postsynaptic axons, for example from the postganglionic trunk of a sympathetic ganglion (ECCLES 1935, 1943) or from ventral roots of the spinal cord (BARRON and MATTHEWS 1936, 1938; ECCLES and PRITCHARD 1937; ECCLES 1946a). But these older techniques are almost completely superseded by the intracellular recording of post-synaptic potentials, which was first applied to the neuromuscular synapses (FATT and KATZ 1950, 1951a, 1952a; NASTUK 1953) then to the following structures: the mammalian motoneurone (BROCK, COOMBS and ECCLES 1951, 1952; WOODBURY and PATTON 1952; FRANK and FUORTES 1955); the moto-neurones of the electric lobe of *Torpedo* (ALBE-FESSARD and BUSER 1952, 1954); the motoneurones of the toad spinal cord (ARAKI, OTANI and FURU-KAWA 1953; ARAKI and OTANI 1955); the crustacean neuromuscular synapses (FATT and KATZ 1953a); the stellate ganglion of *Loligo* (BULLOCK and HAGI-WARA 1955); the mammalian sympathetic ganglion (R. M. ECCLES 1955); the giant ganglion cells of *Aplysia* (TAUC 1955); to quote most of the pioneer investigations performed up to 1955. More recent investigations will be reviewed when the many features of excitatory synaptic action are considered under the various headings.

A. Synaptic delay

Before the advent of intracellular recording, synaptic delay was measured between the arrival time of the presynaptic impulse at the presynaptic terminals and the onset of the postsynaptic depolarization, as recorded extracellularly. Values so derived were as brief as 0.5 and 0.6 msec for the neuromuscular junctions of mammals and amphibia respectively (ECCLES, KATZ and KUFFLER 1941; KUFFLER 1948, 1949) and 0.3 to 0.5 msec for synapses on mammalian motoneurones (ECCLES 1946a; BROOKS and ECCLES 1947b). Sometimes the

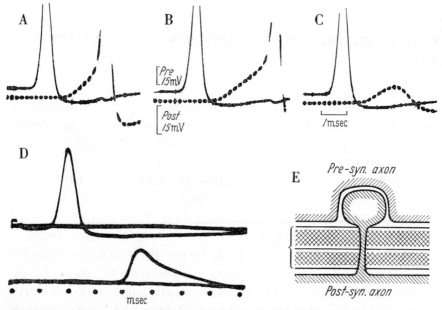

Fig. 12A—E. Intracellular recording from the presynaptic and postsynaptic fibres of the squid stellate ganglion, as in Fig. 8A. The presynaptic spike potentials (continuous line) and responses of the post-synaptic axon (broken line) are recorded simultaneously, the spikes being truncated. In B and C the synaptic transmission started to fail as a consequence of the prolonged repetitive presynaptic stimulation. Voltage scales for presynaptic and postsynaptic potentials are labelled. Temperature, 21—22° C (HAGIWARA and TASAKI 1958). D. As in A—C, but at lower temperature (15—20° C) and showing in lower record the full time course of an EPSP uncomplicated by spike potentials (BULLOCK and HAGIWARA 1957). E. Drawing showing one of the many regions of close contact made by fine axoplasmic processes that extend from the postsynaptic axon towards the presynaptic axon, being there separated by a synaptic cleft as in Figs. 1—3 (HAGIWARA and TASAKI 1958)

arrival time of the presynaptic impulse was calculated on the basis of the observed conduction velocity and conduction distance, but with the amphibian neuromuscular synapse KUFFLER (1948, 1949) applied the stimulation to the nerve in close proximity to the junction, so recording a synaptic delay of 0.6 to 0.9 msec when the presynaptic conduction time was reduced to a negligible value. Alternatively, with extracellular recording of the monosynaptic activation of mammalian motoneurones, the arrival time of the presynaptic impulse at the synaptic terminals and the onset of the EPSP were displayed with the same extracellular records, the synaptic delay being thus shown to be about 0.3 to 0.45 msec (BROOKS and ECCLES 1947b).

Intracellular recording of the postsynaptic potential has given a more precise determination of the onset of the EPSP or EPP, and invariably has confirmed the various values for synaptic delay as determined by extracellular recording. However, it has been suggested (LLOYD 1944, 1955, 1960a) that the synaptic delay would be vanishingly small if allowances were made for the additional but unrecordable delays involved in conduction of presynaptic impulses into the fine presynaptic terminals. This suggestion is difficult to refute for the majority of synaptic junctions, where the presynaptic terminals are so slender that intracellular recording is impracticable, though it would be surprising if the invasion by the presynaptic impulses of the expanded surface of the fine branching presynaptic terminals would produce no detectable extracellular potential.

However, this contention need not be argued, for there is indubitable evidence for a considerable synaptic delay in the giant synapses of the squid stellate ganglion, where the impulse in the giant presynaptic fibre can be displayed by intracellular recording right at the region of the synaptic contacts (BULLOCK and HAGIWARA 1957; HAGIWARA and TASAKI 1958; TAKEUCHI and TAKEUCHI 1962). For example in Fig. 12D, there is a synaptic delay of about 2 msec between the active phase of the presynaptic impulse and the onset of EPSP, both being intracellularly recorded; and in Fig. 12A—C, the synaptic delay of about 1 msec is not lengthened when the EPSP is so depressed by prolonged repetitive stimulation that no impulse is set up postsynaptically. Fig. 12A—D is remarkable in showing that the large depolarizing potential of the presynaptic impulse failed to cause any detectable potential change in the postsynaptic membrane, it thus being a good example of the electric uncoupling considered in Chapter III.

Intracellular recording of the presynaptic spike potential does not give so precise a measurement of the arrival time of the impulse at the terminals as does an extracellular microelectrode in close proximity to the terminal. If located within a very few microns of the terminal, the microelectrode would pick up potentials produced by the currents generated by the presynaptic impulse as it propagates up to the synapse. It would also pick up the postsynaptic current responsible for the postsynaptic potential. It is shown in Chapter VIII that the arrival time of the presynaptic impulse is signalled by the onset of the negatively directed extracellular potential, while the beginning of the postsynaptic current is signalled by the onset of the second negative extracellular potential. In Fig. 46D the synaptic delay so measured is 1.2 msec for the squid giant synapse (TAKEUCHI and TAKEUCHI 1962) and in Fig. 46E it is 0.22 msec for a single neuromuscular synapse of the isolated rat diaphragm, the mean value being 0.217 ± 0.004 (SE) msec for 53 synapses of this type (HUBBARD and SCHMIDT 1963).

This synaptic delay of the mammalian neuromuscular synapse is the briefest yet reported, though an estimate of 0.3 msec has been given for the synapses on mammalian motoneurones (ECCLES 1957), and values as brief as 0.2 msec are indicated when the presynaptic spike potential is recorded by the micro-electrode at the same time as the intracellular EPSP (BROCK, COOMBS and ECCLES 1952, Fig. 9). It seems likely that synaptic delays of about 0.3 msec occur throughout the mammalian central nervous system, as well as at neuro-muscular synapses on striated muscle. These values stand in contrast to the relatively long delays for the autonomic effector system. For example, by allowing for conduction time in presynaptic fibres, the synaptic delays for activation of the cat nictitating membrane and the guinea pig vas deferens were found to be not less than 10 msec (ECCLES and MAGLADERY 1937; BURN-STOCK and HOLMAN 1961); and by stimulating nerve twigs in very close proxi-mity to the presynaptic terminals, BURNSTOCK and HOLMAN (1963, personal communication) could not shorten the synaptic delay below 6 msec. It is still not known how large a fraction of this delay is attributable to conduction time in the fine presynaptic terminals. The various factors contributing to the synaptic delay of chemically transmitting synapses will be considered in Chapter VI.

B. Time courses of excitatory postsynaptic potentials (EPSPs and EPPs)

It will be convenient in the first instance to consider the EPSPs recorded intracellularly from nerve cells. When the postsynaptic potential is produced either by a single impulse or by a virtually synchronous bombardment of impulses, it exhibits a characteristic time course—a relatively rapid rise to a summit from which there is a slower, approximately exponential, decay. As illustrated in Fig. 13 A—I, the size, but not the time course, is changed by varying the volley size, which is an example of spatial summation. Further-more, when several presynaptic impulses synchronously bombard a neurone, the EPSP is virtually identical with the arithmetical sum of the individual EPSPs (ECCLES, ECCLES and LUNDBERG, unpublished observations), as may be seen in the summation of 3 EPSPs in Fig. 13, where $J + K + L = M$. Similarly with frog motoneurones there is a simple summation of hetero-synaptically produced EPSPs (FADIGA and BROOKHART 1962).

The role of spatial summation in building the EPSP will be appreciated even more when it is recognized that the EPSP is composed of superimposed quantal components. As illustrated in Fig. 11 E—H, when synaptic trans-mission is greatly depressed by high magnesium or potassium, presynaptic impulses evoke EPSPs of recognizable quantal composition (KATZ and MILEDI 1963), as will be further discussed in Chapter VI.

In Table 1 there is a wide range in the values of EPSPs for different types of nerve cells, the time to summit varying from 1 to 20 msec and the time constant of decay from 1 to 120 msec. Among the fastest are the neurones of the mammalian central nervous system and the squid stellate ganglion. Not unexpectedly, the motoneurones of amphibia at a temperature of about 15 to 20° C (FADIGA and BROOKHART 1960; FUKAMI 1961) are slower than those of mammals at 37° C. As illustrated in Fig. 14A, the activated synapses must depolarize the postsynaptic membrane by causing an inward flow of current in that part of the postsynaptic membrane acted on by the synaptic transmitter, with a corresponding outflow from the remainder of the membrane.

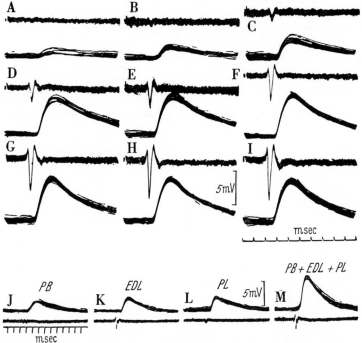

Fig. 13 A—M. Monosynaptic EPSPs recorded intracellularly in motoneurones of lumbar region of cat spinal cord, each record being formed by the superposition of about 25 faint traces. In A—I the EPSP is generated in a medial gastrocnemius motoneurone by an afferent volley from medial gastrocnemius nerve of progressively increasing size, as indicated by the spike potentials in the upper records from the dorsal roots. The EPSP attained its maximum in F, where the afferent volley was probably maximum for group Ia. In J—M, EPSPs are similarly recorded in a peroneous longus motoneurone in response to maximum group Ia volleys from the nerves to peroneus brevis, extensor digitorum longus and peroneus longus, and by all three volleys together, as indicated by the symbols (ECCLES, ECCLES and LUNDBERG 1957a; and unpublished observations)

In general it can be assumed that the time to the summit of the EPSP gives a measure of the duration of the intense phase of transmitter action on the postsynaptic membrane. On the other hand the decay of the EPSP is usually to a large extent determined by the electric time constant of the post-synaptic membrane, but is slowed somewhat by residual transmitter action, as has been particularly well shown by NISHI and KOKETSU (1960) on sympathetic ganglion cells of the frog (Fig. 14B, C). Since these neurones have synapses distributed over their approximately spherical somas and are devoid of dendrites, they provide ideal conditions for comparing the time courses of EPSPs and depolarizations produced by rectangular pulses of current. Almost invariably the EPSPs decay more slowly than the depolarization generated by a current pulse, the mean time constants being 12.1 and 9.7 msec respectively (Table 1). Thus it is concluded by NISHI and KOKETSU that a small residual transmitter action delays the decay of the EPSP, as is revealed in their analysis of the EPSP (Fig. 14 C).

Table 1. *Values for some properties of a representative series of excitatory postsynaptic potentials (EPSP or EPP) for some chemical synapses*
Ranges of values given in brackets. References are cited in the text.

Synaptic type	Synaptic delay	Time to summit	Time constant decay	Time constant postsynaptic membrane	Threshold for spike initiation	Approximate reversal potential for EPSP or EPP
	msec	msec	msec	msec	mV	mV
Motoneurone mammal 38° C	0.3	1.2 (1.0—1.5)	4.9 (3.5—6.1)	3.2 (2.3—3.6)	10 (5—18)	0
Motoneurone frog	(1.0—1.2)	(2.5—3)	(6.5—10)	—	10	—
Motoneurone toad	1.5	2.1	8.0	4.5	10	
Sympathetic ganglion frog	—	2.5—3	12.1 (9.5—14.5)	9.7 (7.5—12.0)	25	— 14 (0 to — 20)
Giant synapse Loligo	1—2	1—1.5	1—1.5	1—1.5	10—15	0
Cardiac ganglion lobster	—	10	20	12	—	— 10
Aplysia, large ganglion cell	—	20	120	45	—	—
EPP frog twitch muscle	0.6—1.0	1.3 (1.0—1.6)	—	—	40	— 15 (— 10 to — 20)
EPP mammalian muscle 38° C	0.2	0.6	1.9	2—3	10—20	—

A similar conclusion is reached by MARTIN and PILAR (1963 a) in their analysis of the EPSPs of the chick ganglion cell, where the dotted line in Fig. 15 E shows that the transmitter action has a duration almost as long as the EPSP. With other spherical neurones devoid of dendrites, the time constant of decay of the EPSP is also longer than the membrane time constant, e.g. ratios of 25/10 and 120/45 for the respective time constants of small and large ganglion cells of *Aplysia* (Fig. 14 D, E; FESSARD and TAUC 1957; TAUC 1958); (30 to 40)/(4 to 6) for the supramedullary cells of the Puffer (HAGIWARA and SAITO 1957, 1959); and with the lobster cardiac ganglion cells the long duration of the synaptic transmitter action (Fig. 15 D) causes the EPSP to decay much more slowly than if it were governed by the time constant of the membrane (HAGIWARA, WATANABE and SAITO 1959). Some of the large discrepancy with *Aplysia* is no doubt attributable to the location of the excitatory synapses on the axon at some distance from the soma (cf. TAUC 1962a, b); as a consequence the EPSPs recorded in the soma would have a considerable

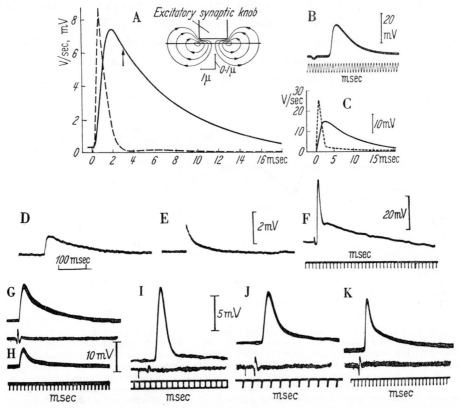

Fig. 14A—K. In A the mean curve of the EPSP of a motoneurone recorded as in Fig. 13, is plotted as a continuous line and analysed on the basis of the membrane time constant as described in the text in order to determine the time course (the broken line) of the postsynaptic currents that generate this potential change. The flow of this current relative to an activated synapse is shown diagrammatically in the inset for a synapse in which the vertical scale is exaggerated tenfold relative to the horizontal (CURTIS and ECCLES 1959). B. Shows an EPSP recorded in a frog sympathetic ganglion cell and C shows such an EPSP analysed as in A to give the time course of the postsynaptic current, the dotted line (NISHI and KOKETSU 1960). D, E. Intracellular records from ganglion cell of Aplysia, D being an EPSP and E a depolarization produced by a brief current pulse applied through another microelectrode in the same cell, which was a large ganglion cell 350 μ in diameter (TAUC 1958). F. EPSP (not spike) recorded intracellularly from a Renshaw cell and evoked by a ventral root volley (ECCLES, ECCLES, IGGO and LUNDBERG 1961). G, H. Monosynaptic EPSPs produced in a gastrocnemius motoneurone, G before and H after deterioration of the motoneurone, the resting membrane potential falling from −61 to −45 mV and the membrane time constant from 5.2 to 1.5 msec. I, J and K are EPSPs of dorsal spinocerebellar tract cells evoked respectively by Group Ia volleys from nerves to plantaris and gastrocnemius-soleus muscles, and by Group Ib volleys from the latter muscle (ECCLES 1961b)

electrotonic slowing of time course, their time to summit being lengthened and their rate of decay slowed. In contrast there is no evidence of a residual transmitter action for the synapses of the stellate ganglion of the squid where the active phase is little more than 1 msec in duration, and the decay of the EPSP is as fast as after an applied depolarizing current (Fig. 12D; HAGIWARA and TASAKI 1958).

In the vertebrate central nervous system, neurones usually have fairly extensive dendritic branches, which introduce considerable distortion by virtue of the electrotonic flow of the applied currents into the dendrites from the assumed location of the intracellular electrode in the soma. The effects of this distortion have been emphasized by RALL (1959, 1960), who has suggested that the difference between the time constants of the postsynaptic membrane as determined by the applied currents and of the EPSP (3.2 and 4.9 msec in Table 1) is completely accounted for without the postulate of a small residual

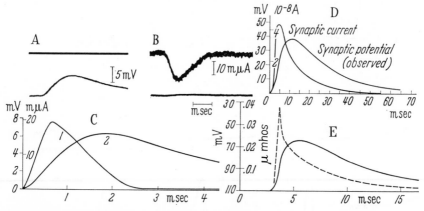

Fig. 15 A—E. EPSPs and time courses of the synaptic currents. A—C. Monosynaptic EPSPs recorded as in Fig. 13 from a cat motoneurone. In A the lower trace shows an EPSP, the upper beam being switched to record the membrane current. B: record of current (upper beam) required for voltage clamping of the membrane at its resting level during the EPSP. The clamped membrane potential is shown in the lower beam. C: tracings of the EPSP in A (curve 2) and the excitatory postsynaptic current in B (curve 1) respectively, the current trace being reversed (ARAKI and TERZUOLO 1962). D shows plotting of EPSP and postsynaptic current flow due to monosynaptic activation of cardiac ganglion cell of lobster (HAGIWARA, WATANABE and SAITO 1959). E shows EPSP and the shunt conductance of the activated synaptic membrane (broken-line) for monosynaptic activation of a chick ciliary ganglion (MARTIN and PILAR 1963a)

active phase of transmitter action (Fig. 14A), and as with frog sympathetic ganglia (Fig. 14C). Unfortunately all attempts to analyse even the most accurate results can at best be but a very crude procedure because there is no information on the geometry of the neurone actually under investigation—not only of the soma and dendrites, but also of the location on it of the activated synapses. On the basis of the careful systematic measurements on lumbar motoneurones of the cat (AITKEN and BRIDGER 1961), it has been shown that RALL's mathematical treatment for the soma-dendrite system results in only a small increase in the membrane time constant, with the consequence that the postulate of a residual transmitter action as in Fig. 14A is not refuted (ECCLES 1961b).

This small residium is also indicated by other independent lines of evidence (CURTIS and ECCLES 1959; ECCLES 1961b). For example the EPSP already in existence is destroyed during the phase of high membrane conductance that occurs when an antidromic impulse propagates up the axon and into the soma and dendrites of a motoneurone; but, even when this invasion begins more than 3 msec after the start of the EPSP (e.g. as late as the arrow in Fig. 14A), there is still an appreciable rebuilding of EPSP after the subsidence of the antidromic spike potential some 2 msec later. There is a comparable rebuilding of EPSP after the spike potential of frog motoneurones that are activated monosynaptically by a single synchronous volley (FADIGA and BROOKHART 1960). But more significant evidence of a prolonged transmitter action is given by the depression of the antidromic spike potential, which occurs throughout most of the duration of the monosynaptically evoked EPSP and which is attributable to the short-circuiting effect of the enduring transmitter action (FADIGA and BROOKHART 1960; Chapter VII). Residual transmitter action is also indicated by Fig. 14H, where the very short membrane time constant of the deteriorated motoneurone (cf. Fig. 14G) results in an initial rapid decay of the EPSP and a prolonged slow decay.

Furthermore, the existence of residual transmitter action is exhibited indubitably at several other types of synapse in the central nervous system, though the actual time course of the synaptic depolarizing action has not yet been determined analytically as in Fig. 14A, C. For example, the EPSP produced by the synchronous synaptic bombardment of a Renshaw cell has a brief intense phase that declines after about 2 msec onto a large residual potential that persists for as long as 50 msec (Fig. 14F). Normally this residual EPSP is responsible for the repetitive discharges that are such a remarkable feature of Renshaw cell responses (Fig. 45 E—H; RENSHAW 1946a; ECCLES, FATT and KOKETSU 1954; ECCLES, ECCLES, IGGO and LUNDBERG 1961). When the enzymic destruction of synaptic transmitter is prevented by a large dose of eserine, a single synchronous synaptic activation can produce a repetitive discharge that persists for as long as two seconds (Fig. 23D; ECCLES, ECCLES and FATT 1956).

In Fig. 14I—K are EPSPs produced in cells of origin of the dorsal spinocerebellar tract by afferent volleys in Group Ia or Ib fibres (ECCLES, OSCARSSON and WILLIS 1961). The neurones were deteriorated, and there was an initial rapid decline of the EPSP, as in Fig. 14H, but thereafter there was a slowly declining component indicative of a prolonged transmitter action. Before deterioration this prolonged transmitter action was adequate to evoke a second spike discharge. Other instances of prolonged synaptic action are exhibited in the many situations where single afferent volleys produce repetitive discharges of cells in the spinal cord; for example a group Ia volley acting on intermediate neurones (ECCLES, FATT and LANDGREN 1956), and a cutaneous afferent volley acting on cells in the dorsal horn (Fig. 45 A—D; McINTYRE, MARK and STEINER 1956; HUNT and KUNO 1959; HAAPANEN, KOLMODIN and SKOGLUND

1958; WALL 1959; ECCLES, ECCLES and LUNDBERG 1960; ECCLES, KOSTYUK and SCHMIDT 1962a). Intracellular recording, as in Fig. 14I—K, often provides evidence that this repetitive discharge can be due to a depolarization that smoothly follows on from the initial spike potential, and often not to later synaptic bombardments via interneuronal relays. In all these types of neurones there has been no direct measurement of the electric time constant, so it is not possible to calculate the approximate time course of synaptic action as in Figs. 14A, C; 15D. Nevertheless the general picture emerges that with most types of excitatory synapse a presynaptic impulse acts on the subsynaptic membrane causing it to produce an initial intense flow of depolarizing current which subsides in a very few milliseconds to a low residual current that may persist for 10 or more milliseconds. When well developed, this residual synaptic action causes a single presynaptic volley to evoke a repetitive discharge, as is most strikingly shown with Renshaw cells.

At higher levels of the mammalian nervous system synaptic action appears generally to be more prolonged than in the spinal cord. For example an ascending dorsal column volley acting on cells of the cuneate nucleus usually evokes a brief repetitive discharge (AMASSIAN and DE VITO 1957; ANDERSON, ECCLES, SCHMIDT and YOKOTA 1963b) that is sufficiently explained by an enduring EPSP of the cuneate cells and not to a delayed interneuronal bombardment. Synaptic excitation of cortical pyramidal cells may give prolonged EPSPs (up to 80 msec) that apparently arise from a brief initial synaptic excitation (PHILLIPS 1961; LI 1961; LI and CHOU 1962). EPSPs of comparable duration may be seen in thalamic neurones on the rare occasions where there is no later IPSP (ANDERSEN, BROOKS and ECCLES 1963). It will be seen later that IPSPs in the brain have a duration often in excess of 100 msec (Chapters X, XIII), which is also the case for all presynaptic inhibitory actions in the brain and spinal cord (Chapter XV). Though there are as yet no investigations of the electric time constants of the postsynaptic membranes concerned in all these prolonged responses, it is hardly possible that it could be the responsible factor. It would therefore seem that in the central nervous system the great majority of synapses are characterized by prolonged transmitter actions.

The geometrical features of the neuromuscular synapse make it possible to apply a different method for determining the time course of transmitter action. The relatively restricted area of the synaptic junction on the long extended cylinders of the muscle fibres is responsible for a very large distortion of the time course of the EPP as recorded intracellularly anywhere along the muscle fibre (FATT and KATZ 1951; BOYD and MARTIN 1956b). Close to the synapse the EPP has an early high peak followed by a very rapid decay, which is largely attributable to the electrotonic spread of the depolarization along the muscle fibres. At progressively further distances from the synapse, the recorded EPPs are progressively slower both in rise and decline. When the total depolarization is integrated for the distributed capacity of the muscle fibre, it is found with both amphibian and mammalian muscle fibres that 2 msec after the onset of the EPP there is an exponential decay of the depolarization with a time course that corresponds closely with the electric time constant of the muscle membrane (FATT and KATZ 1951; BOYD and MARTIN 1956b); hence it can be concluded that the transmitter action has virtually ceased within 2 msec of its onset. However, when the cholinesterase at the junction is inactivated by anticholinesterases, there is a considerable lengthening of the time course of the EPP, particularly its rate of decay (Fig. 16E, F; FATT and KATZ 1951; TAKEUCHI and TAKEUCHI 1959); so the transmitter action would then be continuing throughout the whole duration of the EPP, much as with the residual actions at many types of synapses between neurones.

Excitatory impulses act on crustacean muscle by producing an endplate potential (Figs. 11 B; 66A) which resembles the EPP of vertebrate muscle, but the nerve endings are widely dispersed along the length of the muscle fibre, and correspondingly the EPP is distributed at a fairly uniform size over the whole length of the fibre (FATT and KATZ 1953a; DUDEL and KUFFLER 1961a). BURKE and GINSBORG (1956b) similarly find a distribution of the EPP along the tonic muscle fibres of the frog. As a result of a systematic examination of many crustacean muscles HOYLE and WIERSMA (1958a) show that there are "slow" and "fast" types of motor axons giving distinctive EPPs even in the same muscle fibre. A more striking difference will be described when reviewing the effect of repetitive stimulation. The EPPs produced by adrenergic innervation of smooth muscle fibres have a very slow time course with about 100 msec rise time to the summit and a half decay time of 150 msec, which is attributed to the long duration of the noradrenaline action (BURNSTOCK and HOLMAN 1961). Correspondingly, BROWN and GILLESPIE (1957) report a very slow destruction of the noradrenaline liberated by adrenergic nerve terminals in the spleen.

There have been several investigations designed to give a direct record of the current that flows through the subsynaptic membrane when an EPSP or EPP is produced by a single presynaptic volley. So far as practicable the potential at the postsynaptic membrane is clamped at the resting level and the current flow required for this clamping during synaptic activation can be assumed to be a mirror image of the flow of current across the activated subsynaptic membrane.

By employing this voltage-clamp technique TAKEUCHI and TAKEUCHI (1959, 1960b) have given a very elegant demonstration of the current that flows through the motor endplate in producing the EPP. Thus in Fig. 16B there is a record of the current that has to be applied through a microelectrode at the endplate zone in order just to neutralize the current that would otherwise give the EPP of Fig. 16A. It is seen that this *endplate current* (EPC) runs a much briefer time course than the EPP, which confirms the conclusions from earlier investigations (ECCLES, KATZ and KUFFLER 1941; KUFFLER 1942b; FATT and KATZ 1951) that the EPC has normally a relatively brief duration, the greater part of the declining phase of the EPP being due to a passively decaying electrotonus. However, comparison of Fig. 16E with C shows that inactivation of the acetylcholine esterase (AChE) by eserine causes a remarkable prolongation of the EPC, and this effect of eserine is even more evident in the absence of d-tubocurarine in D and F. These results are readily explicable if the EPC at any instant is taken as a measure of the occupation of

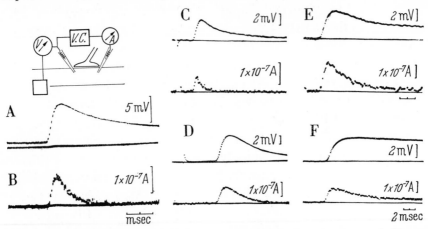

Fig. 16A—F. A is EPP recorded intracellularly from a curarized frog sartorius muscle fibre, and B gives current flow through voltage clamp device (V.C.) in order to prevent membrane potential change, as shown with other beam (see inset diagram), i.e. B gives postsynaptic current that generates the EPP of A. C corresponds to A, B in another fibre, and in E the preparation was soaked in eserine, 1/5000. D corresponds to A, B in another fibre, but transmission was depressed by sodium-deficient RINGER's solution instead of by curare, while in F eserine 1/5000 was added as in E (temperature: 17 to 18° C) (TAKEUCHI and TAKEUCHI 1959)

the ACh receptor sites by ACh. Fig. 16E, F thus shows that, with inactivation of the AChE in the synaptic cleft, the ACh released by a nerve impulse survives many times longer. In passing, it may be recalled that curarizing agents act as if they were competitive with ACh in occupying the ACh receptor sites (DEL CASTILLO and KATZ 1957a). Both the EPP and the EPC are shortened in duration by dTC (Fig. 16D, C; OOMURA and TOMITA 1961), which suggests that with occupation of receptor sites by dTC a greater fraction of the ACh is free and available for enzymic destruction (cf. ECCLES, KATZ and KUFFLER 1942).

Voltage clamping of monosynaptically activated motoneurones (ARAKI and TERZUOLO 1962) is necessarily imperfect because of the synapses on dendrites remote from the application of the clamp; nevertheless there is an initial intense current followed by a barely detectable residual current (Fig. 15B, C), that is very similar to the calculated curve (Fig. 14A). With the large neurones of the cardiac ganglion of the lobster the postsynaptic current has a relatively long duration (Fig. 15 D), the early part of the decline of the EPSP being greatly slowed thereby (HAGIWARA, WATANABE and SAITO 1959). On the other hand with the giant synapses of the stellate ganglion of *Loligo* the postsynaptic current has a very brief duration (HAGIWARA and TASAKI 1958), which corresponds to the finding that the time constant of decay of the EPSP is the same as that of the postsynaptic membrane (Table 1). Unfortunately the technical problems of voltage clamping have so far prevented its application to all but these few excitatory synapses.

C. Ionic mechanism of EPSP and EPP

As shown in Fig. 14A (inset) the activated synapses must cause depolarization of the postsynaptic membrane (the EPSP) by virtue of an inward flow of current in the subsynaptic membrane, which would give the required outflow (and hence depolarization) from the remainder of the membrane. Our

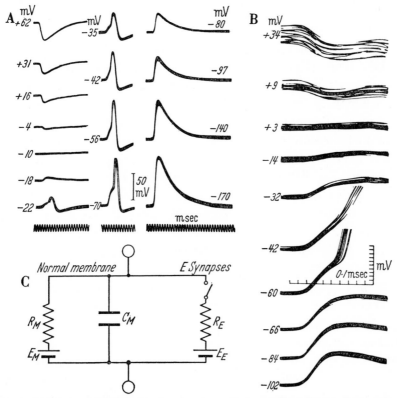

Fig. 17A—C. A. A series of EPSPs set up in a frog sympathetic ganglion cell. Membrane potential was changed from the resting level (−70 mV) by steady current through the recording microelectrode, the actual potential being indicated in mV on each record. Note spike potentials in addition at −22 to −70 mV. Temperature 24—26° C (NISHI and KOKETSU 1960). B. EPSPs set up in a cat biceps-semitendinosus motoneurone at various levels of membrane potential as indicated. Each record is formed by the superposition of about 20 faint traces. The membrane potential was shifted to the indicated values from its resting value of −66 mV by steady currents through the other barrel of the double microelectrode (COOMBS, ECCLES and FATT 1955c). C. Formal electric diagram of a postsynaptic membrane with areas of excitatory synapses as shown on the right side. Further description in text and in Table 2 present problems concern the voltage that causes this postsynaptic current to flow and the ionic mechanisms that are responsible for it. By passing a steady current through the intracellular electrode, the membrane potential can be displaced over a wide range, as illustrated for a frog sympathetic ganglion cell in Fig. 17A (Nishi and KOKETSU 1960). As a consequence it is seen that the EPSP is reversed when the membrane is held at an extreme level of depolarization (-4 mV) or even of reversed potential (16, 31 and 62 mV). On the contrary the EPSP is greatly increased when the membrane is hyperpolarized above the resting potential of -70 mV. There is an approximately linear relationship of the EPSP to the membrane potential, the EPSP being zero at -10 mV, which is thus the *equilibrium potential* for the ionic mechanism that produces the EPSP. The mean value of this equilibrium potential for frog sympathetic ganglion cells is -14 mV (range -8 to -20 mV). With the large neurones of the cardiac ganglion of the lobster, variation of the membrane potential over a wide range reveals its linear relationship to both the EPSP and the postsynaptic current, the equilibrium potential being -10 mV (HAGIWARA, WATANABE and SAITO 1959). A similar experiment on the EPSPs of ganglion cells of *Onchidium* suggests that the equilibrium potential is about 0 mV (KUSANO and HAGIWARA 1961). In a comparable series of EPSPs for a mammalian motoneurone (Fig. 17B) the equilibrium is virtually at zero membrane potential (COOMBS, ECCLES and FATT 1955c). The only other investigations of the equilibrium potential of neuronal EPSPs have been on the toad (ARAKI 1960) and the giant synapse of the squid stellate ganglion (HAGIWARA and TASAKI 1958), where approximate values of 0 mV are obtained by extrapolation. The EPSPs which nerve impulses set up in electroplaques of *Torpedo*, *Narcine*, *Astroscopus* and *Raia* are all reversed by depolarization, the equilibrium potential again being approximately at zero (GRUNDFEST and BENNETT 1961).

Comparable investigations on the EPP of amphibian neuromuscular junctions show that the equilibrium potential lies between -10 and -20 mV, both with the EPP of twitch muscles (DEL CASTILLO and KATZ 1954e; TAKEUCHI and TAKEUCHI 1959, 1960b) and with tonic muscles (BURKE and GINSBORG 1956b). A remarkable feature is the linear relationship of EPP to membrane potential measured relative to the equilibrium potential for the EPP. Using the voltage-clamp technique TAKEUCHI and TAKEUCHI (1959, 1960b) show that the endplate current (EPC) exhibits a similar linear relationship (Fig. 18A, B), which by extrapolation gives an equilibrium potential of -10 to -15 mV. Virtually the same equilibrium potential, -10 to -20 mV, is obtained by testing the effect of the EPC at various times during the large depolarizations produced by a muscle spike potential (DEL CASTILLO and KATZ 1954e). For example in Fig. 19 the EPC initially moves the spike potential downwards in A and B and upwards in D, while in C there is approximately equilibrium at rather less than -20 mV. This effect of the transmitter action on the spike potential is shown diagrammatically in Fig. 19 E.

The linear relationship between membrane potential and EPC (Fig. 18 B) establishes that the EPC is due to ions moving down their electrochemical gradients and not to an ionic pump, for example. Hence the conditions causing the generation of the EPSP or EPP can be shown by a formal electrical diagram (Fig. 17 C), where the activation of the synapses closes the switch shown in the right element of the diagram. A battery E_E has been inserted in this element in accordance with the most reliable determination of the equilibrium potential both for the EPP and the EPSP. The approximate values for the various components are shown in Table 2 for several synaptic junctions.

Table 2. *Approximate values for the various components of Fig. 17 C, derived from a representative series of chemical excitatory synapses*
References are cited in the text. Minimum values are given for R_E.

Synaptic type	R_M Ω	E_M mV	C_M F	R_E Ω	E_E mV
Monosynaptic on motoneurone mammal	1.2×10^6	-70	2.5×10^{-9}	5×10^5	0
Sympathetic ganglion frog	2×10^7	-65	5×10^{-10}	3×10^6	-8 to -20
Twitch muscle frog	$2-3 \times 10^5$	-90	8×10^{-7}	$2-10 \times 10^4$	-10 to -20

As KATZ (1962) has pointed out, the reaction between the excitatory transmitter and the membrane receptors has no regenerative link; the local conductance change produced by the ACh is independent of the level of membrane potential (FATT and KATZ 1951; TAKEUCHI and TAKEUCHI 1960 b). The excitatory transmitter substance must greatly increase the ionic conductance of the subsynaptic membrane and the only ion species in sufficient abundance to participate appreciably in this conductance are sodium, potassium and chloride. The fraction of the total conductance due to each one of these ion species has been assessed by observing the effects that changes in concentration of each have on the equilibrium potential for the EPC (TAKEUCHI and TAKEUCHI 1960 b). For example in Fig. 18 B the open circles and crosses are obtained after replacement of the chloride in the extracellular medium by the presumably impermeable glutamate ion. Since both extrapolated lines cross the base line at the same point, there is virtually no change in the equilibrium potential for the EPC; hence increased chloride conductance can make little if any contribution to the EPC. On the other hand, changes in the relative concentrations either of sodium or of potassium across the membrane cause changes in the equilibrium potential of the EPC which indicate that almost all of the increased conductance is shared between these two ion species, that for sodium being rather larger. Consequently the action of the chemical transmitter on the endplate membrane can be shown diagrammatically as in Fig. 18 C (TAKEUCHI and TAKEUCHI 1960b). The displacement of membrane potential produced by applied ACh has the same equilibrium potential as the EPC (AXELESSON and THESLEFF 1959), and is due to the same ionic permeability (TAKEUCHI 1963), as indeed would be expected if the transmitter substance is ACh.

With the frog neuromuscular junction FURUKAWA, TAKAGI and SUGIHARA (1956) show that ammonium ions can substitute for sodium ions, being even more effective in the process of depolarization produced by synaptic trans-

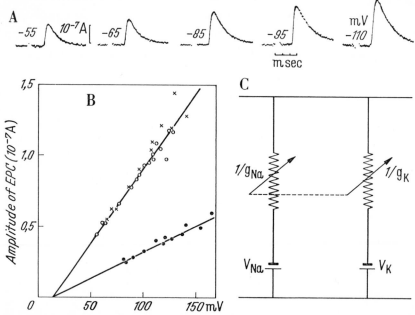

Fig. 18A—C. A are endplate currents (EPCs) recorded under voltage clamp conditions in response to a single nerve volley as in Fig. 16. The membrane potentials are indicated (TAKEUCHI and TAKEUCHI 1959). In B the filled circles plot the EPCs against membrane potential for a series resembling A. The open circles and crosses were obtained after replacement of the chloride in the extracellular medium by glutamate, and the concentration of dTC was also reduced. C shows schematically the assumed changes that occur in sodium (g_{Na}) and potassium (g_K) conductances during an EPC (TAKEUCHI and TAKEUCHI 1960a). The battery V_K should be shown the reverse of V_{Na}

mission and by acetylcholine, as also can hydrazinium (KOKETSU and NISHI 1959). In more systematic studies NASTUK (1959) and FURUKAWA and FURU-KAWA (1959) confirm the effectiveness of ammonium ions and find that many substituted ammonium ions also can replace sodium. For example the various methyl ammoniums are good substitutes, while larger ions such as trimethyl-ethylammonium, choline and dimethyldiethanolammonium are poor. Thus, these preliminary investigations with the EPP suggest that the transmitter has quite a limited action in increasing the permeability of the subsynaptic membrane to cations, there being probably a size limitation with a diameter of hydrated ion no more than twice the diameter of the hydrated potassium ion.

Despite the relative constriction in the pores which the transmitter action opens up in the subsynaptic membrane, the permeability for small cations, K^+

and Na+, must be very high in order to account for the very high conductance of the activated subsynaptic membrane. For example KATZ (1958a) and TAKEUCHI and TAKEUCHI (1960a) both calculate that a miniature EPP is produced by a momentary membrane conductance of 1 to 2×10^{-7} mhos. In the very brief time available (1 to 2 msec) the quantum of acetylcholine can diffuse to only 10 to 20 square microns of receptive surface, which must have its conductance increased to the extraordinarily high value of 1 mho/cm². This conductance is several thousand times larger than for the resting membrane, and even many times the conductance of the muscle membrane during the spike potential (FATT and KATZ 1951). This dominance of the endplate conductance is well illustrated in Fig. 19.

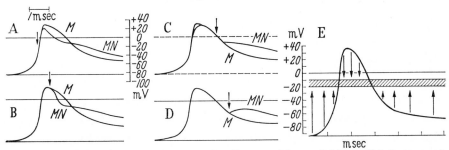

Fig. 19 A—E. A—D superimposed tracings of muscle spike potentials recorded intracellularly at an endplate region. The tracing labelled M is produced by a muscle impulse propagating past the endplate zone. At the times indicated by the arrows a nerve impulse set up an endplate potential that was superimposed on the muscle spike to give the tracing MN. In E, the arrows show directions in which endplate currents affect the muscle spike potentials (DEL CASTILLO and KATZ 1954e)

There is relatively little evidence relating to the ionic permeabilities that are responsible for the currents generating the EPSPs of nerve cells. By electrophoretic injection through an intracellular electrode, large changes can be made in the ionic composition of motoneurones (COOMBS, ECCLES and FATT 1955c; ARAKI, ITO and OSCARSSON 1961; ARAKI, ITO, KOSTYUK, OSCARSSON and OSHIMA 1962). These injections of anions or cations may cause a considerable decrease in the membrane potential and the EPSP is then diminished correspondingly. Otherwise there is no appreciable change in voltage and time course, which contrasts with the large changes simultaneously observed in the spike potential, in the after-hyperpolarization following a spike and in the inhibitory postsynaptic potential. Hence it is concluded that the transmitter substance causes the subsynaptic membrane to become permeable to all these types of injected ions, the largest of which have diameters (in the hydrated state) more than double that of the hydrated K+ and Cl- ions. In the light of the recent evidence that anions are not appreciably concerned in generation of the EPP, further investigation is desirable, particularly with isolated preparations where it will be possible to change the extracellular ions in the way that was done by TAKEUCHI and TAKEUCHI (1960b) in their investigations on the EPP.

CHAPTER V

EXCITATORY TRANSMITTER SUBSTANCES

As pointed out by PATON (1958), CURTIS (1961b) and McLENNAN (1963), several criteria have to be satisfied before one can have full confidence in classifying a substance as a synaptic transmitter: the substance must exist in sufficient quantities in the presynaptic terminals, which must also contain a synthesizing enzyme system; stimulation of the presynaptic nerves must release the substance in adequate quantities from the presynaptic terminals; the action of the substance on the postsynaptic cell must be identical with that of the synaptic action, particularly when applied by micro-electrophoretic techniques; there should be an inactivating enzyme system in the region of the synaptic cleft; when the action of drugs is tested by micro-electrophoretic injection, the pharmacology of the synaptic transmission and of the post-synaptic action of the substance must be similar.

It is not now necessary to argue the case for the existence of chemical synaptic transmission. Chapter I gives in outline the various stages of the dramatic controversy between the exponents of the chemical and electrical hypotheses. In retrospect it is generally recognized that this controversy stimulated much good scientific investigation and led to a deeper understanding of the physiological and pharmacological problems involved in chemical transmission (DALE 1952). Despite the immense efforts of the last decades, no new excitatory transmitter has been identified, though several suggestive developments will be referred to later in this Chapter. Consequently the problems of manufacture, storage, mobilization, release and removal of a chemical transmitter will be treated almost entirely in relation to acetylcholine and noradrenaline. It is not possible to give a comprehensive account of all the metabolic studies on acetylcholine and noradrenaline. Instead, particular examples will be singled out in order to illustrate special features of transmitter metabolism. Subsequently there will be reference to evidence relating to other possible transmitter substances. The recent monograph by McLENNAN (1963) should be referred to for a more comprehensive treatment.

A. Metabolism of excitatory transmitter substances

1. The acetylcholine metabolism of a sympathetic ganglion

The acetylcholine metabolism of sympathetic ganglia has been studied ever since the cholinergic nature of transmission was recognized (FELDBERG and VARTIAINEN 1934; BROWN and FELDBERG 1936; EMMELIN and MAC-INTOSH 1948, 1956; PERRY 1953). However, it is only recently that the investigations of BIRKS and MACINTOSH (1957, 1961) have given the first precise and comprehensive picture of the cellular mechanisms involved in the manufacture of a transmitter substance, as may be seen diagrammatically in Fig. 20. Essentially their technique involves accurate measurements both of the acetylcholine (ACh) content and of the ACh output of the superior cervical ganglion. The ganglia are perfused by oxygenated Ringer Locke or plasma and are studied under resting conditions or under prolonged activation by maximum preganglionic volleys over a wide range of frequencies. The analysis of the metabolic pathways is made

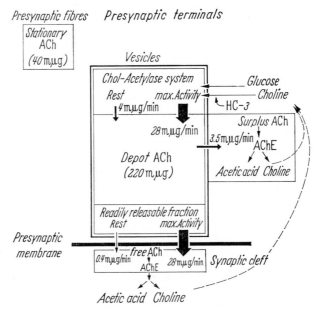

Fig. 20. Diagrammatic representation of the acetylcholine metabolism of the cat superior cervical ganglion according to BIRKS and MACINTOSH (1961). Full description in text

possible both by the use of hemicholinium 3 (HC-3), which has been shown to inhibit ACh synthesis (MACINTOSH, BIRKS and SASTRY 1956; MACINTOSH 1961), and by the suppression of acetylcholinesterase (AChE) by anticholinesterases such as eserine or tetraethylpyrophosphate (TEPP). The AChE of the superior cervical ganglion is virtually all located on the presynaptic terminals (KOELLE and KOELLE 1959).

The synthesis of acetylcholine by choline acetylase is dependent on the continued supply of choline and of glucose. When this is ensured, it has been shown by direct estimation that in the superior cervical ganglion ACh synthesis can be depressed to a negligible level by the drug hemicholinium (HC-3) (BIRKS and MACINTOSH 1957, 1961; MACINTOSH 1961). As would be expected, there is then a profound depression of the release of ACh during prolonged stimulation (Fig. 21 A, oblique crosses), and an associated blockage of transmission through the normally circulated ganglion during stimulation at 20/sec for 20 minutes. This blockage is not a curarizing action due to postsynaptic depression because it develops only during prolonged stimulation, and rest restores transmission, as also does intravenous injection of choline (BIRKS and MACINTOSH 1961).

It will be appreciated that the diagram of Fig. 20 gives a conceptual model in which the experimental data are related to structural features of the gan-

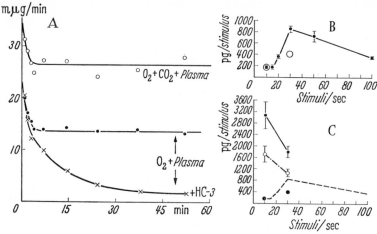

Fig. 21 A—C. Time courses of output of transmitter substances during repetitive stimulation. A: ACh output of a plasma-perfused superior cervical ganglion of cat during 20/sec stimulation of the preganglionic trunk and in the presence of 3×10^{-5} M eserine. Upper curve, mean of 5 experiments in which plasma had been gassed with $CO_2 + O_2$, p_H 7.4. Filled circles, mean of 5 experiments in which gassing was with O_2 only. Crosses, mean of 5 experiments with perfusate containing hemicholinium-3 (HC-3) at concentration 2×10^{-5} M (BIRKS and MACINTOSH 1961). B. Relation between frequency of stimulation and overflow of noradrenaline into the splenic circulation during stimulation of the cat splenic nerves. Each point shows the mean and S.E. of mean of several experiments. The open circles show the mean overflow values at 10 and 30/sec stimulation in 29 preparations that had been rested by decentralization (section of preganglionics) from 19 hours to 6 days previously. C. The curves and points of B are plotted on a reduced ordinate scale and in addition the increased liberation at 10 and 30/sec that occurs under the influence of an adrenergic blocking agent (dibenyline, phentolamine or hydergine). The upper filled circles are means for 12 rested preparations, the open circles for more than 20 normal experiments (BROWN and GILLESPIE 1957; BROWN, DAVIES and FERRY 1961)

glion, and to this extent it is hypothetical. Thus it is postulated that the ACh of the cat superior cervical ganglion is contained in three main compartments. There is firstly about 40 mμg of ACh in a compartment where it cannot be depleted by prolonged stimulation of the presynaptic fibres to a ganglion in which synthesis of ACh is blocked by HC-3, and where it is inaccessible to the AChE of the ganglion. This so-called "Stationary-ACh" is certainly in some extra-synaptic region of the ganglion; and, since the ACh of the preganglionic trunk exhibits similar features, it is assumed to be largely in the presynaptic nerve fibres within the ganglion. The remainder of the extractable ACh of the ganglion exists in compartments that are in diffusional relationship; and it must be in the presynaptic terminals because presynaptic volleys release ACh from the principal component (the Depot-ACh), which has a normal level of about 220 mμg. As shown in Fig. 20 it is assumed that the Depot-ACh is contained in the synaptic vesicles and that the other fraction of the ACh in the nerve terminals (Surplus-ACh) is contained in the extra-vesicular space, where it is exposed to hydrolysis by the AChE of the presynaptic terminals (KOELLE and KOELLE 1959; McISAAC and KOELLE 1959). When this AChE is inactivated, the Surplus-ACh progressively accumulates; hence an explanation is provided for the paradox that, during activation of a ganglion perfused by eserinized Ringer Locke, there is progressive decline of the output of ACh to a low level despite a well maintained content of ACh in the ganglion (BROWN and FELDBERG 1936; KAHLSON and MACINTOSH 1939). Most of this content would then be the Surplus-ACh, which is not available for release by nerve impulses.

When the preganglionic nerve to the superior cervical ganglion is severed, the choline-acetylase in the distal segment virtually disappears in a few days (BANNISTER and SCRASE 1950), while there is even a transitory increase in the segment proximal to the section; hence it seems that the ACh manufacturing system is produced in the nerve cell and travels thence along the axon to the site of manufacture of ACh in the nerve terminals (HEBB and WAITES 1956). This manufacture of ACh by the choline-acetylase system is assumed to occur within the compartment containing the Depot-ACh, which presumably is the synaptic vesicles. As shown in Fig. 20 the Depot-ACh is directly replenished at the resting rate of ACh manufacture, about 4 mμg/min. Only about 10% (0.4 mμg/min) of this resting production appears in the effluent of the ganglion; the remainder (about 3.5 mμg/min) diffuses into the Surplus-ACh compartment, where it normally would be hydrolysed by AChE, but where in the presence of anti-AChE it accumulates at this rate of 3.5 mμg/min to reach eventually a level in excess of the Depot-ACh (BIRKS and MACINTOSH 1961).

Activation of the ganglion by presynaptic volleys effects two changes in the ACh metabolism. There is firstly an increase in the rate of liberation of ACh, so that, under optimal conditions of perfusion (plasma equilibrated with CO_2 and O_2), a steady rate as high as 28 mμg/min is reached and maintained indefinitely (Fig. 21 A, open circles). Correspondingly there is an increase in the synthesis of ACh so that it, too, reaches a level of about 28 mμg/min. The synthesis of ACh is of course dependent on a continued supply of choline, and it is necessary to add choline when perfusing by Ringer Locke. However, when perfusing by plasma, the addition of choline does not increase the rate of synthesis even when ACh hydrolysis is prevented; hence normally there is no significant feed-back of the choline liberated by AChE hydrolysis, as was proposed by PERRY (1953) and as is indicated by the broken lines in Fig. 20. Similarly VOLLE and KOELLE (1961) found that choline did not alleviate the failing transmission of repetitively stimulated ganglia treated with anti-AChE.

It is further shown in Fig. 20 that calcium ions are essentially concerned in the liberation of ACh during activity. Concentrations up to 10 to 20 mM greatly increase the output of ACh from the stimulated ganglion (HARVEY and MAC-INTOSH 1940; HUTTER and KOSTIAL 1954). Barium can act as a substitute for calcium (DOUGLAS, LYWOOD and STRAUB 1961) and magnesium is an antagonist, just as at the neuromuscular synapse (Chapters III, VI). It is suggested by BIRKS and MACINTOSH (1961) that the increased ACh liberation resulting from the action of CO_2 and the plasma factor may be due to an influence on this calcium effect, or may be independent of it.

The diagram does not attempt to account for the two essential responses to activation by presynaptic volleys; the increased release of ACh (up to 70 times the resting rate) and the increased synthesis of ACh (up to 7 times the resting rate). The manner in which nerve impulses increase the release of ACh will be considered in relation to neuromuscular transmission (Chapter VI), where it has been very thoroughly investigated. However the diagram does indicate that less than one quarter of the Depot-ACh (the readily releasable fraction) is immediately available for release by nerve impulses, and is later replenished from the main reserves in the Depot (BIRKS and MACINTOSH 1961). Furthermore, the release of ACh would be quantal, presumably by synaptic vesicles, because the Surplus-ACh outside the vesicles is not available for release by nerve impulses.

The diagrammatic arrangement in Fig. 20 would suggest that activation by presynaptic volleys depletes the Depot-ACh and so increases the rate of synthesis of ACh. However, accurate measurement of the Depot-ACh in ganglia perfused by plasma or blood fails to disclose any depletion even during 2 hours of stimulation at 20/sec (BIRKS and MACINTOSH 1961). As suggested by these authors, the influence of depletion of ACh in stimulating its synthesis should be considered at the level of the quantal mechanism for release of transmitter and presumably in relation to individual synaptic vesicles, not to the collective assemblage diagrammed in Fig. 20. Calculation shows that, if the Depot-ACh is contained in synaptic vesicles, it must be in such a high concentration, isotonic or even higher (Chapter III), that it can be assumed to retard further synthesis. When activation causes a vesicle to release its ACh into the synaptic cleft (Chapter VI), there would be an immediate resumption of synthesis of ACh in that vesicle, i.e. the synthesis would be occurring only in the small fraction of the vesicles that had released their ACh. Hence the rate of synthesis is maintained at a high level even though the total Depot-ACh is not appreciably depleted. It is relevant to this explanation that on extraction from the ganglion the choline-acetylase synthesizes ACh more than 4 times faster than the maximum rate in the ganglion (BANNISTER and SCRASE 1950). It will be appreciated that this explanation of the way in which ACh output accelerates synthesis accounts for the indefinite maintenance of ACh synthesis at maximal level (Fig. 21 A) when the ganglion is maintained under physiological conditions of perfusion either with plasma plus CO_2 or with blood, and stimulated at a frequency of about 20/sec. It also accounts for the rapid decrease of synthesis on cessation of stimulation. It may be a general phenomenon that synaptic vesicles are recharged after they have unloaded their quantum of transmitter into the synaptic cleft; and this accumulation of recharging vesicles may contribute to the formation of the organelles that GRAY (1959, 1963) describes on the presynaptic side of the active zone of the synapse (Chapter II).

2. Acetylcholine metabolism of the neuromuscular synapse

The acetylcholine metabolism at neuromuscular synapses is much more difficult to investigate because they form such a minute part of a nerve-muscle preparation. The release of ACh by nerve impulses (DALE and FELDBERG 1934; DALE, FELDBERG and VOGT 1936) was indeed one of the principal experimental bases for the hypothesis of cholinergic transmission at the neuromuscular synapse. More recently there have been investigations designed to give a quantitative measure of the output of ACh by a single impulse at a motor synapse.

From the measured output during repetitive stimulation EMMELIN and MACINTOSH (1956) calculated an output of 5×10^{-12} g ACh from the cat tibialis anticus muscle in response to a single maximal volley. Assuming single synapses on 10^5 muscle fibres, there would be about 5×10^{-17} g per synapse. However the rate of stimulation (20 to 25/sec) was too high for maintenance of maximum ACh output per impulse. In the isolated rat diaphragm preparation STRAUGHAN (1960) obtains an output of 3.5×10^{-16} g/impulse at a synapse when stimulating at 6/sec and KRNJEVIĆ and MITCHELL (1961) find outputs up to 5 times greater still when stimulating at 2/sec. As with the superior cervical ganglion, the output per impulse falls as the rate of stimulation is increased. The maximum rate of production (about 3×10^{-9} g/min from the rat hemi-diaphragm) is attained at frequencies of 20 to 50/sec (STRAUGHAN 1960). The resting output of ACh has been given as 300 to 400×10^{-12} g/min from the rat hemidiaphragm (STRAUGHAN 1960; MITCHELL and SILVER 1963) or less than half that amount (KRNJEVIĆ and MITCHELL 1961). Certainly it is much larger than the value expected from the resting quantal release of ACh that is responsible for the miniature EPPs. Presumably it arises from structures other than the nerve endings because after denervation it continues at about 50% of normal (MITCHELL and SILVER 1963). However, HEBB (1962) suggests that the very small level of choline-acetylase activity surviving in the denervated muscle may actually be in the degenerated nerve and its endings and could be sufficient to account for the observed output of ACh.

Just as with the superior cervical ganglion, intravenous injection of HC-3 into normally circulated muscles results in depression of neuro-muscular transmission during prolonged tetanization (DESMEDT 1958; REITZEL and LONG 1959). After the tetanus there is a very slow recovery, which is quite different from the rapid recovery to the post-tetanic potentiation that occurs with muscles partly blocked by dTC (Fig. 38C). DESMEDT (1958, 1961) finds that the post-tetanic depression of myasthenic muscle closely resembles that of HC-3 treated muscle and hence proposes that the essential lesion in myasthenia is impairment of ACh synthesis, either by some circulating substance acting like HC-3, or by some defect in the supply of choline-acetylase to the nerve endings. Intracellular recording from excised intercostal muscle fibres from myasthenic patients gives strong support to DESMEDT's hypothesis (DAHLBACK, ELMQVIST, JOHNS, RADNESS and THESLEFF 1962). Miniature EPPs are infrequent and are not increased in high potassium solutions, and there is little or no sign of the post-tetanic potentiation normally observed; all of which accords with the postulate that there is a severe deficiency in transmitter formation and release.

It is of great interest that, during prolonged tetanization at 10 to 20/sec of muscles treated with HC-3, there is a progressive and severe diminution of the miniature EPPs virtually to extinction and there is a parallel diminuition of the EPPs (ELMQVIST, QUASTEL and THESLEFF 1963). This diminution is not attributable to a curarizing action of the HC-3, because at very low frequencies both the EPP and the min. EPP are diminished only by 10 to 20% to a plateau that is reached in 5 to 10 min. It seems likely that this action of HC-3 during severe tetanization is the first experimental demonstration of a reduction in the quantal size of ACh. Reference to Fig. 20 shows that this effect is explicable by HC-3 acting as a competitor to choline in the process of absorption to the site of ACh manufacture, as has been postulated by BIRKS and MACINTOSH (1961) and MACINTOSH (1961). An alternative explanation of the diminution in min. EPPs is that the desensitization of receptor sites (Fig. 22E) during the high frequency tetanization may be more severe in the presence of HC-3.

HC-3 also has been shown to cause neuromuscular block by acting as a curarizing agent when applied to rat or frog muscles *in vitro*, decreasing their sensitivity to directly applied ACh and also decreasing the size of the miniature EPPs without affecting their frequency or the quantal numbers of the EPPs produced by nerve stimulation (Chapter VI; MARTIN and ORKAND 1961; THIESS and BROOKS 1961). However, these experiments are not in conflict with those of THESLEFF because the ACh reserves of the nerve terminals would not be seriously depleted by their testing stimulations in which a total of no more than a few thousand stimuli were applied, whereas THESLEFF applied up to 50,000 stimuli.

3. Noradrenaline output from adrenergic terminals

In 1946 VON EULER showed that the adrenergic transmitter is noradrenaline, not adrenaline as had been originally believed, though much evidence had accumulated to the contrary (cf. BACQ 1935). It appears that adrenaline is not a transmitter of any synapses (VON EULER 1959). There is evidence paralleling that for ACh that noradrenaline is stored and possibly manufactured in the adrenergic terminals (VON EULER and HILLARP 1956). Presumably it, too, is contained in the synaptic vesicles that are observed in adrenergic nerve terminals on smooth muscle (CAESAR, EDWARDS and RUSKA 1957; RICHARDSON 1958; YAMAMOTO 1960) from which it is quantally released (BURNSTOCK and HOLMAN 1961, 1962a), just as with ACh. By a powerful new histochemical technique it has been possible to discover that there is a very high noradrenaline content in nerve fibres descending the spinal cord to ramify around the neurones of the intermedio-lateral horn (CARLSSON, FALCK, FUXE and HILLARP 1963). Hence it seems likely that for the first time an adrenergic synaptic action has been identified in the central nervous system. It is of particular significance that these postulated adrenergic synapses are on neurones that are believed to be the cells of origin of the sympathetic preganglionic fibres. These fibres act cholinergically on the sympathetic ganglion cells that in turn are largely adrenergic activators of peripheral effector organs, i.e. the sequence would be: adrenergic-cholinergic-adrenergic, which corresponds to the alternation suggested by FELDBERG and VOGT (1948).

By chemical extraction and chromatographic identification, BROWN and GILLESPIE (1957) and BROWN, DAVIES and FERRY (1961) have shown that stimulation of the splenic nerves results in an output of noradrenaline from the spleen which on pharmacological assay is found to be appropriate for precise study. A characteristic curve is obtained when the frequency of stimulation is varied (Fig. 21 B), there being a maximum output per volley at a frequency of 30/sec. The output at low frequencies is greatly increased in the presence of substances blocking adrenergic action, such as dibenamine and dibenyline, whereas at high frequencies there is very little increase (Fig. 21 C, open circles). This effect is attributed to the action of the adrenoceptive sites in binding and destroying the liberated noradrenaline, an action which is proportionally much less efficient at high frequencies because of the saturation of the receptor sites. Since inactivation of monamine oxidase does not affect the output of noradrenaline into the perfusion fluid (BROWN and GILLESPIE 1957), this enzyme does not seem to be important in destruction of liberated noradrenaline. Other enzymic inactivating processes have been suggested (AXELROD 1959).

After prolonged inactivity of the splenic nerve (BROWN, DAVIES and FERRY 1961) there is an increased liberation of noradrenaline, but the uptake and destruction by receptor sites is so much increased that less appears in the effluent (open circles, Fig. 21 B; lower filled circles, Fig. 21 C), the increased output being apparent only when the receptor sites are blocked (upper filled circles in C). In general the effect of frequency on output of noradrenaline is much the same as with acetylcholine. The output per impulse declines with frequencies above 10/sec (Fig. 21 C) and is temporarily increased after a conditioning tetanization.

As noted in Chapter III the action of reserpine in greatly reducing the noradrenaline content of adrenergically innervated organs (BURN and RAND 1959) is paralleled by the diminution it produces both in the frequency of the min. EPPs and in the size of EPPs of the adrenergically innervated smooth muscle (BURNSTOCK and HOLMAN 1962b), but there is little if any diminution in the size of the min EPPs. Conceivably a large diminution in the quantal content of noradrenaline might be brought about by tetanization as severe as that used by ELMQVIST, QUASTEL and THESLEFF (1963) for cholinergic synapses.

B. Action of excitatory transmitter substances on the subsynaptic membrane

Strictly speaking, an investigation of the effects produced by controlled application of the transmitter substance on the subsynaptic membrane has been performed only with the known cholinergic synapses: amphibian and mammalian neuromuscular synapses; sympathetic ganglion synapses; and the synapses on Renshaw cells in the spinal cord. However, the investigations already reviewed (Chapter IV) show that the transmitter released by presynaptic impulses has much the same kind of action at all excitatory synapses; so it can be presumed that the investigations with acetylcholine at the neuromuscular synapse have a wide implication. Acetylcholine action on sympathetic ganglion synapses is given special consideration in Chapter VIII.

With micro-electrophoretic injection it is possible to apply very minute quantities of acetylcholine in close proximity to a neuromuscular synapse whose responses are registered by an intracellular microelectrode as is illustrated diagrammatically in Fig. 22 (NASTUK 1953, 1959; DEL CASTILLO and KATZ 1955a, 1956b, 1957a, b, c; KATZ and THESLEFF 1957b; THESLEFF 1958, 1960a; KRNJEVIĆ and MILEDI 1958; MILEDI 1960a, b). When great care is exercised to apply the micropipette charged with acetylcholine (2—4 M ACh chloride) within a few microns of the endplate, the ACh emission produced by a very brief (0.1 to 1.0 msec) and small outward current causes a depolarization of the muscle fibre that has a time course almost as fast as the EPP produced by a nerve impulse (KRNJEVIĆ and MILEDI 1958). For example in Fig. 22B the rise time is about twice as long as for the EPP (1.3 msec in A), but the rates of decline are very similar. In view of the rate of diffusion of ACh, such a rapid response indicates that the micropipette was within $4\,\mu$ of the endplate. It was calculated that 1.5×10^{-14} g of ACh was injected in Fig. 22 B, and significant muscle depolarizations have been produced by injections as small as 1.5×10^{-15} g (KRNJEVIĆ and MILEDI 1958).

These quantities of ACh are very little larger than the observed output of ACh which is given as 1.5×10^{-15} g per impulse under the most favourable conditions (KRNJEVIĆ and MITCHELL 1961). Thus with the improved microtechniques there has been a virtual bridging of the gap between the quantity of ACh released by an impulse and that required to produce an equivalent muscle depolarization. In fact as pointed out by FATT (1954, 1959) and EMMELIN and MACINTOSH (1956) the gap is surprisingly narrow when it is realized how vastly different are the conditions of application. The presynaptic impulse causes the release of ACh at a multitude

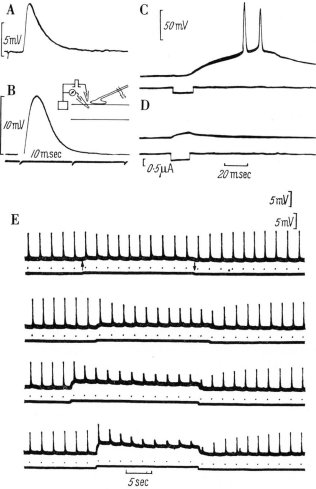

Fig. 22 A—E. A. End-plate potential evoked by stimulation of phrenic nerve. The muscle was paralysed by 15.0 mM magnesium. B. Acetylcholine potential evoked in another fibre by a 1 msec pulse of current (3.5×10^{-8} amp) from an ACh-filled micropipette in close proximity to an endplate (inset diagram). In both cases, muscles were rat diaphragms, at 24—25° C.; the potentials were recorded with intracellular electrodes (KRNJEVIĆ and MILEDI 1958). C, D. External and internal application of acetylcholine to a motor endplate. In C, ACh was injected by a 16 msec current pulse (see lower trace) as in B and evoked a large depolarization that generated two spike potentials. Between C and D the micropipette entered the muscle fibre. The same current pulse now produced merely the small catelectrotonic potential due to passage of the current across the fibre membrane (DEL CASTILLO and KATZ 1955a). E. Application of ACh to the outside of an endplate by twin pipettes with intracellular recording as in B and C. Brief testing injections of constant size were applied at intervals of about 2.5 sec from one barrel, and gave the brief depolarizations shown in each upper trace. An intercurrent low steady injection of ACh was applied through the other barrel for 20 to 30 sec as shown by the lower monitor trace for each series. The intensity of this injection was increased from above downwards (see monitor records) (KATZ and THESLEFF 1957b)

(100 to 300) of sites that open directly into the synaptic cleft. The diffusion distance is thus no more than 1μ for the application of ACh to a very large

fraction of the subsynaptic membrane. Even with the most favourable location of the micropipette the acetylcholine will be injected at a site several microns from the endplate and will diffuse radially therefrom in all directions. As a consequence only a relatively small fraction would reach the edge of the synaptic cleft and diffuse into the cleft to reach receptor sites on the subsynaptic membrane (cf. FATT 1954; DEL CASTILLO and KATZ 1955a). Moreover, the injection technique would be inefficient also because of the gross inequality of ACh application to the receptor sites, the adjacent ones being overloaded, the more remote being uninfluenced. DEL CASTILLO and KATZ (1955a) showed that, with progressive increase in the distance between injection site and endplate, there was the falling off in size and the slowing of time course of response that would be expected from the diffusion equations.

Recently MILEDI (1960b) has shown that the ACh receptor sites are not restricted to the actual subsynaptic membrane, but extend in progressively diminishing concentration for up to 300μ away from the endplates on muscle fibres of the rat diaphragm, where the actual endplate is less than 30μ in diameter (COLE 1957). These sparsely distributed receptor sites contribute to the depolarization produced by relatively large ACh injections at sites remote from the endplate (Fig. 22C). However, the quick responses to extremely small injections occur only when the micropipette is accurately located over the endplate; and DEL CASTILLO and KATZ (1957a, b) have shown that the subsynaptic receptor sites are readily accessible to d-tubocurarine applied by electrophoretic injection, as evidenced by the depression it produces in the EPP.

When the injecting micropipette is inserted intracellularly below the subsynaptic membrane, the injection of ACh by an outward current pulse produces merely a small catelectrotonic potential (Fig. 22D), which is entirely due to the current flow across the muscle membrane (DEL CASTILLO and KATZ 1955a). The ineffectiveness of the internally injected ACh cannot be explained by postulating its destruction by AChE, for the stable choline-ester, carbachol, is similarly ineffective. Hence it can be concluded that ACh receptor sites are exclusively located on the outer surface of the endplate membrane and that the membrane itself is so impermeable to ACh that these external receptor sites are not accessible to internally injected ACh (DEL CASTILLO and KATZ 1955a).

Electrophoretic injection of ACh on to the endplate receptor sites has been employed to study the desensitization of these receptors when subjected to a prolonged dose of ACh (THESLEFF 1955; KATZ and THESLEFF 1957b; AXELSSON and THESLEFF 1958). A steady low ejection rate produces in a few seconds a considerable desensitization that is best demonstrated by the decreasing depolarizations produced by standard brief testing ejections of ACh (Fig. 22E). The desensitization comes on slowly with a half-time of about 5 sec and passes off at about the same rate when the steady background of ACh is withdrawn.

Evidently, these results show that, when ACh is combined with "receptor molecules" for several seconds, they are slowly degraded into a form that is no longer able to produce and maintain the high ionic permeability that occurs with brief ACh actions (KATZ and THESLEFF 1957b; DEL CASTILLO and KATZ 1957c). On cessation of the steady injection of ACh, the testing pulses of ACh recover their full depolarizing action (Fig. 22E), which indicates a reversed transformation from the degraded to active receptors. Kinetic studies suggest that this latter transformation occurs only after the ACh combination has dissociated (KATZ and THESLEFF 1957b). The actions of decamethonium and succinylcholine on endplate receptors are in part due to a similar process of desensitization, though in part the block of neuro-muscular transmission is due to a prolonged endplate depolarization (BURNS and PATON 1951; ZAIMIS 1953; DEL CASTILLO and KATZ 1957b, c; THESLEFF 1955, 1958). By a similar technique TAUC and BRUNER (1963) demonstrate a desensitization of ACh receptors on the body of ganglion cells of Aplysia and other Mollusca, which differs only in the longer time course.

Simple curarizing agents can also be studied by the method of electro-phoretic injection (DEL CASTILLO and KATZ 1957a, b). It was confirmed that d-tubocurarine does not alter the membrane potential or ionic permeability of the endplate membrane. Its equivalent effectiveness in blocking both neuromuscular transmission and the depolarizing action of electrophoretically applied acetylcholine can be explained by its competitive occupation of the ACh receptor sites (DEL CASTILLO and KATZ 1957b; JENKINSON 1960). As would be expected, d-tubocurarine is ineffective when injected into the muscle fibre at the endplate region, just as was observed with ACh in Fig. 22D.

By histochemical techniques it has now been established that acetylcholin-esterase (AChE) is concentrated on the subsynaptic membrane of the neuro-muscular junction, especially in the region of the junctional folds (COUTEAUX 1958). Thus the enzymic receptor sites for ACh are located in close proximity to the receptor sites responsible for its depolarizing action (cf. ŽUPANČIĆ 1952). These two types of receptor are of course readily differentiated by the action of their specific inhibitors, the anticholinesterases on the one hand and curari-form compounds on the other. In Chapter VIII there will be presented pharma-cological evidence suggesting that there are two types of receptor sites for ACh on ganglion cells, one type resembles the endplate receptor, the other is a specific site for anti-AChEs as well as for ACh. Nearly all anti-AChEs are slowly acting, so their effect in increasing the sensitivity of the endplate to applied ACh is more difficult to demonstrate when they are applied electro-phoretically. However, a rapidly acting anti-AChE, edrophonium (NASTUK and ALEXANDER 1954), when injected electrophoretically increases the depo-larization produced by an injection of ACh applied a fraction of a second later, but has no effect on the response to a carbachol injection (KATZ and THESLEFF

1957c). A rapid anti-AChE action of decamethonium and choline can similarly be demonstrated (DEL CASTILLO and KATZ 1957c).

Because the synaptic transmitter substances have not been identified for other junctions, comparable investigations have not been possible; but the pharmacological results with neuro-muscular transmission help in attempting to explain the action of pharmacological agents on other synaptic transmissions and also in attempting to assess the credentials of suspected transmitters.

The concept of receptor sites is conveniently used in all discussions relating to chemical synaptic transmission, yet practically nothing is known about their structure or distribution on the postsynaptic side of the synaptic cleft. When muscles are paralysed by radio-active curarine, the number of receptor sites at a single endplate can be estimated by an ingenious technique based on auto-radiography (WASER 1960, 1961). Block of neuromuscular transmission occurs when approximately 3×10^6 molecules of curarine are combined with each endplate. Since depression of the EPP to about one fourth is required for paralysis, it is assumed that there can be no more than 4×10^6 receptor sites altogether. WASER points out that the number of ACh molecules released by a single impulse at a neuromuscular junction is of the same order of magnitude, for example 200 quanta each of 10,000 molecules (Chapters III and VI). 4×10^6 molecules of curarine cover less than 1 per cent of the surface area of the muscle endplate membrane including the junctional folding, hence WASER concludes that the receptor sites are sparsely distributed over the endplate membrane.

The population of cholinoceptive sites is believed to be much greater on the electric organ of *Electrophorus electricus*, which thus provides very favourable conditions for the study of the chemical nature of the ACh "receptor substance"; and it was first utilized for this purpose by CHAGAS and his colleagues (CHAGAS 1959; HASSÓN and CHAGAS 1961; HASSÓN 1962). Their investigations and those of EHRENPREIS (1960, 1961, 1962) were essentially based on the attempt to discover what chemical components of electric organs form complexes with curarizing agents. One of these substances is an acid polysaccharide (HASSÓN 1962), others are protein components (EHRENPREIS 1960, 1961). Unfortunately these investigations into the molecular biology of specific receptor sites have not yet given an insight into their mode of combination with the transmitter substance.

C. Acetylcholine as an excitatory synaptic transmitter in the central nervous system

The synaptic endings on Renshaw cells are of particular interest because they are the neurones in the vertebrate central nervous system for which there is the best evidence for activation by a known synaptic transmitter, acetylcholine. As illustrated in Fig. 23 the evidence for this statement is entirely pharmacological (ECCLES, FATT and KOKETSU 1954; ECCLES, ECCLES and FATT 1956; CURTIS, ECCLES and ECCLES 1957; CURTIS and R. M. ECCLES 1958a, 1958b; LONGO, MARTIN and UNNA 1960; CURTIS, PHILLIS and WATKINS 1961b). It contains no anomalous features when the blood-brain barrier is circumvented by the micro-electrophoretic injection of drugs into the immediate environment of the Renshaw cell under observation (CURTIS 1963a). The absence of a membrane potential ensures that the injection is not made with

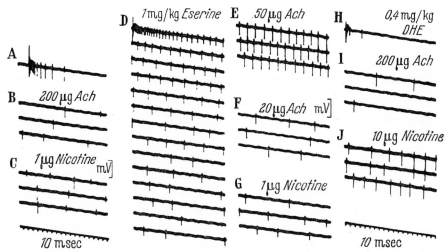

Fig. 23 A—J. Responses of a Renshaw cell as recorded by means of a microelectrode in close proximity. There was no spontaneous discharge. A is response to a single antidromic volley in L_7 ventral root, while B and C each show three successive sweeps at the height of the responses evoked by intra-arterial injection of 200 μg of acetylcholine and 1 μg of nicotine, respectively. Several minutes after the intravenous injection of 1.0 mg eserine/kg, the response evoked by an antidromic volley (A) was changed to the enormously increased and prolonged response (D); while E, F and G show, respectively, three successive records at the heights of the responses evoked by the intra-arterial injections of 50 μg acetylcholine, 20 μg acetylcholine and 1 μg nicotine. As expected there is a greatly increased sensitivity to acetylcholine but no change for nicotine. Records H, I and J were obtained during the maximum of the depression produced by the intravenous injection of 0.4 mg dihydro-β-erythroidine hydrobromide/kg; H shows the greatly depressed response evoked by the antidromic volley; and I and J, the responses to intra-arterial injections of 200 μg acetylcholine and 10 μg nicotine respectively, show that the sensitivity of the Renshaw cell had been reduced to about one tenth (ECCLES, ECCLES and FATT 1956)

the microelectrode in an intracellular position, as is for example shown in Fig. 6, where it is in an astroglial cell. It has been suggested that the absence of any extracellular space except the 200 Å clefts makes an extracellular location impossible for an electrode with a tip diameter measured in microns; however this objection does not take into account the fact that the microelectrode creates its own extracellular space by destruction of the cells it penetrates. The pharmacological actions then closely resemble those observed at vertebrate ganglionic synapses rather than neuromuscular synapses (CURTIS and RYALL 1963).

All Renshaw cells are readily excited to discharge impulses by acetylcholine and related choline esters as well as by tetramethyl ammonium and by nicotine

(Fig. 23 B, C). Blocking agents on peripheral cholinergic synapses are likewise effective on the synapses on Renshaw cells. Dihydro-β-erythroidine (Fig. 23 H—J) is much more effective than both d-tubocurarine and procaine (CURTIS and ECCLES 1958b). All anti-AChEs that have been tested by micro-electrophoretic injection (for example eserine, prostigmine and edrophonium) prolong the response of Renshaw cells to synaptic excitation via motor axon collaterals and increase their responses to electrophoretically applied acetylcholine (CURTIS and ECCLES 1958b; CURTIS, PHILLIS and WATKINS 1961b); but it is not possible to apply the different anticholinesterases with selectivity adequate to distinguish between inhibitory actions on acetylcholinesterase and on pseudo-cholinesterase. It is of interest that prostigmine is usually much less effective than eserine (Fig. 23 D, E, F) when given intravenously (ECCLES, FATT and KOKETSU 1954; ECCLES, ECCLES and FATT 1956), though they are about equally effective when electrophoretically injected so as to avoid the blood-brain barrier (CURTIS and ECCLES 1958b).

Many experimental investigations have been undertaken in the hope of discovering other cholinergic synapses in the mammalian spinal cord. However, in recent critical surveys (PERRY 1956; PATON 1958; FELDBERG 1957; HEBB 1957, 1959; CURTIS, PHILLIS and WATKINS 1961b; FLOREY 1961; McLENNAN 1963) this work has been evaluated as giving no more than suggestive evidence of the existence of such cholinergic synapses. Since dorsal roots contain such minute amounts of acetylcholine and cholineacetylase (MacINTOSH 1941; FELDBERG 1945, 1957; FELDBERG and VOGT 1948; HEBB 1957, 1961) it is generally agreed that primary afferent fibres do not form cholinergic synapses; thus the monosynaptic reflex pathway to motoneurones, the monosynaptic excitation of interneurones and finally the various monosynaptic relays up ascending tracts (the dorsal spino-cerebellar, the ventral spino-cerebellar, and the ipsilateral cutaneous) would not be cholinergically activated. But there remains a wide diversity of synapses made by interneurones that conceivably could be cholinergic, particularly in view of the investigations of FELDBERG, GRAY and PERRY (1953) and of FERNANDEZ DE MOLINA, GRAY and PALMER (1958). However, out of the many hundreds of interneurones and motoneurones tested, there is not even a single example of a pharmacological action suggestive of cholinoceptive receptor sites (CURTIS, PHILLIS and WATKINS 1961b; CURTIS 1963a).

Antidromic impulses in the motor axons of frog motoneurones produce a dorsal root potential (BARRON and MATTHEWS 1938; ECCLES and MALCOLM 1946; KOKETSU 1956a) and pharmacological investigations (KIRALY and PHILLIS 1961; MITCHELL and PHILLIS 1963) indicate that somewhere in the central pathway there are cholinergically transmitting synapses. Presumably this ACh transmission is located at the central synapses formed by the motor-axon collaterals, just as occurs with motor-axon collaterals and Renshaw cells (Fig. 82C, D).

There have been several very extensive investigations of the cholinoceptive pharmacology of neurones in various brain nuclei, the lateral geniculate (CURTIS and DAVIS 1962, 1963), the ventrobasal complex of the thalamus (CURTIS and ANDERSEN 1962), various nuclei in the brain stem (BRADLEY and WOLSTEN-CROFT 1962; SALMOIRAGHI and STEINER 1963), and the cerebral cortex, particularly the pyramidal cells of the visual and auditory cortex (JUNG 1958; SPEHLMANN and KAPP 1961; SPEHLMANN 1963) and of many regions of the neocortex (KRNJEVIĆ and PHILLIS 1961, 1962, 1963a, 1963b).

Neurones fired by electrophoretic application of ACh are found in all these regions of the brain, often in very high proportion, for example up to 90% for Betz cells in the precruciate cortex (KRNJEVIĆ and PHILLIS 1962), but the responses are characteristically much slower in onset, with a delay of several seconds, and much longer in after-discharge than for excitation of these neurones by acidic amino acids or for excitation of Renshaw cells by ACh (CURTIS and ANDERSEN 1962; CURTIS 1963a). Two other characteristic features are the insensitivity of the neurones to nicotine and the effectiveness of atropine and hyoscine as blocking agents, whereas dTC is ineffective. In all these respects the ACh action on these brain neurones differs from its action on Renshaw cells or sympathetic ganglion cells, being muscarinic in type rather than nicotinic. However, it is now recognized that sympathetic ganglion cells have muscarinic as well as nicotinic type receptors (R. M. ECCLES and LIBET 1961; Chapter VIII).

There is as yet no compelling evidence that these muscarinic receptor sites on neurones in the brain are employed in synaptic transmission. For example, though atropine blocks ACh excitation of thalamic neurones, it does not depress synaptic transmission through the thalamus or the spindle bursts generated in the thalamus (CURTIS 1963a). However, there are many other excitatory pathways onto these neurones that have yet to be tested pharmacologically. For the present these cholinoceptive sites on cerebral neurones can be regarded as no more than suggestive that ACh or a related substance plays a limited role as a transmitter for certain synapses that are as yet not identified. Possibly the very slow reactions of these muscarinic type receptors allows them to have a background facilitatory function. An important conclusion from these pharmacological investigations on cholinoceptive neurones is that acetylcholine is not concerned in a large number of the synaptic transmissions in the vertebrate central nervous system.

Preceding these micro-electrophoretic observations there were many other investigations providing less direct evidence that ACh is a synaptic transmitter substance in the central nervous system. There is firstly the biochemical evidence that the choline-acetylase activity of some regions of the central nervous system, for example the cortex, basal ganglia, geniculate bodies and thalamus, is very high (FELDBERG and VOGT 1948; HEBB and SILVER 1956), and that this distribution corresponds with the concentration of ACh (MAC-INTOSH 1941; FELDBERG 1945; PATON 1958). There is reasonable correlation with the distribution of AChE (BURGEN and CHIPMAN 1952; KOELLE 1954; GEREBTZOFF 1959; DE LORENZO 1961); hence the suggestion that ACh is likely to be a synaptic transmitter in these nuclei (FELDBERG 1954, 1957; HEBB 1957, 1959; HEBB and WHITTAKER 1958; DE LORENZO 1961).

In an attempt to separate material containing the particulate fraction of the brain that is specially concerned in acetylcholine metabolism, homogenates of brain have been subjected to gravity centrifugation (HEBB and SMALLMAN 1956; HEBB and WHITTAKER 1958; WHITTAKER 1959; GRAY and WHITTAKER 1960; WHITTAKER and GRAY 1962; DE ROBERTIS, PELLEGRINO DE IRALDI, RODRIGUE X DE LORES ARNAIZ and SALGANICOF 1962; R. W. RYALL, personal communication). Electron-microscopy has proved to be of great value in identifying the particulate material in the various fractions. In the fraction that is rich in acetylcholine and 5-hydroxytryptamine there are large numbers of particles that could be recognized as presynaptic terminals containing vesicles and mitochondria (GRAY and WHITTAKER 1960; WHITTAKER and GRAY 1962; DE ROBERTIS et al. 1962). This method will undoubtedly be of great value as a first stage of purification in the attempt to isolate the various transmitter substances in the central nervous system.

These procedures of extraction and particulate analysis relate acetylcholine metabolism to synaptic structures in the brain. Further evidence of this relationship is given by investigations on the output of ACh from the cerebral cortex (MACINTOSH and OBORIN 1953; MITCHELL 1963). In the presence of anti-AChE, ACh is continuously released from the cerebral cortex at a rate up to 6×10^{-9} g/min/cm², the rate being approximately proportional to the electrical activity of the cortex. Since the rate is increased by direct cortical stimulation or by stimulation of afferent pathways to the cortex, generation by synaptic activation appears likely. However, this production is so low that only a small fraction of synapses may be concerned (MITCHELL 1963).

D. Excitatory actions of acidic amino acids on neurones of the central nervous system

Since the conclusion from these thorough studies is that the great majority of excitatory synaptic actions is not mediated by ACh or by such other possible transmitters as noradrenaline or 5-hydroxytryptamine, special attention must be directed to other substances that are highly potent neuronal excitants. There can be no doubt that central synapses operate by the mediation of highly specific chemical transmitters. We can regard these substances as keys that operate the locks that are the specific receptor sites for the post-synaptic membrane. Yet the immense range of non-cholinergic excitatory synapses exhibits almost no pharmacological action relating either to the keys or to the locks. The one notable exception is the specific blocking action of 5-hydroxytryptamine and related substances on synaptic transmission from the optic nerve through the lateral geniculate nucleus (CURTIS and DAVIS 1962). It is therefore important to examine the credentials of a group of substances, the acidic amino acids, that on electrophoretic injection are powerful excitants of neurones (CURTIS, PHILLIS and WATKINS 1960, 1961a; CURTIS and WATKINS 1960b, 1961, 1963; CURTIS 1961a, 1961b; CURTIS and KOIZUMI 1961; KRNJEVIĆ and PHILLIS 1961, 1963a; CURTIS and DAVIS 1962).

Micro-electrophoretic injection of such acidic amino acids as aspartic, glutamic and cysteic in close proximity of a neurone causes it to discharge repetitively just as with Renshaw cells responding to ACh. The dosage is similar, as also is the rapid onset of the response and its cessation on termination of the injection. No comparable effects are produced when these substances are injected intracellularly; hence it can be assumed that their actions are on receptor sites on the external surfaces of neurones. The action of such highly potent substances on nerve cells is very relevant to the problems arising in the identification of synaptic transmitter substances and in the understanding of their actions on the postsynaptic membrane. These acidic amino acids also depolarize motoneurones in the way that would be predicted for the excitatory transmitter substance. By means of a coaxially arranged double micro-electrode (Fig. 24 inset) it is possible to inject one of these species of ions extracellularly by current flow from the outer barrel and employ the inner barrel to record intracellularly the resulting change of membrane potential (cf. Fig. 24A). This depolarization can sum with a synaptically produced depolarization and so initiate impulse discharge; and, as with all membrane depolarizations, the inhibitory postsynaptic potential is reversibly increased during this depolarization (cf. Fig. 24D, F, H).

There is an apparent similarity between the depolarizing action produced by the acidic amino acids and the depolarizing action of excitatory synapses; yet CURTIS, PHILLIS and WATKINS (1960) argue against identification with the synaptic transmitting agent, and suggest instead that they are non-specific excitants that act at receptor sites on the subsynaptic membrane other than the sites of action of the synaptic transmitters. The original objections were based on evidence which indicated that the excitatory action has a nonspecific character: all nerve cells including the cholinergically activated Renshaw cells are equally affected; and both optical forms of glutamic and aspartic acids have identical action. Moreover, there seems to be no enzymic mechanism for removal of these excitatory amino acids from the surfaces of nerve cells. The argument based on Renshaw cells has now been countered by the demonstration of non-cholinergic synapses on these cells (CURTIS, PHILLIS and WATKINS 1961 b); and the first discriminative study of receptor sites for excitation by acidic amino acids has shown that these correspond to the synaptic areas on crustacean muscle fibres (TAKEUCHI and TAKEUCHI 1963).

However, an investigation of the equilibrium potential for the depolarizing action of the acidic amino acids shows that in the same motoneurone it is at a much less depolarized level than the equilibrium potential for the synaptic

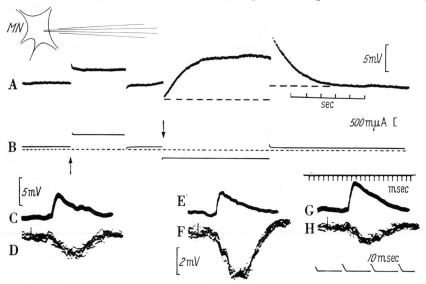

Fig. 24 A—H. A. The alteration in the resting potential of a cat gastrocnemius motoneurone recorded intracellularly by means of an electrode, containing 0.6 M-K$_2$SO$_4$, which was the inner projecting barrel of a co-axial assembly (see inset). The resting potential of the cell was -68 mV over the time recorded and upward deviation indicates depolarization. B, recorded simultaneously with A, indicates the current flowing in the outer barrel of this electrode, which contained sodium aspartate solution. The dotted line indicates zero current, there being originally a cationic current of 200 mμA flowing. This was increased by 720 mμA (upward arrow) and later reversed at downward arrow so that a total anionic current of 520 mμA passed aspartate from the electrode into the environment of the neurone, causing the slowly developing depolarization, which slowly reversed on cessation of the current. C, E, G, monosynaptic EPSPs generated by a gastrocnemius volley, before, during the aspartate injection, and after recovery, i.e. corresponding to the A, B, tracings immediately above. D, F, and H, polysynaptic IPSPs generated by a peroneal nerve volley at similar times (CURTIS, PHILLIS and WATKINS 1960)

depolarizing action (CURTIS 1962a). It is still possible to maintain that the excitatory transmitter substance is related to these acidic amino acids, and that this discrepancy arises because these latter substances give an ionic permeability change which is biassed slightly more for K$^+$ ions relative to Na$^+$ ions than is the permeability produced by the transmitter (Chapter IV; Fig. 18; TAKEUCHI and TAKEUCHI 1960b). At the neuromuscular junction TAKEUCHI and TAKEUCHI (1960b) have shown that chloride ions are not appreciably concerned in the depolarization of the endplate potential, which must be accounted for by a permeability change only to cations with an equilibrium potential set by the relative permeabilities to Na$^+$ and K$^+$ ions. An alternative possibility is that the acidic amino acids depolarize by increasing the membrane permeability to all small ions, Cl^-, Na^+ and K^+.

Relevant to this suggestion that the synaptic transmitter may be related to the acidic amino acids is the recent discovery (CURTIS and WATKINS 1961, 1963; CURTIS, PHILLIS and WATKINS 1961a) of similar substances that are much more powerful excitants of nerve cells when tested either by electrophoretic injection or by topical application to the cat cerebral cortex or to the isolated spinal cord of the toad. Homocysteic acid has a more powerful action than that of L-glutamic acid, two times for the L form and five times for the D form when tested by micro-electrophoretic injection; but the most potent substance is N-methyl-D-aspartic acid, which is about 10 times more potent than L-glutamic acid when similarly tested. It has an even greater relative potency (70 times) when tested by the toad spinal cord or (200 times) when tested by topical application to the cerebral cortex, where the initiation of spreading depression is the test response. It is of great interest that N-methyl-L-aspartic acid is little if any more active than either the D or L forms of glutamic and aspartic acids. Such high potencies certainly indicate that these molecular configurations are accurately keyed to very extensive receptor sites on the cell surface. Even if these sites are not concerned in the operation of excitatory transmitter substances, they are of great interest both pharmacologically and physiologically.

It has been suggested (ECCLES 1957, p. 63) that the passage of current across the postsynaptic membrane might accelerate the removal of transmitter substance that was electrically charged, and hence indicate whether it was cationic or anionic. If the transmitter is a cation, e.g. acetylcholine, the passage of a depolarizing current across the postsynaptic membrane would be expected to aid in the removal of transmitter from the receptor sites on the subsynaptic membrane and, more generally, from the synaptic cleft. It is, therefore, of interest that with two types of cholinergic synapse strong depolarizing currents accelerate the decay of the excitatory synaptic potentials and currents: with the frog neuromuscular junction (TAKEUCHI and TAKEUCHI 1959); and with the frog sympathetic ganglion cells (NISHI and KOKETSU 1960). With the former junction strong hyperpolarizing currents have the opposite action, prolonging the endplate current, an effect which TAKEUCHI and TAKEUCHI (1959) suggest as being due to interference with the removal of the transmitter from the endplate area. In view of these results with a known transmitter, it is of interest that the passage of hyperpolarizing currents across the cat motoneuronal membrane causes a decreased effectiveness of the excitatory transmitter, the increase in the size of the EPSP being much less than the theoretically expected linear relationship of EPSP to membrane potential (Fig. 17B, -84 and -102 mV; COOMBS, ECCLES and FATT 1955c). Also the earlier summit and faster decay of the EPSP suggest a more rapid elimination of the excitatory transmitter from the synaptic cleft. These observations certainly indicate that the transmitter for monosynaptic excitatory action is an anion, which revives the hope that it may be closely related to the negatively charged amino acids, glutamic, aspartic and cysteic acids, that mimic the transmitter so closely (Fig. 24; CURTIS, PHILLIS and WATKINS 1960, 1961a; CURTIS and WATKINS 1960b, 1961, 1963).

E. Excitatory transmitter substances in invertebrates

As pointed out by FLOREY (1961), ACh has been shown to be an excitatory transmitter at very few invertebrate synapses, for example at neuromuscular synapses in the longitudinal muscle of the leech (BACQ and COPPÉE 1937) and in the retractor muscles of the holothurian (BACQ 1939). TAUC and GERSCHEN-FELD (1962) have also presented evidence that ACh is an excitatory transmitter to their D-type of *Aplysia* ganglion cells. As illustrated in Fig. 81 the depolarizing action of electrophoretically applied ACh is depressed by dTC, as also is the EPSP, and atropine and hexamethonium are similarly effective. Since both ACh and AChE are normally present in the Molluscan nervous system, the excitatory transmitter action of ACh seems highly probable.

In 1960 WELSH and MOORHEAD showed that 5-hydroxytryptamine (5 HT) is present in a wide variety of Molluscan nervous systems, and more recently there is evidence that 5 HT may be an excitatory transmitter onto some neurones in Mollusca. Selective chromatographic and pharmacological tests reveal a concentration of 5 HT in the snail's brain usually in excess of 1 in 10^5, and specific enzyme systems for its manufacture and destruction have been demonstrated in the snail (KERKUT and COTTRELL 1963). Matching this chemical evidence is the pharmacological evidence that application of 5 HT in concentrations not higher than 10^{-6} has a powerful excitatory action on some neurones of the snail's brain (KERKUT and WALKER 1962). The D-cells of *Aplysia* are also readily excited by 5 HT (GERSCHENFELD and TAUC 1961). However, there is as yet no evidence directly implicating 5 HT as the excitatory transmitter; it has not been shown to be released during activation of synapses, and there is no pharmacological evidence corresponding to the competitive inhibitions of cholinergic and adrenergic synaptic receptor sites. Such pharmacological antagonism occurs on the snail's heart, which is sensitive to 5 HT even in concentrations as low as 10^{-12} (KERKUT and COTTRELL 1963); hence 5HT may well be the excitatory transmitter substance to the heart.

CHAPTER VI

THE RELEASE OF TRANSMITTER BY PRESYNAPTIC IMPULSES

A. Release of transmitter by single impulses

1. Quantal composition of transmitter release

It is not possible directly to demonstrate that a nerve impulse evokes an EPP by causing the release of a hundred or more packets of ACh within a fraction of a millisecond, for there is an almost synchronous superposition of the constituent miniature EPPs. However, if the magnesium concentration of the extracellular fluid is increased from the normal level of 1 mM to about 10 mM, the EPP becomes very small and fluctuates in amplitude, from zero in a step-like manner (DEL CASTILLO and KATZ 1954b, 1956b; BOYD and MARTIN 1956a; LILEY 1956b). Decrease of calcium acts similarly and cumulatively. Comparison between the random min. EPPs and the EPPs in Fig. 25A—C suggests that this fluctuation is attributable to variations in the number of packets released by a nerve impulse, 0, 1, 2 or more, and the quantal composition of the EPPs can actually be recognized when cooling increases the temporal dispersion (Fig. 25 D, E). Statistical analysis using POISSON's theorem gives a precise confirmation of this quantal composition of the EPPs, and shows that the quanta are identical with those randomly released to give the min. EPPs. As illustrated in Fig. 9A, B extracellular recording of min. EPPs is much more selective than intracellular; hence the quantal fluctuations of the extracellular EPPs are much more in evidence than with the intracellular EPPs. Extracellular recording thus is of special advantage in revealing quantal composition when the intracellularly recorded EPPs have a rather high quantal content (DEL CASTILLO and KATZ 1956a). The same POISSON tests have shown that at other synaptic regions besides the neuromuscular synapses of frog and mammal the postsynaptic potentials are composed of varying numbers of quanta; for example the EPSPs of the sympathetic ganglion cells of the frog (BLACKMAN, GINSBORG and RAY 1962) and the EPPs of the crustacean neuromuscular synapse (DUDEL and KUFFLER 1961b). Unfortunately, the

EPSPs of frog motoneurones are unsuitable for the Poisson analysis (Fig. 11 E—H: Katz and Miledi 1963). Probably there is an extreme range of min. EPSPs, which occurs because some EPSPs are generated on remote dendritic sites (cf. Fadiga and Brookhart 1960).

Estimates of the number of quanta normally released by a nerve impulse at a neuromuscular synapse have been derived by several methods: by statistical analysis; from the relative sizes of the EPPs and the miniature EPPs; and recently from a comparison of the relative conductance changes (Ta-

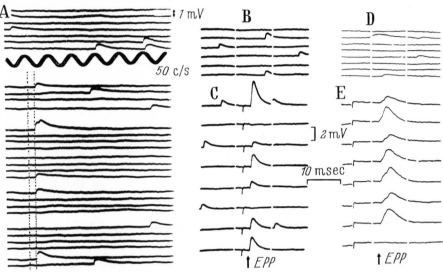

Fig. 25 A—E. Quantal components of endplate potential. A. Intracellular recording from a frog neuromuscular synapse showing a few spontaneous min. EPPs in the top record and in the lower part the responses to a single nerve impulse when in a calcium-deficient and magnesium-rich medium. Stimulus artifact and response latency are indicated by a pair of dotted lines. There was a high proportion of failures, and only 5 unit responses to twenty four impulses (Del Castillo and Katz 1954b). B—E are intracellular records from a rat diaphragm. B gives control spontaneous miniatures for C and D for E, C and E showing in addition EPPs set up by a nerve impulse. Medium has low calcium and high magnesium, 1 mM and 6 mM respectively (Liley 1956b)

keuchi and Takeuchi 1960a). The estimates lie usually in the range of 150 to 300 for the endplates both of amphibia (Del Castillo and Katz 1954b; Martin 1955) and of mammals (Boyd and Martin 1956b; Liley 1956b), though the lower value of about 100 is derived from the conductance change. Burke (1957) gives the value of 100 to 300 per cm length of amphibian tonic muscle fibre.

Thus it has been conclusively established that nerve impulses generate the EPP by producing for a fraction of a millisecond an enormous increase in the rate of quantal emission of acetylcholine. For example, Katz (1958a) states "we have come to regard the miniature EPP as the basic coin, as the quantal unit of action at the neuromuscular junction. We believe that the impulse, by depolarizing the membrane of the motor nerve terminal, momentarily increases the statistical chances of quantal release, by a factor of several hundred thousand, provided we have normal amounts of calcium and magnesium present."

In Fig. 10B a limited range of depolarization increases the frequency of min. EPPs in a very steep logarithmic relationship, about 10-fold for every 15 mV depolarization (LILEY 1956c). If this linear relationship is extrapolated to the much larger depolarizations produced by the nerve impulse in the presynaptic terminals, the observed release of quanta of transmitter is quantitatively accounted for in respect both of amount and of temporal dispersion (LILEY 1956c; ECCLES and LILEY 1959). For example with 90 mV depolarization the frequency would be increased by a factor of 10^6.

However, it still remains to explain how depolarization brings about this great acceleration in the frequency of quantal emission. DEL CASTILLO and KATZ (1956b) and KATZ (1958a, 1962) postulate that the synaptic vesicles are in continuous movement due to thermal agitation and have receptive sites sterically related to receptive sites on the inner surface of the presynaptic membrane, the locking together being a preliminary to ejection of the contents of the vesicle into the synaptic cleft. They further explain the effect of depolarization by postulating that it produces a large increase in the number of these presynaptic attachment sites. A final postulate is that the number of these attachment sites is dependent on the action of calcium ions on the membrane, for the size (quantal content) of the EPP is approximately proportional to the external concentration of calcium (DEL CASTILLO and STARK 1952; DEL CASTILLO and KATZ 1954d; LILEY 1956c); while magnesium acts as a competitor for the active sites available for calcium occupation (DEL CASTILLO and ENGBAEK 1954; JENKINSON 1957; HUBBARD 1961; KATZ 1962).

Fig. 26C shows that the squid synapse resembles the neuromuscular synapse in that the size of the excitatory postsynaptic current increases with the external calcium concentration, while D illustrates the severe depressant action of magnesium. It is of interest that there are no concomitant changes in the presynaptic spike. Calcium and magnesium act similarly on the EPSPs of *Onchidium* ganglion cells (KUSANO and HAGIWARA 1961).

In conclusion it is postulated that the release of transmitter by a nerve impulse at a neuromuscular synapse is due to the following sequence of events (KATZ 1962): firstly, depolarization of the presynaptic terminal; secondly, a consequent increase on the inner surface of the terminal of attachment sites for the preformed packets of transmitter (presumably the attachment sites are at the active zones and the packets are synaptic vesicles); thirdly, the attachment of synaptic vesicles to these sites and the discharge of their contents into the synaptic cleft. Calcium is an essential "co-factor" for the second or third stages.

At most synapses it is not possible to demonstrate that the EPSP has a quantal composition, though this may be presumed on account of the comparable occurrence of synaptic vesicles in all presynaptic terminals that act by liberation of chemical transmitter (Chapter II), and on account of the miniature postsynaptic potentials that are recognizable with most types of chemical synapse (Chapter III).

2. *Relation of size of presynaptic spike potential to transmitter release*

It will be assumed that the size of the EPP or EPSP may be employed as a measure of the amount of transmitter liberated, provided that the post-

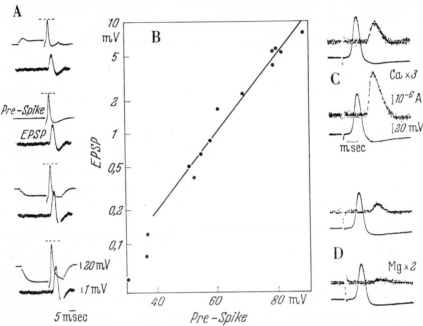

Fig. 26A—D. Presynaptic spike potentials and excitatory postsynaptic potentials. A gives specimen intracellular records from a giant synapse of the squid stellate ganglion both presynaptically (upper trace) and postsynaptically (lower trace), the disposition of electrodes being as in Fig. 8A. A presynaptic spike potential (upper trace) with the resultant EPSP (lower trace) is shown towards the end of each sweep. At the onset of the uppermost record a depolarizing pulse was applied to the presynaptic fibre, while there were hyperpolarizing pulses in the two lowermost records as shown. The dotted lines show absolute height of the control presynaptic spike. In B the amplitudes of the EPSPs are plotted logarithmically against the heights of the presynaptic spikes for the series partly illustrated in A. In C are presynaptic spikes (lower traces) and currents producing EPSPs (upper traces) to show effect of increased calcium in increasing the EPSP with no change in the presynaptic spike. In D similarly but for the depressant action of magnesium (TAKEUCHI and TAKEUCHI 1962)

synaptic membrane is under comparable conditions. There are now several independent investigations which show that the larger the spike potential of the presynaptic impulse, the larger the EPP or EPSP; hence, on the above criterion, the larger the output of transmitter.

Only with the squid giant synapse can a quantitative evaluation be made between height of the presynaptic impulse and size of EPSP, because only with this synapse has it been possible simultaneously to record from both the presynaptic and postsynaptic components (HAGIWARA and TASAKI 1958;

TAKEUCHI and TAKEUCHI 1962). With the electrode arrangements as in Fig. 8 A, the presynaptic membrane potential is displaced in either the depolarizing or hyperpolarizing directions and a presynaptic impulse and the resultant EPSP are recorded to give the upper and lower traces of the specimen records of Fig. 26 A. Hyperpolarization increases the height of the presynaptic spike potential, though it reduces the absolute potential of the summit, the control height being given by the dotted line in each record. Concomitantly there is a large increase in the EPSP. Conversely, presynaptic depolarization reduces the presynaptic spike and the EPSP. The points of the plotted curve published by TAKEUCHI and TAKEUCHI (1962, Fig. 8) have been replotted in Fig. 26 B on semilogarithmic coordinates to show that the logarithm of the EPSP bears an approximately linear relationship to the presynaptic spike potential, as would be expected on LILEY's (1956 c) hypothesis. However the factor of proportionality is less, a 10-fold increase for every 30 mV, as against 15 mV in Fig. 10 B.

It should be noted that the presynaptic spike height is measured relative to the membrane potential, and is not the absolute value plotted in the much steeper curve of HAGIWARA and TASAKI (1958, Fig. 13). The assumption is made in plotting Fig. 26 B that, within 20 msec of displacing the membrane potential, there is full adjustment of the transmitter-releasing mechanism. If it were incomplete, there would be a corresponding decrease in the steepness observed for the relationship of presynaptic spike potential to transmitter-release, which otherwise would approximate more closely to Fig. 10 B.

With the rat diaphragm a polarization of the nerve terminals also increases the sizes both of the presynaptic spike potential and of the EPP. However, HUBBARD and WILLIS (1962 a, b) find a remarkable difference if the current is applied through a microelectrode that is placed in such close apposition to the nerve terminal, that it picks up min. EPPs extracellularly (cf. Fig. 9 A, B). When a prolonged current is applied through the electrode in the direction that hyperpolarizes the nerve terminal, there is an enormous increase in the EPP that very slowly builds up over many seconds (Fig. 27 A—F) and slowly declines on cessation of the current (Fig. 27 G). In contrast, the presynaptic spike potential merely shows the immediate small increase that would be expected because of the hyperpolarization produced by such a current. Furthermore, the potentiation of the EPPs must be due entirely to an increase in the number of released quanta of ACh, because there is no associated increase in the size of the min. EPPs. The applied current must slowly effect a large building up of the available transmitter. Presumably it does this by causing an electrophoretic migration of the ACh packets up to the presynaptic membrane fronting the synaptic cleft. The increase in EPP may be as much as 20-fold, so there should be a remarkable concentration of synaptic vesicles close to the synaptic cleft, if indeed synaptic vesicles are the preformed packets of ACh. It would be of great interest to test whether a corresponding concentration of synaptic vesicles can be observed by electron-microscopic examination of such polarized nerve terminals.

This mobilization of transmitter by a hyperpolarizing current is observed when neuromuscular transmission is blocked either by dTC as in Figs. 27, 36A—G, or by excess magnesium (Fig. 36H—J). However, a depolarizing current does not exercise the reverse effect of producing a slowly developing depression of EPPs. There is merely the immediate small diminution attributable to the depression of the presynaptic spike potential in the depolarized terminals, and this diminution is proportional to the current intensity (Fig. 28; HUBBARD and WILLIS 1962c). The significance of these results will be discussed in relation to the replenishment of transmitter during repetitive stimulation.

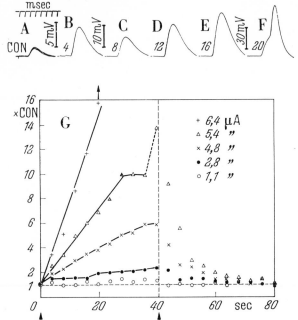

Fig. 27 A—G. The effect of hyperpolarizing currents on the amplitude of EPPs in a curarised preparation. A—F shows sample records from an experiment in which, after 4 superimposed records were taken (A), a current of 6.4 μA was applied as described in text. EPP amplitudes recorded at 4 sec intervals increased progressively during current flow and became large enough to generate a spike potential (F). The 5 mV scale applies to A and B, the 10 mV scale to C, D, E, and 30 mV scale to F. The graph (G) plots the results of this and other experiments with smaller currents at the same junction. EPP amplitudes are shown as multiples of the respective control sizes. Stimulation was at 4 sec intervals before, during and after the application of current. The turning on and off of the current is indicated by the arrows below the abscissa. The arrow above the symbol for 6.4 μA (at 20 sec) indicates the generation of an action potential while the dotted line (triangles) indicates the development of a local response (HUBBARD and WILLIS 1963)

By applying polarizing currents diffusely through large electrodes placed on the dorsal and ventral surfaces of the cat spinal cord, it is possible to produce a considerable polarization of the Group Ia fibres that monosynaptically excite motoneurones (ECCLES, KOSTYUK and SCHMIDT 1962c). Correspondingly, as shown in the specimen records of Fig. 29 A, the monosynaptic EPSPs are increased by a current that hyperpolarizes the presynaptic terminals and decreased with depolarization. The motoneuronal polarization produced by the applied current (Fig. 29 C) has the opposite action on the EPSP (cf. Fig. 17 B) from that actually observed (Fig. 29 B). Thus the influence of presynaptic polarization on the amount of transmitter released by a presynaptic volley would be even larger than is indicated by Fig. 29A and B. The effect of presynaptic depolarization in diminishing the output of transmitter will be used to explain presynaptic

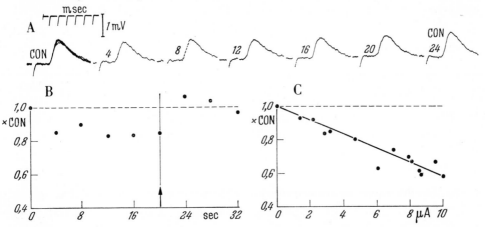

Fig. 28A—C. Reduction of end-plate potential amplitude by depolarizing current applied as in Fig. 27. A shows four superposed controls followed by end-plate potentials elicited at 4-sec intervals after the onset of a depolarizing current of 3.5 µA. Current turned off after 20 sec. B, End-plate potential amplitudes in A plotted as function of control amplitude against time (sec) after onset of depolarizing current. Current turned on at time 0 and off at arrow and vertical bar. C, End-plate potential amplitudes (ordinate) as fraction of control 4 sec after onset of a range of depolarizing currents (0—10.1 µA.). Curarized rat diaphragm (HUBBARD and WILLIS 1962c).

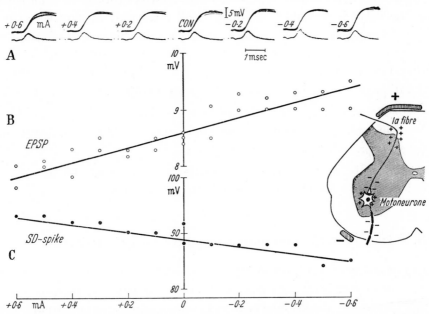

Fig. 29A—C. Changes produced in monosynaptic EPSPs by polarizing current across the cord. Intracellular recording from a motoneurone supplying the anterior biceps muscle, the membrane potential being −70 mV. A shows specimen records of EPSPs under the influence of increasing currents in both directions, as indicated (in mA) for each record, CON being the control value. Each record consists of many superimposed faint traces. The upper traces are the intracellular records, which are differentiated in the lower traces. In B amplitudes of the EPSPs (in mV) for the series partly shown in A are plotted against the direction and strength of the polarizing currents. C shows the amplitudes of antidromically evoked SD-spikes measured under the influence of the same currents. In A, B and C, (+) and (−) indicate the polarity of the dorsal electrode. In inset diagram + and − signs are on the dorsal and ventral electrodes, respectively. Voltage calibration in A is for intracellular recording only (ECCLES, KOSTYUK and SCHMIDT 1962c)

inhibition (Chapter XV). The effect of hyperpolarization in increasing the output of transmitter will provide in part an explanation of posttetanic potentiation in the last two sections of this Chapter.

3. The factors involved in synaptic delay

At the present level of understanding of chemical synaptic action three factors can be considered as contributing to the synaptic delay as measured between the arrival of the impulse at the presynaptic terminal and the onset of the EPP or EPSP. This delay is as brief as 0.22 msec at the mammalian neuromuscular synapse (HUBBARD and SCHMIDT 1963), and is also of this order at mammalian central synapses.

a) The *liberation of transmitter* probably occurs to an appreciable extent only when the presynaptic impulse is approaching its summit, as is indicated by precise study of the variation in latencies in the quantal components of the EPP (LILEY 1956c; ECCLES and LILEY 1959). Furthermore, there may be a lag period between the triggering potential and the actual quantal ejection of the transmitter into the synaptic cleft.

b) The *diffusion of the transmitter* across the synaptic cleft. This component of the delay is probably negligibly small for a cleft as narrow as 200 Å (cf. ECCLES and JAEGER 1958). However a considerable spread of transmitter to receptive sites, particular down the junctional folds of the muscle endplate (Fig. 1 B), would involve more delay and contribute as much as 1 msec to the duration of the rising phase of the postsynaptic current (cf. Figs. 14, 16).

c) The *attachment of the transmitter* to the receptor sites and the subsequent onset in ionic permeability of the subsynaptic membrane probably accounts for an appreciable part of the synaptic delay.

Evidently much more precise methods of investigation are required in order to define the relative contributions of these factors.

B. Release of transmitter during repetitive synaptic activation

Under natural conditions synapses are activated by trains of impulses that may be of relatively high frequency. Characteristically, receptor organs fire repetitively, as also do interneurones, while motoneurones normally discharge repetitively in evoking muscle contractions. In all these situations frequency of discharge signals intensity of activation, and frequency modulation provides the means for transmitting information from receptors along interneuronal pathways and the final common paths to the effectors (cf. ADRIAN and BRONK 1929; GRANIT 1955). It is therefore imperative to study the operation of synapses during repetitive activation.

1. Investigations with double stimulation

In the simplest situation a second impulse activates a synapse at various times after a conditioning impulse. At the curarized amphibian neuro-muscular synapse, the second endplate potential and endplate current are greatly potentiated at brief test intervals (Takeuchi and Takeuchi 1959), the effect passing off after 100 to 200 msec (Eccles, Katz and Kuffler 1941; Lundberg and Quilisch 1953a). An initial phase of potentiation is also observed with most other types of synaptic junction, though it is often merely a relative potentiation superimposed upon a prolonged depression, as is characteristically seen with the following synapses: curarized mammalian neuromuscular synapses (Liley and North 1953; Lundberg and Quilisch 1953a, b; Hubbard 1959, 1963); monosynaptic synapses on motoneurones (Curtis and Eccles 1960); curarized synapses of sympathetic ganglia (Eccles 1943; Laporte and Lorente de Nó 1950; Job and Lundberg 1953); giant synapses of the squid stellate ganglion (Takeuchi and Takeuchi 1962). Evidently two antagonistic factors are in operation, a brief potentiating influence and a more prolonged influence of depression.

The depression has been specially investigated by Takeuchi (1958) with the amphibian EPP, by Hagiwara and Bullock (1957) in the "follower cells" of the lobster cardiac ganglion, the depression being there called "de-facilitation," and by Hubbard (1963) in the curarized rat diaphragm. There is usually a potentiation of the EPP at brief intervals that passes over to a depression persisting for as long as 2 to 10 sec. During this initial potentiation the presynaptic spike potential is always slightly depressed (Hubbard and Schmidt 1963). In the giant synapse of the squid, on the contrary, there is an increase in the presynaptic spike size at intervals up to 15 msec after a single conditioning impulse, and presumably this accounts, at least in part, for the associated increase in EPSP (Takeuchi and Takeuchi 1962).

2. Investigations with repetitive stimulation

Further information on the potentiation and depression has been derived from investigations on the steady state of synaptic activity that quickly develops during repetitive activation at a constant frequency. The possibility that potentiation during and after tetanization (cf. Sections C_1 and C_2 below) might be due to an increased sensitivity of the postsynaptic membrane to the transmitter has been eliminated by direct tests with acetylcholine on the sympathetic ganglion (Larrabee and Bronk 1947) and on the mammalian neuro-muscular junction (Hutter 1952).

a) Neuronal synapses. Repetitive synaptic action has been studied in detail by intracellular recording of the excitatory postsynaptic potentials (EPSPs) generated monosynaptically in motoneurones, which provide a direct and quantitative measure of synaptic efficacy (CURTIS and ECCLES 1960). Fig. 30A shows monosynaptic EPSPs set up in a motoneurone by repetitive stimulation. It is seen that a steady-state is attained after the first few EPSPs, even over a wide range of frequencies; and it is found that this steady state is maintained for hundreds of responses. Evidently, there is an initial phase of adjustment of the EPSP to the steady-state size characteristic of that frequency. By a superposition technique it is possible to measure accurately the sizes of EPSPs during this steady-state, as in the specimen records of Fig. 30B. When the sizes of the superimposed EPSPs for the series that is partly illustrated are plotted against either the frequency or the volley interval (scaled

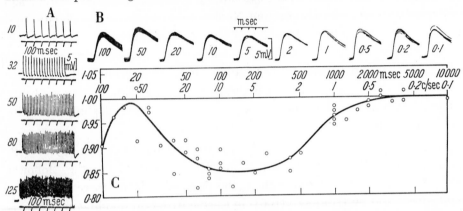

Fig. 30A—C. A. Repetitive monosynaptic EPSPs recorded intracellularly from a cat gastrocnemius motoneurone (cf. Fig. 13) with a DC amplifier, the frequency of the maximum group I volleys from gastrocnemius nerve being shown to be left of each record. B. Repetitive monosynaptic EPSPs formed by superimposed traces at the indicated frequencies (c/sec) when the EPSP had attained a steady state. C. The EPSPs partly illustrated in B are expressed as fractions of the mean size obtaining at 0.4 c/sec or slower and plotted against the respective stimulus frequencies on a logarithmic abscissal scale. Above the frequency scale, the corresponding stimulus intervals are shown in msec (CURTIS and ECCLES 1960)

logarithmically), the points on the extreme right of Fig. 30C reveal that there is no appreciable change in the sizes of the EPSPs until the frequency is in excess of 0.4/sec. There is a progressive depression as the frequency is raised to 5—10/sec. With further increase in frequency, the EPSP increases to a maximum at about 50/sec, being then almost as large as at the lowest frequencies. All the motoneurones so investigated have exhibited a trough at 5—20/sec and an increased EPSP as the frequency is raised to 50—100/sec.

Above 100/sec each successive EPSP is superimposed on the tail of the preceding responses so that its size has to be determined by a subtraction technique. It is shown in this way (CURTIS and ECCLES 1960) that above 100/sec the size of the added EPSP declines with increasing frequency, particularly above 200/sec (Fig. 31A). It may be assumed that the size of the EPSP is approximately proportional to the amount of transmitter that is acting on the neurone (cf. Fig. 13 J—M), so it is possible to obtain an approximate measure of the amount of transmitter that is produced by repetitive stimulation in unit time by multiplying the size of the EPSP during the steady state by the frequency. As so measured (Fig. 31 B) the rate of liberation of transmitter increases as the frequency is raised to 300/sec; but above that frequency a plateau is attained, the rate of liberation of transmitter being then almost three times greater than for stimulation at 100/sec.

Fig. 31 B recalls the observation of BIRKS and MacINTOSH (1961) that the rate of output of ACh from the superior cervical ganglion increases with frequency up to 20/sec, beyond which a plateau is attained (Chapter V). The critical frequencies differ more than tenfold, which may be attributed to in-

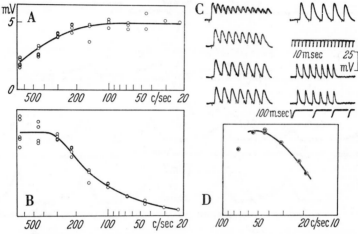

Fig. 31 A—D. A, the sizes of the last EPSPs of brief repetitive stimulations have been measured as described in the text, and plotted against the frequency of stimulation, as shown by the logarithmic abscissal scale. The repetitive stimulations were prolonged sufficiently for attainment of the steady-state. B. The results plotted in A have been recalculated to give the total production of EPSP in unit time, the sizes of the EPSPs being multiplied by the respective stimulus frequencies and plotted on an arbitrary scale. Note that a plateau is attained for frequencies above 300/sec. Biceps-semitendinosus motoneurone with a resting potential of − 78 mV (CURTIS and ECCLES 1960). C. Repetitive EPSPs intracellularly recorded from ganglion cell of rabbit superior cervical ganglion. The frequencies can be derived from the time scales, all but the last two being at the faster sweep. D. The sizes of the last EPSPs of the records in C are calculated as for A and the total production of EPSP in unit time is plotted as in B (R. M. ECCLES 1955)

trinsic differences between the fast motoneuronal and the slow ganglionic synapses. However, with the ganglionic EPSPs also (R. M. ECCLES 1955), the critical frequency at which a ceiling is attained has been found to be much higher than 20/sec, being above 40/sec in Fig. 31 D, which is derived from intracellular records illustrated in Fig. 31 C. These observations are probably not inconsistent because it can be assumed that the intracellular recording would be from the largest ganglion cells, which are likely to have a faster presynaptic mechanism than the average response given by the whole assemblage of presynaptic terminals that are activated in BIRKS and MacINTOSH's experiments on ACh output.

Since the potentiation during repetitive stimulation is dependent on increased release of transmitter from the presynaptic terminals, it is not unexpected that large differences sometimes are observed between the potentiations for different types of synapses on the same neurone. The neurones of the ventral spinocerebellar tract (ECCLES, HUBBARD and OSCARSSON 1961) regularly exhibit a large absolute potentiation of the EPSPs monosynaptically produced by Group Ib afferent volleys (up to 200% at 100/sec in Fig. 32A), whereas with Group Ia afferent volleys (Fig. 32B) there is merely a relative potentiation at frequencies of about 50/sec which is even less well developed than in Fig. 30C. With some interneurones in the intermediate nucleus

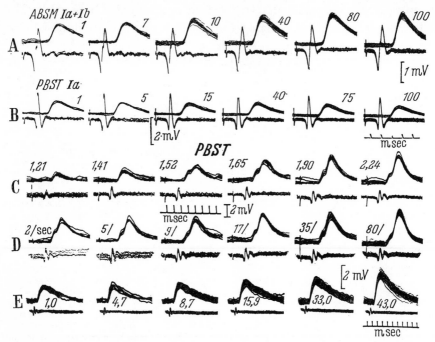

Fig. 32A—E. Monosynaptic EPSPs recorded at the steady-state during a wide range of frequencies, as indicated in c/sec for each series of superimposed traces (A, B, D and E). A and B give respectively Group Ib and Ia activation of the same cell of the VSC tract. The lower traces show the afferent volleys entering the spinal cord through L₇ dorsal root (ECCLES, HUBBARD and OSCARSSON 1961). C shows graded stimulation at the strengths indicated relative to threshold, and by the clear double composition of the EPSP it gives evidence of the converging Ia and Ib activation of a neurone in the intermediate nucleus of the spinal cord with stimulation of the posterior biceps-semitendinosus nerves. In D maximum Ia Ib volleys are applied at the frequencies indicated (ECCLES, KOSTYUK and SCHMIDT, unpublished records). In E are monosynaptic EPSPs of a thoracic motoneurone innervating the external intercostal muscle (SEARS 1963)

there is also monosynaptic innervation by Group Ia and Ib afferent volleys as shown in the threshold series of Fig. 32C. In Fig. 32D there is at high frequencies a large potentiation of the later Ib component of the combined EPSP and little change in the earlier Ia component. It is tempting to conclude that Ib afferent fibres differ from Ia in having synapses that are much more efficient at high frequencies. However, when Ia and Ib fibres converge onto the same neurone of the dorsal spino-cerebellar tract, there is little if any more potentiation for the EPSPs set up by the Ib afferent voleys than for the Ia, both giving curves like Fig. 30C (ECCLES, OSCARSSON and WILLIS 1961).

An observation even more disturbing to any attempt at generalization is that the monosynaptic Group Ia synapses on respiratory motoneurones of the thoracic cord regularly exhibit a large frequency potentiation (SEARS 1963), which in Fig. 32 E is as large as for the Ib synapses in Fig. 32 A. Recently FADIGA and BROOKHART (1962) have described another example of differing frequency-potentiation for two monosynaptic pathways onto the same moto-neurone. Frequency-potentiation is very highly developed for the pyramidal monosynaptic pathway onto motoneurones of the forelimb muscles of the baboon, and it is remarkable that it is very poorly developed for the Group Ia synapses on these same motoneurones (LANDGREN, PHILLIPS and PORTER 1962; PHILLIPS, personal communication 1963). It seems that frequency-potentiation is very highly developed at the synaptic terminals of pyramidal cell axons. Possibly electron-microscopy may reveal special structural features at these synapses. We are yet at an early stage of investigation into frequency-potentiation, but clearly it has great functional significance.

b) Neuromuscular synapses. With repetitive activation of the curarized amphibian neuromuscular synapse there is an initial phase of potentiation that passes off after several volleys (FENG 1940; ECCLES and MACFARLANE 1949). When the EPP produced by single impulses is greatly depressed by low calcium or high magnesium (DEL CASTILLO and KATZ 1954c), the potentiation is greatly increased and prolonged (Fig. 33 A). Intracellular recording at the endplate zone (Fig. 33 B) shows that with severe calcium depletion many im-pulses fail to produce any EPP; but during repetitive stimulation the successive impulses become on the whole more effective, there being apparently a greater probability for the release of quanta of transmitter, each of which produces an EPP resembling the miniature EPPs in the second and fourth base lines of Fig. 33 B. Statistical analysis of a great many records such as those of Fig. 33 B establishes that this is indeed the case, the sizes of the EPPs being accurately in accord with predictions from POISSON's theorem. This is also the case for the similarly produced EPPs of mammalian muscle (Fig. 33 E; BOYD and MARTIN 1956b; LILEY 1956b). The sizes of the EPPs evoked by these quanta are not changed by calcium depletion, which corresponds to the observation of DEL CASTILLO and STARK (1952) that the sensitivity of the endplate to acetyl-choline is not changed by variation in the extracellular calcium concentration from 0.45 to 7.2 mM.

Repetitive responses of curarized mammalian neuromuscular synapses are much more dominated by depression (Fig. 33 C; LUNDBERG and QUILISCH 1953a, b; LILEY and NORTH 1953; HUBBARD 1959), though at the steady state there is a relative potentiation at frequencies of 50 to 100/sec as in Fig. 30 (HUBBARD 1963). It was suggested by THESLEFF (1959) that this depression is due to a desensitization of the receptor sites on the postsynaptic membrane comparable with that occurring in Fig. 22 E during electrophoretically applied

ACh. In Fig. 34A, B there is a progressive decline of the repetitively evoked EPPs in a curarized mammalian muscle, and even after the brief tetanus

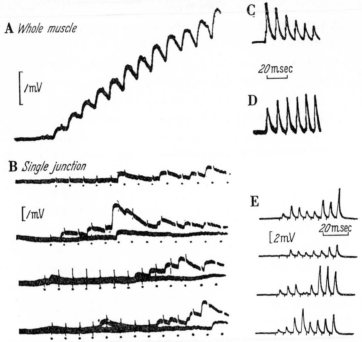

Fig. 33A—E. A, B. Frog nerve muscle preparations blocked by high magnesium (14 mM) and calcium deficiency (0.9 mM), the nerve being stimulated at 100/sec. In A external recording from endplate region of frog sartorius and in B intracellular recording at endplate zone of a frog muscle fibre, the stimuli being indicated by dots (DEL CASTILLO and KATZ 1954e). C, D. EPPs recorded from curarized rat diaphragm on repetitive supramaximal stimulation of the phrenic nerve. In C the extracellular calcium concentration was normal (2.5 mM). In D it was reduced to 0.28 mM (LUNDBERG and QUILISCH 1953b). E. Intracellular EPPs of a rat diaphragm in high magnesium solution (10 mM) with repetitive stimulation at 160/sec (LILEY 1956b)

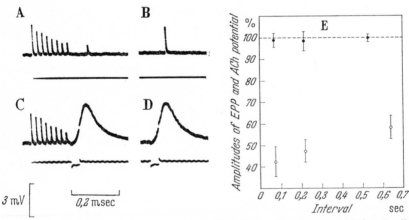

Fig. 34A—E. EPPs and ACh potentials to show effect of a brief repetitive stimulation, 8 volleys at 50/sec, in a rat nerve-muscle preparation treated with 5×10^{-7} dTC. In A the test EPP was 0.08 sec after end of tetanus and in B it was 1.9 sec, showing almost complete recovery. In C and D injections of ACh were applied extracellularly as in Fig. 22 as shown by the current record in the lower trace. E shows plotting of amplitudes of EPPs (open circles) and of ACh potentials (filled circles) against the testing interval for the series partly illustrated in A—D. Each point is mean of five separate determinations and the vertical line shows the $\pm$S.D. (OTSUKA, ENDO and NONOMURA 1962)

recovery takes many seconds (OTSUKA, ENDO and NONOMURA 1962). There is no associated depression of the ACh sensitivity of the postsynaptic membrane (Fig. 34C, D, E), so it can be assumed that the output of ACh progressively declines; and at the end of the tetanus there is a slow recovery of a test EPP to the original control size. The concept of available ACh very satisfactorily accounts for such observations. The packets of ACh that are available for release into the synaptic cleft by a nerve impulse in a fraction of a millisecond must be in very close proximity to the presynaptic membrane fronting this cleft, which corresponds to the aggregations of synaptic vesicles in Fig. 1B, and it is assumed that a significant fraction of this available ACh is released by an impulse, so that a series of impulses in quick succession evokes a progressively declining series of EPPs as in Fig. 34A, C. The frog neuromuscular junction also gives unchanged ACh responses after a tetanization in which the EPPs had been much diminished (OTSUKA, ENDO and NONOMURA 1962).

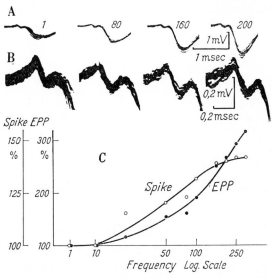

Fig. 35A—C. Extracellular EPPs and presynaptic spike potentials during repetitive stimulation at frequencies from 1 to 320/sec. A. Records of extracellular EPPs made by superimposing 30—60 faint traces during stimulation at the stated frequencies. B. As A but taken simultaneously at a much higher gain to show detail of the spike potential. C. Spike amplitudes (open circles) and EPP amplitudes (filled circles) plotted as a function of frequency of stimulation. The amplitudes of spike and EPP during stimulation at 1/sec were taken as 100%. Note different ordinates for spike and EPP amplitudes (HUBBARD and SCHMIDT 1962)

Under conditions where the release of ACh is greatly depressed as for example with excess magnesium or deficient calcium in the external medium, it would be expected that depletion of available ACh would be negligible and that there would be little or no decline during a repetitive series of EPPs. In fact there is a progressive increase under these conditions (Figs. 33A, D, 36H, 37A), which indicates that there is some compensatory physiological process concerned in increasing the output of ACh during repetitive stimulation. One example is illustrated in Fig. 35, where a microelectrode picks up the extracellular potentials in the immediate vicinity of a single neuromuscular junction. The series in A and C shows the large potentiation of the magnesium-depressed EPPs during the steady state attained at various frequencies of tetanization. In B and C there is also seen to be an increase in the spike potential recorded from that single nerve terminal. The logarithm of the increase in the EPP is approximately proportional to the increase in spike potential (HUBBARD and SCHMIDT 1963), which may be correlated with other curves indicating a logarithmic relationship of transmitter output to presynaptic depolarization (Figs. 10A, B; 26B). However an additional explanation is derived from the process of transmitter mobilization, as will emerge in the next section.

The crustacean neuromuscular synapse normally responds to single and repetitive stimulation in a manner closely resembling the responses of vertebrate synapses subjected to calcium deficiency. During low frequency stimulation, motor nerve impulses release transmitter only intermittently at several synaptic areas, while with higher frequency the probability of release increases, just as in Fig. 33B, E (DUDEL and KUFFLER 1961b). Statistical analysis also shows that the transmitter is released in quanta comparable to those giving min. EPPs. Thus the potentiation during repetitive stimulation is due to an increase in the probability of release of quanta by the nerve impulses, and is not due to an increased invasion of nerve terminals or to an increased sensitivity of the postsynaptic membrane to the transmitter substance. Many crustacean muscles have been investigated by HOYLE and WIERSMA (1958a) and by WIERSMA and BOBBERT (1961) in a comparative study of responses to repetitive nerve stimulation. There may be "fast" and "slow" innervation of the same muscle fibre. In general with the "fast"innervation a larger EPP is produced by single impulses, but with repetitive stimulation there is more potentiation of the EPP produced by the "slow" innervation. Summation of EPPs at high frequency results in the attainment of a plateau at about half of the resting membrane potential (WIERSMA and BOBBERT 1961). Presumably the sizes of the EPPs under these various conditions are explicable in terms of the quantal release mechanism demonstrated by DUDEL and KUFFLER (1961a, b).

Responses resembling those of crustacean muscle, but on a much slower time scale, have recently been reported for the action of hypogastric nerve impulses on the smooth muscle of the guinea pig vas deferens (BURNSTOCK and HOLMAN 1961, 1962a, 1962b). With repetitive stimulation as slow as 2 or 3/sec there is a progressive potentiation of the successive EPPs, so that eventually a spike potential may be generated. There is much the same relative potentiation when the EPPs are diminished either by partial denervation or by reserpinization.

3. Mobilization of transmitter

Important evidence relating to the postulated mobilization of transmitter is provided by investigations on the enormous potentiation that gradually develops during application of a hyperpolarizing current to presynaptic terminals (Fig. 27). This potentiation also occurs throughout a repetitive series of curarized EPPs (Fig. 36A—G; HUBBARD and WILLIS 1963); but the relative potentiation is greater for the first EPP of each repetitive test series, which corresponds to Fig. 27, and progressively declines for the later responses. It appears therefore that, effective as is the mobilization produced by the hyperpolarizing current, it is not adequate to sustain the same high level of potentiation during a repetitive series, though of course there is a considerable potentiation throughout the whole series of 10 EPPs of the test series in Fig. 36D. The potentiation is over 6-fold for the last response (Fig. 36G). Fig. 36H—J further shows that the hyperpolarizing current produces a large and progressive potentiation of magnesium-blocked EPPs. Under such conditions the initial EPP of a repetitive series may be the largest (Fig. 36J).

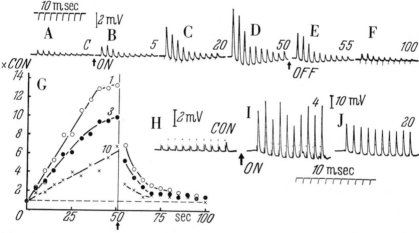

Fig. 36A—J. Effect of hyperpolarizing current on brief tetanic trains of EPPs in a curarized preparation. A shows a control record of a tetanic train produced by 10 stimuli at 100/second. After A, a current of 4.5 μA was begun, as indicated by the first arrow. B—D are records taken during the current at the indicated times in seconds. Two seconds after D, the current was turned off and records E and F were taken. Stimulation was at 5 sec intervals throughout the experiment. G shows the time course of changes in the amplitudes of the first (open circles), the third (filled circles) and the tenth (crosses) EPPs; note that they are plotted relative to their respective control heights. H—J, series as in A—D, but for a neuromuscular junction treated with excess Mg., the current strength being 9 μA. The 2 mV scale applies to H and I, the 10 mV to J. The effect of cessation of current is not illustrated, but there was complete reversibility as in F (HUBBARD and WILLIS 1963)

Again, on cessation of the current there is the same slow recovery illustrated in Figs. 27G and 36G.

Evidently an electric current flowing so as to hyperpolarize the terminals provides a powerful force mobilizing the packets of ACh. Probably the current is acting electrophoretically on negatively charged particles. It may therefore be asked why the current in the reverse direction causes merely a small rapid depression of the EPSP (Fig. 28) with no slowly developing large depression matching the large potentiation of Figs. 27 and 36. This difference presumably arises because the observation is restricted to a measurement of the available transmitter, i.e. the transmitter in very close proximity to the synaptic cleft, and not to the distribution of the transmitter throughout the whole presynaptic terminal. According to the electrophoresis explanation the hyperpolarizing current would cause the mobilization even of remote transmitter, hence the long phase of progressively increasing effectiveness. On the contrary the depression of transmitter release by a depolarizing current would be fully effective as soon as it had caused a very small movement of the available transmitter away from its strategic site in close proximity to the synaptic cleft (HUBBARD and WILLIS 1962 b). There is one observation apparently at variance with this explanation of transmitter mobilization by applied hyperpolarizing current, namely that there is no associated change in the frequency of the min. EPPs. In part at least this discrepancy can be attributed to the calcium-independent fraction of the min. EPPs (HUBBARD 1961), which does not form a component of the EPP (Chapter III).

4. Reserves of transmitter in presynaptic terminals

It is of interest to attempt some numerical assessment of the population of synaptic vesicles in presynaptic nerve terminals and their probable rate of discharge during repetitive stimulation. For example the total length of the long finger-like nerve terminals of an amphibian neuromuscular junction is at least 500μ and a nerve impulse causes the discharge of about 200 quanta of transmitter, which is about one quantum for 3μ length of nerve terminal, or $10 \mu^2$ of synaptic contact (cf. BIRKS, HUXLEY and KATZ 1960). The rat neuromuscular junction is smaller in area and the quantal liberation is also about 200, so one quantum would be liberated for an area little more than $1 \mu^2$. The areas of synapses on motoneurones would usually not be larger than 2 to $3 \mu^2$ (HAGGAR and BARR 1950; SZENTAGOTHAI and RAJKOVITS 1955; PALAY 1958), while the total population of synaptic vesicles in a large presynaptic terminal (a hemispherical dome 2μ in diameter) may be calculated as about 20,000, it being assumed that vesicles (spheres of about 350 Å in diameter) occupy about 20 % of the total volume of the knob. On the assumption that the $3 \mu^2$ of synaptic contact of such a knob has about the same density of quantal liberation as at a rat neuro-muscular junction, there would probably be no more than two quanta liberated by an impulse from one knob. With such a small liberation per impulse, the synaptic knob would have a reserve supply for only 10,000 impulses, for example 200 seconds at a frequency of activation of 50/sec. Calculations based on the ACh content of sympathetic ganglia and the amount released by an impulse likewise give a reserve supply of ACh for about 10,000 impulses (BIRKS and MacINTOSH 1957, 1961).

If, as seems likely, the quantal liberation of transmitter is due to the discharging of the contents of synaptic vesicles into the synaptic cleft, the available transmitter (cf. PERRY 1953; LILEY and NORTH 1953; BIRKS and MacINTOSH 1957; TAKEUCHI 1958) at any one instant would be the transmitter in the synaptic vesicles in immediate juxtaposition to the presynaptic membrane at an active zone (Figs. 1 to 3, 7), for only such vesicles could be discharged in this way by an impulse. There are few vesicles in such a strategic position; consequently depletion may be evident even after only one impulse (Figs. 33C, 34). Besides causing the discharge of some vesicles, the presynaptic impulse can be envisaged as causing other vesicles to move into the strategic zone, which would be the structural manoeuvre involved in mobilization. This movement would be greatly potentiated by impulses in quick succession, but no such interaction occurs with longer intervals (50 msec or longer in Fig. 30C) between successive presynaptic impulses; hence depletion then dominates mobilization.

Electron-microscopic investigations may eventually provide a crucial test for these speculations on the structural correlations of the depletion and mobilization phenomena of repetitively activated synapses. At present the evidence is equivocal. DE ROBERTIS (1956, 1958) finds that with disuse of several days the vesicles are smaller in size. Immediately after prolonged intense stimulation there is a large depletion of vesicles, while a small increase is observed after 100/sec stimulation. In contrast, at neuromuscular synapses BIRKS, HUXLEY and KATZ (1960) could see no significant depletion after intense stimulation.

Evidently the prolonged activation of synapses at relatively high frequencies raises two problems: firstly, the mobilization of quanta of transmitter within a presynaptic terminal, vesicles moving up to the synaptic surface preparatory to their discharge; and secondly, the replenishment of transmitter either by formation of new vesicles or by recharging of vesicles that have discharged their contained transmitter. The movement of vesicles into strategic sites on the membrane of the motor nerve terminals was indicated to BIRKS, HUXLEY and KATZ (1960) by the observed distribution of the vesicles. Not only were they mobilized in the zone of the terminal fronting the synaptic cleft, but they tended to be concentrated opposite the junctional folds (Fig. 1B), where they would be liberated in proximity to a large subsynaptic surface and hence be most effective. We are far from understanding the forces thus moving synaptic vesicles into strategic sites; yet these forces must play a vital role in the efficiency of operation of synapses during prolonged repetitive activation.

C. Synaptic potentiation and depression subsequent to activation

1. After single or brief repetitive stimulation

Investigation of neuromuscular synapses gives three important advantages when attempting to analyse the various factors that determine the effect of conditioning stimulation on the output of transmitter by a subsequent testing impulse. Firstly, min. EPPs signal the spontaneous release of transmitter, which in many respects runs parallel to the release of transmitter by nerve impulses. Secondly, by increasing the extracellular magnesium the output of transmitter by the conditioning stimulation can be reduced to a negligible level; consequently the effect of conditioning stimulation can be examined virtually uncomplicated by the depletion of transmitter and the reactions thereto. Thirdly, curarization by dTC or a related curarizing agent reduces competitively the size of the EPP so that it can be observed uncomplicated by the generation of postsynaptic spike potentials.

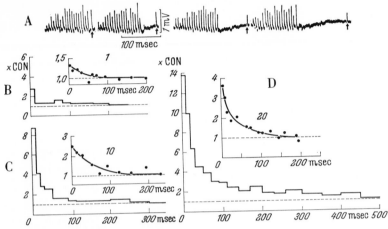

Fig. 37 A—D. Potentiation of EPP amplitude and min. EPP. frequency after 1—20 nerve impulses in a magnesium-poisoned rat diaphragm preparation. A shows intracellularly recorded EPPs in response to 20 stimuli at 200/sec, and to a testing stimulus (arrow) at various intervals after the short tetanus. In the graphs inset in B, C and D the amplitude of the EPP response to a testing stimulus is plotted after 1 (B) impulse and 10 (C) and 20 (D) impulses at 200/sec, for intervals up to 200 msec. Each point represents the average EPP amplitude determined from 10—15 trials at each interval and expressed as a multiple of the average EPP amplitude in the absence of stimulation. In the main graphs in B, C and D, the increased min. EPP frequencies found after the same number and frequency of stimuli are shown. The line length in these graphs indicates the time interval over which this frequency was computed in each case. The frequencies were obtained by comparing, in 200—300 trials, the number of min. EPPs in the selected interval after stimulation, with the number expected in the absence of stimulation. The graphs thus show the probability of min. EPP occurrence at various intervals after stimulation as a multiple of this probability in the absence of stimulation. B, C, D were all obtained from the same junction. The temperature was 36° C (HUBBARD 1963)

In Fig. 37A are four specimen records of a magnesium-depressed neuro-muscular synapse being activated by 20 impulses at 200/sec and tested by a single impulse (arrow) at various intervals later (HUBBARD 1963). During the tetanization there is the usual progressive potentiation of the successive EPPs (cf. Figs. 33, 36H), and the testing EPPs show simply the post-tetanic decline of this potentiation, the full series being plotted in D. After conditioning by 10 impulses there is a similar curve of post-tetanic potentiation, but at a lower level (C); and there is even potentiation for almost 100 msec after a single conditioning impulse (B).

DEL CASTILLO and KATZ (1954c) and DUDEL and KUFFLER (1961b) have observed that, even if an impulse fails to release a single quantum, it still induces potentiation of the transmitter released by a subsequent impulse.

By statistical treatment of over one thousand observations in half of which the conditioning impulse released no transmitter, HUBBARD (1963) has confirmed that the potentiation following a single impulse, as in Fig. 37B, is quite independent of the release of transmitter; hence it seems justifiable to assume this also for the similar curves C and D. Apparently the presynaptic impulse directly initiates the process of transmitter mobilization, and there is a large facilitation of this process when presynaptic impulses follow at high frequency.

Another index of mobilization after synaptic activation is the increased frequency of min. EPPs (LILEY 1956a; BROOKS 1956; HUBBARD 1959, 1963) which in Fig. 37B—D has a time course and a relative intensity matching the EPP potentiations except for the more prolonged low intensity phase. Just as with the EPP the increase in min. EPP frequency after a single impulse (B) is not dependent on its effectiveness in releasing transmitter (HUBBARD 1963), so presumably this independence also obtains for the min. EPP curves plotted in C and D, which differ only in their larger size and somewhat longer duration. This increased frequency is not attributable to an increase in potassium concentration in the synaptic cleft because it is not diminished by application of a hyperpolarizing current to the muscle through a microelectrode inserted into the muscle at the motor endplate, which would deplete the cleft of excess potassium (TAKEUCHI and TAKEUCHI 1961). Repetitive activation also results in an increased frequency of the min. EPPs of a crustacean muscle (DUDEL and KUFFLER 1961b).

In the magnesium-treated preparation repetitive stimulation results in the cumulative potentiation illustrated in Fig. 37B to C to D, only when at a frequency above 10/sec. With increasing frequency up to 300/sec there is a corresponding increase in the post-tetanic potentiation following the same small number of stimuli. Evidently each impulse has two independent actions on the transmitter mechanism in the presynaptic terminals: there is firstly a brief jet of transmitter release, no more than 1 msec in duration; and, quite independently, there is a process of mobilization of transmitter that is at a maximum within 3 msec and has declined to zero by about 100 msec. It should be noted that the increased spike potential illustrated in Fig. 35B, C is observed at the steady state reached during prolonged tetanization and it does not occur for the brief tetani of Figs. 37 and 38.

The complications introduced by the additional factor of transmitter depletion are illustrated by the response of a curarized neuromuscular synapse (Fig. 38; HUBBARD 1963). In Fig. 38A a conditioning tetanus of 20 impulses at 200/sec results in the usual severe depression of the successive EPPs (cf. Figs. 34A, C and 36A), and the testing stimulus reveals that post-tetanically this depression passes over to a small potentiation at 125 msec. In the plotted series (Fig. 38B, filled circles) the maximum potentiation is at 100 msec and is followed by a further depression of about 1 sec duration. With conditioning by 10 impulses (open circles in B) the potentiation is less, so that it merely causes a relative decrease in a depression that itself is about 1 sec duration. Finally after 50 impulses there is again merely a relative potentiation, with a maximum at about 100 msec, but subsequently after 400 msec there is a large and very prolonged potentiation (C).

The depressed EPPs during the tetanization in Fig. 38A were attributed in the preceding section to depletion of the available transmitter. The simplest explanation of the curves of Fig. 38B, C is that there is a transient potentiation

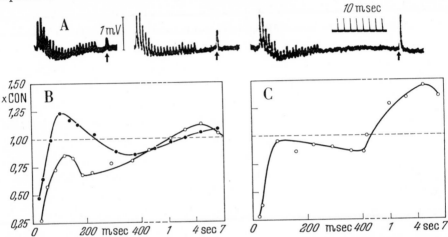

Fig. 38A—C. EPP magnitude after 10, 20 and 50 stimuli at 200/sec, intracellularly recorded from a curarised rat diaphragm preparation in vitro. A shows EPP responses during and after (arrows) 20 stimuli at 200/sec. Note the increased EPP amplitude at the longest interval after the tetanus. In the graph B (full circles), the amplitude of this EPP response to a testing stimulus is shown as a multiple of the EPP amplitude in the absence of stimulation. All the points are averages obtained from 5—10 trials at each interval. Also plotted in B (open circles) are the EPP amplitudes similarly obtained after 10 stimuli at 200/sec. In C, the conditioning tetanus was 50 impulses at 200/sec. These results were all obtained from the same neuromuscular junction. It will be noted that after 20 impulses at 200/sec (B filled circles) the EPP amplitude was larger than the control at intervals of 100—200 msec after the tetanus. After 50 impulses this potentiation was lost, but a later phase of post-tetanic potentiation was found beginning about a second after the conditioning tetanus. The temperature was 36° C (HUBBARD 1963)

due to transmitter mobilization superimposed on a prolonged depression due to depletion. After 20 impulses the mobilization quickly terminates the depression and for a while it more than compensates for the depletion, but after 50 impulses the depletion is more severe and compensation is incomplete. However it does not seem that the post-tetanic potentiation that occurs independently of transmitter depletion (Fig. 37) can account for all of the potentiation occurring after 20 impulses in Fig. 38; in Fig. 37D the potentiation has declined almost to zero by 100 msec, whereas it is then maximal in Fig. 38B.

The synapses concerned in monosynaptic activation of motoneurones resemble curarized neuromuscular synapses in many of their postactivation responses. In the series (CURTIS and ECCLES 1960) plotted in Fig. 39A, B, C and illustrated in the inset records, the conditioning tetani of 40 volleys were at 640, 400 and 100/sec respectively and ceased at zero on the time scale. Only one testing stimulus was applied after each conditioning tetanus, and the sizes of the EPSPs were measured as the maximum slopes of the rising phases, as illustrated in the inset records. It will be seen that a conditioning tetanus of 400/sec is as effective as that at 640/sec, but after a tetanus at 100/sec there

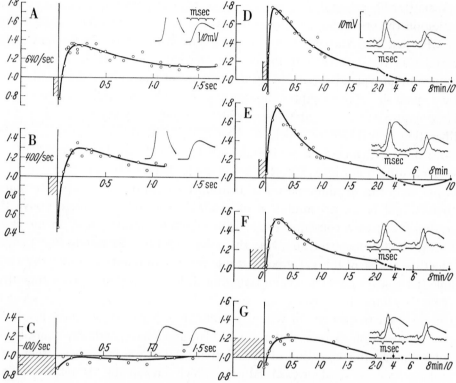

Fig. 39A—G. A—C. Curves showing early post-tetanic potentiation following brief conditioning tetani. The points plot the potentiation of the steepest part of the rising slope of the EPSPs as a fraction of the mean control. Intracellular records from the biceps—semitendinosus motoneurone (resting potential, −60 mV) are shown as insets, the first being the response at about 0.2 sec post-tetanically, the second the control. Note spike origin in A and B. Conditioning tetani of 40 impulses, the respective frequencies being 640/sec, 400/sec and 100/sec for A, B and C and the durations being indicated by the initial hatched blocks. D—G. Post-tetanic potentiation of monosynaptic EPSPs (see inset records of potentiated and control EPSPs) following long conditioning tetani (3200 volleys). The respective conditioning tetani for D, E, F, G were 640/sec for 5 sec, 400/sec for 8 sec, 200/sec for 16 sec and 100/sec for 32 sec, as shown by the hatched blocks. Thus each horizontal row AD, BE and CG has the same frequency of the conditioning tetanus. Note the large difference in time scales (about 100) between A—C on the one hand and D—G on the other (CURTIS and ECCLES 1960)

is no potentiation relative to the control EPSP. Since the total duration of the conditioning tetanus was only 0.4 sec in Fig. 39C, and since the potentiation in A and B had declined very little by 0.4 sec after the tetanus, it is evident that the increased temporal spread of the conditioning volleys is not responsible for the absence of potentiation in Fig. 39C. A conditioning tetanus of 200/sec gives a small potentiation, whereas 100/sec is often followed by depression. Thus it is frequency rather than number of impulses that is of particular significance in producing post-tetanic potentiation after brief conditioning tetani. These potentiations or depressions of the EPSP after brief conditioning tetani correspond to the post-tetanic potentiations or depressions of monosynaptic reflexes under comparable conditions (ECCLES and RALL 1951; LLOYD 1952).

It seems that there is a correlation between the changes in the rate of transmitter liberation during the steady-state of responses to repetitive stimulation on the one hand and the potentiations that occur in the testing EPSP or EPP just after the cessation of these tetani on the other. In discussing this correlation it is convenient to use the concept of "available transmitter," a measure of which is provided by the amount of transmitter that is liberated by a given size of presynaptic impulse. For example, on termination of repetitive synaptic stimulation at 300/sec or higher, there is a sudden cessation of the liberation of transmitter which has been running at the maximum attainable rate; albeit with an output per impulse much below the level for a single impulse under resting conditions (Fig. 31 A, B). It would therefore be expected that, after cessation of this maximum drain of transmitter from the presynaptic terminal, there would be an accumulation of available transmitter therein above the resting level; as a consequence, a testing impulse would cause an increased liberation of transmitter, so giving the potentiated EPSPs seen in Fig. 39 A, B. The time course of this early post-tetanic potentiation indicates that the available transmitter goes on accumulating for as long as 200 msec after repetitive synaptic stimulation ceases and then declines slowly over several seconds. During lower frequencies of synaptic stimulation (e.g. 200/sec) there is a lower rate of liberation of transmitter (Fig. 31 B), and correspondingly there is less potentiation after cessation of stimulation. After low frequencies there is a prolonged phase of depressed EPSPs, which presumably is related to the depression observed during low frequency tetani (Fig. 30 B, C). After a brief conditioning tetanus at 100/sec there is apparently an approximate balance between the potentiation and the depressant action (Fig. 39 C).

2. After long repetitive stimulation

After long conditioning tetani the potentiation of synaptic transmission, as indicated by the size of a testing EPSP, rises much more slowly and is much more prolonged than after the brief tetani, its total duration being measured in minutes instead of seconds. In this series the potentiation was much the same after 3200 impulses at 640 or 400/sec (Fig. 39 D, E), corresponding to the similar potentiations following 40 impulses at these two frequencies (A, B). Contrary to the findings with brief tetani (Fig. 39 C), there was a considerable potentiation after 3200 impulses at 100/sec (Fig. 39 G), while following tetanization at 200/sec there was an intermediate level of potentiation (Fig. 39 F). In all these respects the observations with EPSPs correspond closely with previous investigations employing the monosynaptic reflex as a test of potentiation (cf. LLOYD 1949; ECCLES and RALL 1951). However, a difference arises when the relative amounts of potentiation are compared. Usually reflexes display much larger potentiations because the changes in synaptic efficacy are sampled by the responses of a population of moto-neurones of which many are brought into the discharge zone by a relatively small increase of EPSP. On the other hand the size of the EPSP of a single motoneurone can be assumed to be proportional to the synaptic efficacy, which is thus shown to be potentiated to no more than 1.5 to 2.0 times the control.

The most likely explanation for the potentiation (cf. LLOYD 1949) that follows a long high-frequency tetanus is that under such conditions there is a prolonged after-hyperpolarization of the presynaptic fibres, with as a conse-quence an increase in the presynaptic spike potential (WALL and JOHNSON 1958; ECCLES and KRNJEVIĆ 1959a, b; BISHOP, BURKE and HAYHOW 1959; HUBBARD and SCHMIDT 1963); such an increased presynaptic spike can be expected to have an increased synaptic excitatory action (LLOYD 1949; ECCLES and RALL 1951; DEL CASTILLO and KATZ 1954d; HAGIWARA and TASAKI 1958; TAKEUCHI and TAKEUCHI 1962; ECCLES, KOSTYUK and SCHMIDT 1962c; HUBBARD and SCHMIDT 1963), and the increase in the monosynaptic EPSP of motoneurones has a comparable time course (ECCLES, KRNJEVIĆ and MILEDI 1959; ECCLES and KRNJEVIĆ 1959b). The alternative explanation is that there is an increased availability of transmitter, which is strongly suggested for the neuromuscular junction by the greatly increased frequency of miniature endplate potentials that is observed post-tetanically (LILEY 1956b; BROOKS 1956; HUBBARD 1959, 1963). This latter explanation is, of course, specially applicable to the post-tetanic potentiation after brief tetani, such as 40 impulses at 600/sec, because there is unlikely to be an appreciable after-hyperpolarization of the nerve terminals (cf. Fig. 7A of ECCLES and KRNJEVIĆ 1959a).

Another factor that may be operative during post-tetanic potentiation, but acting in the opposite direction, is the receptor desensitization of the post-synaptic membrane. The prolonged action of the synaptic transmitter may depress the effectiveness of many receptor sites on the postsynaptic membrane, just as occurs after prolonged action of a low concentration of acetylcholine on the neuromuscular synapse (Fig. 22E; THESLEFF 1955; KATZ and THESLEFF 1957b; AXELSSON and THESLEFF 1958). After a few impulses there is no sign of receptor desensitization with either rat or frog neuromuscular synapses (OTSUKA, ENDO and NONOMURA 1962). But evidence of desensitization is seen after the decline of the potentiation as in Fig. 39E at 4 to 10 minutes post-tetanically after 3200 impulses; desensitization may also be partly responsible for the delayed onset of post-tetanic potentiation after a prolonged condi-tioning tetanus (cf. LLOYD 1949). The receptor desensitization would thus be envisaged as forming a background depression on which were superimposed the more powerful potentiating factors. With synaptic transmission in the lateral geniculate body, post-tetanic depression is so large that it often dominates the potentiation (EVARTS and HUGHES 1957; HUGHES 1958; BISHOP, BURKE and HAYHOW 1959). It may persist for hours after a moderate tetanus, but after a much longer tetanus (10 min) there is no depression. It is possible that in part at least this enigmatic behaviour may eventually be explicable in terms of receptor desensitization.

DUDEL and KUFFLER (1961 b) noted that some seconds after the end of a severe conditioning tetanus, the frequency of miniature EPPs of crustacean muscle exhibits a prolonged depression (minutes) below the resting frequency. No such depression is seen with mammalian muscles (LILEY 1956b; HUBBARD 1959, 1963).

CHAPTER VII

THE GENERATION OF IMPULSES BY THE EXCITATORY POSTSYNAPTIC POTENTIAL AND THE ENDPLATE POTENTIAL

Except in rare circumstances, such as with the chick ciliary ganglion (Chapters II, IX), there is at the chemically transmitting synapse a complete break in the cable-like transmission that characterizes propagation along nerve-fibres up to the synapse. Usually the chemical transmission mediates a sequence of events that leads to the postsynaptic generation of a new impulse, as will be described in this Chapter. However, there are many examples of excitatory chemical transmission in which postsynaptic impulses are not generated. The synaptically induced depolarization is adequate in itself either to provide the currents for the discharge of an electric organ such as that of *Raia*, *Astroscopus*, *Narcine* and *Torpedo* (GRUNDFEST 1957a; BENNETT 1961); or to evoke a muscle contraction, as with the slow tonic muscles of the frog (KUFFLER and VAUGHAN WILLIAMS 1953; BURKE and GINSBORG 1956a, b).

With most synapses a single synchronous synaptic bombardment is adequate to generate a postsynaptic impulse, but with others the temporal summation of synaptic excitations is required. It is proposed to consider firstly the simpler situation of impulse generation by a single synchronous bombardment before treating the more complex phenomena resulting from repetitive synaptic activation.

A. Generation of impulses by a single synchronous synaptic activation

As shown in Fig. 40B—D, if the EPSP attains a critical threshold level, it causes the neurone to discharge an impulse, the latency being briefer, the larger the EPSP. In Fig. 40B—D this was brought about by increasing the size of the presynaptic volley, i.e. by increasing the number of activated synapses on the motoneurones. A similar result can be produced with the potentiation of the EPSP that follows a conditioning tetanization (Fig. 39A, B, inset records). As would be expected, a subliminal EPSP can also be made to generate an impulse by procedures that change the membrane potential towards the critical threshold level. For example in Fig. 40F—H the same EPSP as in Fig. 40E was made effective by the operation of a background depolarizing current which was commenced 12 msec before, and with an intensity shown in each record in mμA. The impulse arises at the arrows when the total level of depolarization is about 18 mV, which is made up in varying proportions by the conditioning depolarization and the superimposed EPSP. The threshold level of depolari-

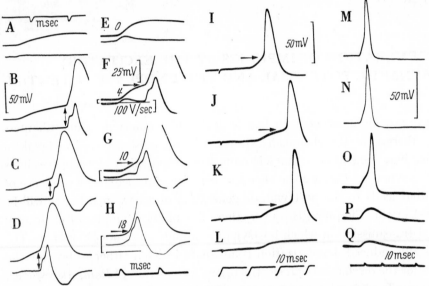

Fig. 40A—Q. A—D. Intracellularly recorded potentials of a cat gastrocnemius motoneurone (resting membrane potential −70 mV) evoked by monosynaptic activation that was progressively increased from A to D. The lower traces are the electrically differentiated records, the double-headed arrows indicating the onsets of the IS spikes in B—D. E—H. Intracellular records evoked by monosynaptic activation that was applied at 12.0 msec after the onset of a depolarizing pulse whose strength is indicated on each record in mμA. A pulse of 20 mμA was just below threshold for generating a spike. E shows control EPSP in the absence of a depolarizing pulse. Lower traces give electrically differentiated records. Note that spikes are truncated (COOMBS, CURTIS and ECCLES 1957b). I is the action potential recorded intracellularly from a cell of the rabbit superior cervical ganglion in response to a maximum presynaptic volley, and in J—L the volley size is progressively diminished. Arrows mark the origin of the spike (R. M. ECCLES 1955). M—Q are action potentials similarly recorded, M resembling I. N—Q show effect of progressive curarization, the presynaptic volley being maximum throughout and the membrane potential unchanged (R. M. ECCLES 1963)

zation may be attained also by superimposing the EPSP on the depolarization produced by a preceding EPSP, which provides a sufficient explanation of the reflex phenomenon known as temporal facilitation (LLOYD 1946a; ECCLES 1946a, 1953). Comparable observations have been made with the EPSPs generated in a wide variety of nerve cells. For example with sympathetic ganglion cells, varying the size of the presynaptic volley gives a series of EPSPs and spike potentials (Fig. 40I—L) closely resembling Fig. 40A—D, but with a time scale several times slower, and in Fig. 40M—Q curare is seen to block by depressing the EPSP below the threshold level (R. M. ECCLES 1963). There are a large number of investigations that conform with the hypothesis that synaptic excitatory action is effective in generating an impulse solely by the depolarization of the neurone, i.e. by producing an EPSP that attains the threshold level of depolarization (ECCLES 1953, 1957; COOMBS, ECCLES and FATT 1955c; R. M. ECCLES 1955; FRANK and FUORTES 1956b, 1961; COOMBS, CURTIS and ECCLES 1957b; KOLMODIN and SKOGLUND 1958; MACHNE, FADIGA and BROOKHART 1959; HAGIWARA, WATANABE and SAITO 1959; PHILLIPS, 1959, 1961; FADIGA and BROOKHART 1960; NISHI and KOKETSU 1960; SPENCER and KANDEL 1961a; ARAKI and TERZUOLO 1962; FURSHPAN and FURUKAWA 1962).

Alternatively it has been postulated (LLOYD and McINTYRE 1955; HUNT 1955) that monosynaptic excitatory impulses are effective in evoking motoneuronal discharges by a mechanism of "transmitter potentiality" which can be assessed solely by the criterion of the motoneuronal discharge. On the contrary it has been argued that the experimental basis for this postulate is perfectly compatible with the EPSP generation of discharges (ECCLES 1957, pp. 64—65; FRANK and FUORTES 1961). Recently HUNT and PERL (1960) have again questioned the adequacy of the EPSP explanation, but adduce no new evidence of substance. For example, it is argued that lateral gastrocnemius volleys are more powerful than medial gastrocnemius in evoking discharges from lateral gastrocnemius motoneurones, yet less powerful in producing EPSPs; however this argument overlooks the fact that in the latter situation the soleus nerve was separated from the lateral gastrocnemius nerve (ECCLES, ECCLES and LUNDBERG 1957b), whereas in the former it was not (LLOYD, HUNT and McINTYRE 1955; LLOYD and McINTYRE 1955). Medial gastrocnemius volleys produce an EPSP in lateral gastrocnemius-soleus motoneurones which has a mean value only 0.51 times that produced by a lateral gastrocnemius-soleus volley (ECCLES, KRNJEVIĆ and MILEDI 1959), which is a ratio that accounts satisfactorily for the observed differences in evoking reflex discharges. HUNT and PERL (1960) also refer to the small variations in the threshold level of depolarization observed by FRANK and FUORTES (1956b) and KOLMODIN and SKOGLUND (1958) when the mode of stimulating a motoneurone is varied. However, both groups of investigators satisfactorily explained these small deviations in terms of the EPSP hypothesis, without having to postulate an additional mechanism for generating discharges.

When the spike potentials generated by an EPSP are recorded at sufficient speed, they are seen to have an inflexion on the rising phase comparable with that occurring with the spike potential generated in the motoneurone by antidromic invasion from its motor axon (ARAKI, OTANI and FURUKAWA 1953; ARAKI and OTANI 1955; FATT 1957b; FUORTES, FRANK and BECKER 1957; COOMBS, CURTIS and ECCLES 1957a, 1957b; MACHNE, FADIGA and BROOKHART 1959). The double composition of the motoneuronal spike potential is particularly evident when it is recorded after electrical differentiation, as in the lower records of Figs. 40 B—D; and 41 A, B. The first spike, beginning at the doubled-headed arrow in Fig. 41 B, is called the IS-spike because there is convincing experimental evidence that it is generated in the *initial segment* of the motoneurone (the non-medullated part of the motor axon plus the axon hillock from which the axon arises); the second spike arises when the IS spike has depolarized the soma membrane to its much higher threshold level (the SD horizontal line in Fig. 41 A, B), being called the SD spike because it is produced by the soma and dendrites. These identifications have been definitively established by TERZUOLO and ARAKI (1961) and by ARAKI and TERZUOLO (1962) who employed two powerful techniques: simultaneous extracellular

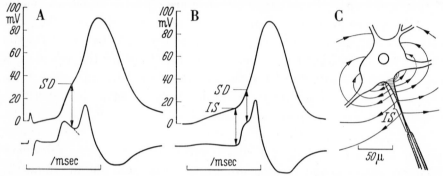

Fig. 41 A—C. Tracings of intracellularly recorded spike potentials evoked by antidromic (A) and mono-synaptic (B) stimulation of a motoneurone, respectively (COOMBS, CURTIS and ECCLES 1957b, Fig. 9 A, B). The lower traces show the electrically differentiated records. Perpendicular lines are drawn from the origins of the *IS* and *SD* spikes, as indicated in the differentiated records, the respective threshold depolarizations being thus determined from the potential records, and indicated by horizontal lines labelled respectively *IS* and *SD*. C shows diagramatically the lines of current flow that occur when a synaptically induced depolarization of the soma-dendritic membrane electrotonically spreads to the initial segment

and intracellular recording from the same motoneurone; and voltage clamping of a motoneuronal soma that is impaled by a double microelectrode.

With normal motoneurones the threshold level of depolarization is always, as in Figs. 40 B—D, 41 A, B, much higher for the SD membrane than for the IS membrane. There is a considerable range in the threshold values for cat motoneurones that are shown by their resting and spike potentials to be in good condition; for the IS membrane 5 to 18 mV (mean about 10 mV) and for the SD membrane 19 to 37 mV (mean 25 mV) (COOMBS, CURTIS and ECCLES 1957b; FUORTES, FRANK and BECKER 1957; TERZUOLO and ARAKI 1961; ARAKI and TERZUOLO 1962). However, for any one motoneurone the SD threshold is never less than twice the IS threshold. With frog motoneurones a comparable difference is observed with mean values of about 9 mV and 26 mV for the threshold depolarizations for initiating IS and SD spikes respectively (MACHNE, FADIGA and BROOKHART 1959). Some toad motoneurones are exceptional in that a gradually rising local response initiates the full spike potential without any evident step characteristic of an IS spike (ARAKI and OTANI 1959, ARAKI 1960).

With other types of nerve cells the spike potentials often display a double composition comparable with the IS-SD potentials of motoneurones, but there are considerable variations, and in some types no IS-SD separation is detectable. The site of initiation of the impulses is then indeterminate. With pyramidal cells of the neocortex and hippocampus there is an IS-SD composition of the intracellular spike potential (PHILLIPS 1961; LI 1961; KANDEL, SPENCER and BRINLEY 1961); hence it is likely that, as with motoneurones, the initial segment has a much lower threshold than the soma and dendrites. Consequently it is the usual site of initiation of impulses. In the spinal cord there is much variation with respect to the threshold discrimination between the IS and SD regions of nerve cells. For example, the same large discrimination as with motoneurones is seen with the cells in the dorsal horn on which large cutaneous fibres make synaptic contacts (ECCLES, ECCLES and LUNDBERG 1960; KOSTYUK 1960), while there is no sign of IS-SD separation with the intermediate neurones that relay the group I a and I b afferent impulses from muscle (ECCLES, ECCLES and LUNDBERG 1960). Possibly these are amongst the interneurones in which HUNT and KUNO (1959) could find no IS-SD separation. On the contrary with the cells of the ventral spinocerebellar tract (ECCLES, HUBBARD and OSCARSSON 1961) and the cells of CLARKE's column (CURTIS, ECCLES and LUNDBERG 1958) there is a considerable threshold separation for the IS and SD spikes. With the frog sympathetic ganglion cells the threshold for generation of the IS spike is so high, mean about 26 mV with range 18—35 mV, that only occasionally is it possible to detect an inflexion signalling the later origin of the soma spike, which has a threshold of 30—40 mV on such occasions (NISHI and KOKETSU 1960), and with synaptic stimulation of mammalian sympathetic ganglion cells an inflexion signalling a later origin for the SD spike is never seen (Fig. 40I—K; R. M. ECCLES 1955, 1963).

Where the IS threshold is much lower than the SD threshold, as in the motoneurone, the EPSP produced by the activation of synapses covering the soma and dendrites is effective not by generating an impulse in these regions, but by electrotonic spread of the depolarization to the initial segment, as is illustrated by the lines of current flow in Fig. 41 C. By recording the impulse discharged along the motor nerve fibre in the ventral root, it is found that usually this impulse starts to propagate down the medullated axon about 0.05 msec after the initiation of the IS spike, i.e. the medullated axon usually is excited secondarily to the initial segment (COOMBS, CURTIS and ECCLES 1957b). In normal motoneurones, synaptic excitatory action usually generates an SD spike not directly by its depolarizing action, but indirectly through the mediation of an IS spike which lifts the depolarization of the SD membrane to threshold by currents that flow in the reverse direction from those drawn in Fig. 41 C (COOMBS, CURTIS and ECCLES 1957b, TERZUOLO and

ARAKI 1961; ARAKI and TERZUOLO 1962). A similar sequence has been observed in the ganglion cells of *Aplysia* (ARVANITAKI and CHALANOZITIS 1956; TAUC 1960b). TAUC (1962a, 1962b) has shown that in *Aplysia*, the axonal initiation of the spike is attributable not only to the lower threshold of the initial segment of the axon, but also to the location of the synaptic endings thereon and not on the soma.

Exceptionally the timing of the impulse in the ventral root fibres shows that it is generated in the medullated axon just before the onset of the IS spike, so presumably it is initiated in the first node (COOMBS, CURTIS and ECCLES 1957b). Such a site of impulse initiation is comparable with that produced by the Pacinian corpuscle (DIAMOND, GRAY and SATO 1956; DIAMOND, GRAY and INMAN 1958; LÖWENSTEIN and RATHCAMP 1958; GRAY 1959; LÖWEN-STEIN 1959).

The generation of an impulse in the axon at some distance from the soma is more directly demonstrated by EDWARDS and OTTOSON (1958) who record the spike potential simultaneously through electrodes located extracellularly on the soma and axon of a crustacean stretch receptor cell. In this way it is shown that a generator potential initiates the discharge of an impulse at a site remote from the cell body, which is itself invaded by antidromic propagation about 0.3 msec later. Synaptic excitatory action also causes the initiation of spikes in the axon at some distance from the soma of ganglion cells of the lobster cardiac ganglion (HAGIWARA and BULLOCK 1957; HAGIWARA, WATANABE and SAITO 1959; HAGIWARA 1961) and the impulse never invades the soma, which is electrically inexcitable. In an extraordinarily rigorous topographical investigation of the Mauthner cell of the goldfish, FURSHPAN and FURUKAWA (1962) show that the synaptically generated impulse discharge arises as a full-sized spike in the axon hillock or adjacent axon, while the cell body and large dendrites have little if any ability to produce even partial spike potentials.

With the amphibian and mammalian neuromuscular junction the EPP generates a spike potential when the depolarization attains a critical level (Fig. 42K; FATT and KATZ 1951; BOYD and MARTIN 1956b). The exact site of generation is not known, but surface recording from single isolated muscle fibres (KUFFLER 1942a, 1942b) shows that it is in close proximity to the endplate region. With intracellular recording the spike potential at the endplate region is depressed by the shunting effect of the high ionic permeability that is produced by the action of the transmitter (acetylcholine) on the subsynaptic membrane (Figs. 19, 42L; FATT and KATZ 1951; DEL CASTILLO and KATZ 1954e; OGATA and WRIGHT 1960). Similarly with amphibian sympathetic ganglion cells the spike potential is diminished if it is superimposed on the early phase of the EPSP (Fig. 42M; NISHI and KOKETSU 1960). As shown in Fig. 14C there would then be a high conductance of the subsynaptic membrane as a result of continued transmitter action. With mammalian motoneurones there is little or no depression of the spike potential under these conditions (COOMBS, CURTIS and ECCLES 1957a), but a depression comparable with that of Fig. 42M is seen with synaptic activation of amphibian motoneurones (MACHNE, FADIGA and BROOKHART (1959) and of the cells of CLARKE's column in the cat spinal cord (ECCLES, OSCARSSON and WILLIS, unpublished observations).

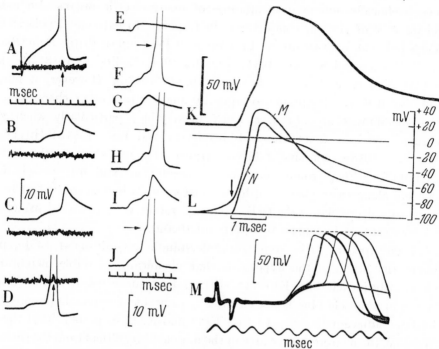

Fig. 42A—M. A—J. Intracellular responses of a chromatolysed motoneurone showing partial responses and the discharge of impulses. Upper traces in A—C (lower in D) are intracellular records from a flexor digitorum longus motoneurone (spike potential, 84 mV) whose motor axon had been severed 16 days previously in L7 VR. Lower tracings are from the filament of L7 VR that contained the motor axon. A shows response to a depolarizing current pulse that generated a spike potential; B—D are responses at same amplification and sweep speed, but evoked by a group I maximum afferent volley in the nerve to flexor digitorum longus. E—J are responses as in B—D, which are selected to show the wide range of variability of partial responses that are superimposed on the EPSP (E) and evoke full spikes when the depolarization attains the critical level (about 13 mV) shown by the arrows in F, H and J (ECCLES, LIBET and YOUNG 1958). K, L intracellular records at endplate zone of a frog muscle fibre, K being generated by a nerve impulse with the spike arising from an initial EPP, while in L there are superimposed tracings of such a response (N) and the spike produced by an impulse propagating along the muscle fibre (M) (DEL CASTILLO and KATZ 1954e). M shows spike potentials arising from the EPSPs of a frog sympathetic ganglion cell, the earliest spike having a depressed summit just as in L (NISHI and KOKETSU 1960)

There is now a voluminous literature in support of the concept that those areas of postsynaptic membrane which are selectively sensitive to the action of chemical transmitting substances are electrically inexcitable (GRUNDFEST 1957a, b, 1959, 1960a, b, 1961a, b). Several examples can be given of post-synaptic membranes which have extensive areas of synaptic contact and which exhibit no sign of electric excitability even when subjected to extreme depolarization. Motor nerve terminals are widely dispersed over the surface of the tonic muscles of amphibia, and no increase of sodium conductance can be detected even with extreme depolarization (KUFFLER and VAUGHAN WILLIAMS 1953; BURKE and GINSBORG 1956a). The somas of the large cells of the lobster cardiac ganglion have been shown to be virtually devoid of electrical excitability and at the same time to be the probable site of generation of the EPSP (HAGIWARA, WATANABE and SAITO 1959; HAGIWARA 1961). The chemically activated membranes of many electric organs also exhibit no increase of sodium conductance in response to extreme depolarization: *Torpedo* (ALBE-FESSARD 1951; FESSARD and POSTERNAK 1950); *Raia* (BROCK, R. M. ECCLES and KEYNES 1953; BROCK and R. M. ECCLES 1958; BENNETT 1961); *Narcine* and *Astroscopus* (GRUNDFEST 1957b). However, it may be questioned if it is justifiable to argue by analogy that other chemical receptive membranes are also electrically inexcitable, particularly when some cardiac and crustacean muscle fibres (FATT and KATZ 1953a; HOYLE and WIERSMA 1958a) combine a diffuse transmitter sensitivity with electrical excitability. Furthermore, denervated mammalian and frog muscle fibres develop along their whole length a sensitivity to ACh even equivalent to that at a normal endplate (Fig. 99B), and yet retain their electrical excitability (AXELSSON and THESLEFF 1959; MILEDI 1960a).

There appears to be some misunderstanding (GRUNDFEST 1961c, p. 97) about the origin of the hypothesis that chemically excitable membrane is electrically inexcitable. KUFFLER (1942a) first suggested that the endplate region of a muscle fibre is not electrically excitable, the muscle impulse being initiated adjacent thereto. In 1951 FATT and KATZ suggested "that the endplate, i.e. the neuroreceptive area of the muscle fibre, differs from the surrounding fibre surface not only in its specific sensitivity to chemical stimulants, but in its lack of sensitivity to electric currents." Subsequently investigation by DEL CASTILLO and KATZ (1954e) supported this postulate, but they clearly stated that the electrical inexcitability would obtain only for the actual receptor areas and need not extend over the whole endplate membrane of the muscle, which might be a mosaic of chemically and electrically excitable patches. Subsequently this concept was reformulated and greatly elaborated by ALTAMARINO, COATES and GRUNDFEST (1955) and by GRUNDFEST (1955, 1957a, b, 1959, 1960a, b, 1961a, b).

Recently it has been claimed that electrical inexcitability has been demonstrated for the areas of the frog neuromuscular junction that are excited by the transmitter (WERMAN 1960, 1963). Impulses are generated in muscle by direct stimulation and propagated past the region of the nerve ending. With extracellular recording by a microelectrode in close proximity to the fibre at an endplate site (identified by fast miniature EPPs) there is either a purely positive potential or there is superimposed on it a negative spike potential that is smaller than when the microelectrode is elsewhere on the muscle fibre. It should be pointed out that the absence of a negatively directed spike need indicate merely that the spike potential at the endplate region is lower than elsewhere. External recording samples the extrinsic flow of current deriving from inequalities in the membrane currents at any instant. It cannot establish that there is no inward sodium current at any region. The most that could be demonstrated is that the spike potential of endplate sites is smaller than elsewhere along the muscle; but not that these sites have an electrical inexcitability comparable with that of the tonic muscles of amphibia (BURKE and GINSBORG 1956a). As pointed out by SPYROPOULOS and TASAKI (1960) it seems impossible at present to prove or disprove GRUNDFEST'S hypothesis that all chemically excitable membrane is electrically inexcitable.

In this context it should be mentioned that electrical inexcitability of the soma has been inferred from observations on the very large positively directed spikes that are observed by an extracellular microelectrode in close proximity to motoneuronal surface membranes (FREYGANG 1958; FREYGANG and FRANK 1959). The immediately subjacent membrane is acting as a source for some remote excited membrane. Since the exploring microelectrode always fails to find this excited membrane, it can be concluded that the observations probably mean no more than that the injurious action of the microelectrode renders the immediately subjacent membrane electrically inexcitable.

By a rigorous study of simultaneous extracellular and intracellular recording from a motoneurone, TERZUOLO and ARAKI (1961) have proved that the soma membrane is actively concerned in producing the SD spike. However, measurements of the current flow generating the SD spike show that the membrane conductance increases only about 7 times above the resting value (ARAKI and TERZUOLO 1962), which is less than one fourth of the change that occurs in other excitable membranes (COLE and CURTIS 1939; HODGKIN 1951, 1958; HODGKIN and HUXLEY 1952; FATT and KATZ 1951). A considerable proportion of this discrepancy could be explained if the high proportion of the soma membrane covered by synapses (WYCKOFF and YOUNG 1956; PALAY 1958) is inexcitable. Other factors that would tend to diminish the relative conductance change would be the glial coverage of so much of the soma membrane and the constricted extracellular spaces which apparently are constituted solely by 200 Å clefts between the glial and nervous elements (PALAY 1958; HORSTMANN and MEVES 1959; DE ROBERTIS and GERSCHENFELD 1961).

There is now much other evidence that the somas and dendrites of most neurones are less readily excitable than the immediately adjacent non-medullated zone of the axon. The threshold depolarization is usually two or three times higher for the soma-dendritic spike than for the IS spike (COOMBS, CURTIS and ECCLES 1957a, 1957b; FUORTES, FRANK and BECKER 1957, ARAKI and TERZUOLO 1962); and the conduction velocity in dendrites and possibly over the soma is very slow, being usually much less than 1 m/sec for dendrites

(Lorente de Nó 1947; Fatt 1957a; Cragg and Hamlyn 1955; Andersen 1960a). By microelectrode recording from neurones in tissue culture under direct visual observation Hild and Tasaki (1962) have demonstrated conduction of impulses along dendrites, at least for 100 μ from the soma, the velocity being at the very slow rate of about 0.1 m/sec.

Even if half of the soma-dendritic membrane is electrically inexcitable because of its synaptic coverage, the resulting shunting of the regenerative depolarization of incipient impulses would produce a relatively small increase in threshold to electric excitation. It has therefore been argued (Eccles 1957, p. 52) that there is some intrinsic difference between the soma-dendritic membrane and the adjacent membrane of the initial segment, and this has been confirmed by threshold determinations using the voltage clamp (Araki and Terzuolo 1962). It is also strongly indicated by the after-potentials following a spike, the after-hyperpolarization being large after the SD spike and negligible after the IS spike (Coombs, Eccles and Fatt 1955a). Possibly the dense synaptic coverage of the soma-dendritic membrane is the cause of this differentiation in its properties relative to the uncovered membrane. An analogous example of a spreading influence from synaptic areas might be provided by the specific receptors to acetylcholine which spread widely beyond the normal neuromuscular junction, a progressively decrementing distribution being observable for some hundreds of microns (Miledi 1960b). However, such a synaptic influence certainly cannot apply to the giant ganglion cells of *Aplysia* which are also electrically much less excitable than their axons, despite the restriction of the synapses to the axon at some distance from the soma (Tauc 1962a, 1962b). Furthermore, the somas of frog spinal ganglion cells are less excitable than their axons, though there is a complete absence of synaptic endings (Svaetichin 1951, 1958; Ito 1957). It would seem therefore that somas are less excitable than axons regardless of the synaptic connections they may or may not have on their surfaces.

The electrical inexcitability of dendrites of cortical pyramidal cells has been inferred from two observations on the curarized cortex (Purpura and Grundfest 1956; Grundfest 1958): the absence of a negative surface potential indicates that the antidromic invarion of pyramidal cells does not extend up the apical dendrites; stimulation by an electrode at a depth of 0.8 mm fails to produce a negative potential of the cortical surface immediately above. If may be conceded that under the conditions of these experiments impulses do not propagate up the apical dendrites, but it is unjustifiable to draw the further conclusion that the apical dendrites are inexcitable electrically. The experiments merely indicate that impulse propagation did not occur along the length of an apical dendrite. Under more favourable conditions, as for example a background of synaptically induced depolarization, propagation of impulses may occur, or at least there may be partial spike responses, as in Fig. 42B—J, which would add to the synaptically induced depolarization. Several factors would contribute to the low safety factor for impulse propagation from soma along dendrites (cf. ANDERSEN 1960a): the threshold for initiation of an impulse is much higher (PHILLIPS 1959, 1961); the profuse branching introduces a considerable expansion of the surface to be invaded; finally, impulse propagation becomes less efficient in very fine nerve fibres. In the crustacean stretch receptor cell there is evidence that blockage or delay of antidromic propagation occurs not only at the axon-soma junction but also at various sites along dendrites (EYZAGUIRRE and KUFFLER 1955b; EDWARDS and OTTOSON 1958). However, antidromic invasion normally penetrates far enough along the dendrites to be able to affect the generator sites at their terminals, and there is no evidence to suggest that, apart from geometrical factors, dendrites have properties different from the soma from which they arose.

On both anatomical and physiological grounds the dendrites of motoneurones become of progressively less significance for the purposes of synaptic function the further they extend from the soma. The density of synaptic knobs falls off progressively (BARR 1939; BODIAN 1952; LORENTE DE NÓ 1938b; WYCKOFF and YOUNG 1956), and the increased electrotonic decrement causes the postsynaptic currents generated by activation of a synapse to have progressively less effect on the membrane potential of the initial segment of the axon, which is the site of the effective excitatory and inhibitory actions of synapses, at least with most types of neurones. It has been calculated that the length constant for a dendrite 5μ in diameter is about 300μ (COOMBS, ECCLES and FATT 1955a), so it will be appreciated that synapses on dendrites are virtually ineffective if situated on the more remote regions of dendrites that are about 1 mm in length.

A remarkable regional distribution of synaptic endings has been demonstrated on frog motoneurones (FADIGA and BROOKHART 1960; BROOKHART and FADIGA 1960). By a careful systematic study of the fields of extracellularly recorded synaptic potentials and by correlation both with the intracellular potentials and with the potentials in the ventral roots, it was shown that a dorsal root volley and a lateral column volley monosynaptically excite quite different regions of motoneurones. The former volley acts on the distal zones of the dorsally directed dendrites, the latter on the soma and on the dendrites adjacent thereto. From these sites of production the EPSPs spread electrotonically over the motoneuronal surface and along the axon to the ventral root. The generation of an impulse occurs if the initial segment is depolarized above threshold, hence the synapses of the dorsal root fibres are very unfavourably located (FADIGA and BROOKHART 1960).

An active role of dendrites in initiating impulses is exhibited by motoneurones that are suffering from chromatolysis on account of severance of their axon some weeks previously (ECCLES, LIBET and YOUNG 1958; McINTYRE,

BRADLEY and BROCK 1959). For example a synaptically induced depolarization (Fig. 42 E) may induce one or more partial spike responses (G, I), which in turn may generate further partial spikes so that eventually a full-sized neuronal spike is set up (F, H, J). It is further seen in Fig. 42 that an impulse is discharged down the motor axon by the large spike (D) and not by the partial responses, B and C. These partial responses are often generated in the dendrites, remote from the soma, and usually there is no evidence of an intermediate stage of IS-spike as in Fig. 41 B. Presumably the full impulse arises in the soma or dendrites and propagates thence down the axon. The afferent nerve terminals of the amphibian muscle spindle exhibit a similar phenomenon (KATZ 1950), there being local responses probably at strategic branching sites, that may or may not build up into propagated impulses. These observations conform with the suggestions (CLARE and BISHOP 1955; BISHOP 1958) that in the apical dendrites of cortical cells the synaptically induced depolarization may evoke partial spike responses that greatly aid the electrotonic spread of the depolarization to the soma or adjacent axon where the propagated impulse is initiated. This suggestion is particularly valuable as it provides a mechanism whereby the remote synapses on the apical dendrites of a pyramidal cell can contribute effectively to the generation of an impulse at the axon-soma region. Recently, with intracellular recording from the pyramidal cells of the hippocampus, SPENCER and KANDEL (1961 b) have shown that synaptic excitation of the apical dendrites generates local responses which propagate to the soma and may produce sufficient depolarization to initiate the discharge of an impulse, just as occurs with chromatolysed motoneurones (Fig. 42 B—J). Usually no IS spike can be seen preceding the SD spike, so it seems likely that the local dendritic response is able to initiate the propagated impulse either in the dendrites, as found by CRAGG and HAMLYN (1955) and by ANDERSEN (1960a), or in the soma, without the mediation of an IS spike response. Synaptic excitation of pyramidal cells of the motor cortex also appears to evoke local responses of dendrites (PHILLIPS 1959, 1961).

In summary of the available evidence, it can be concluded that both dendrites and somas are less readily excitable electrically than axons; as a consequence impulse propagation is very slow, usually below 1 metre/sec for dendrites; and blockage may occur at sites of particularly low safety factor, as at the axon-soma junction or at branching points of dendrites. There is probably much variability between different types of nerve cells and between the same type under different experimental conditions, but there is no justification for assuming from the experimental evidence that the surface membrane of dendrites is devoid of electrical excitability. On the balance of evidence it seems likely that the chemical receptor patches at synapses are electrically inexcitable, but it is not known if these patches are coextensive with the subsynaptic membrane, nor is it known what fraction of the dendritic membrane is specialized in this way.

If, surrounding receptor sites for transmitter, there was an extensive "forbidden zone" for the sodium-conductance mechanism, then the generalization that chemically excitable membrane is not electrically excitable would be of great interest because it would raise problems concerning the means whereby this exclusiveness is effected. Problems of this character will be considered in Chapter XVI. However two recent developments have now made the generalization of little interest. Firstly the concept of "forbidden zone" has now become so restricted that it may be merely of molecular dimensions (GRUNDFEST 1961 c; BENNETT 1961); so that it comes to mean no more than that a transmitter receptor site with the associated ionic channel cannot also be an ionic channel for electrical excitation. There is of course no evidence to the contrary, and in fact this generally has been a tacit assumption. Secondly the concept of electrical excitability has been extended beyond the sodium and potassium conductances responsible for the nerve impulse. Apparently it now includes any non-linearity in the membrane ionic currents that flow in response to applied membrane potentials—for example the delayed rectification of the slow tonic muscles of amphibia (GRUNDFEST 1961 c, p. 99). One wonders how non-linear a process has to be before it is designated "a peculiar variety of electrical excitability."

B. Accommodation and adaptation of neurones

The generation of spike potentials by prolonged synaptically induced depolarizations will be considered in relation to neuronal responses produced by polarizing currents applied through an intracellular electrode. Such investigations have been performed most extensively on cat, rat and toad motoneurones.

On cat motoneurones rectangular depolarizing or hyperpolarizing currents induce firstly potential changes with approximately exponential time courses that are largely governed by the membrane time constant (Fig. 43 A, B; ARAKI, ITO and OSHIMA 1961). The potentials reach a summit at about 15 msec and thereafter there is a slow decline to a final steady level of potential after about 100 msec that is on the average about 70 % of the summit potential. On cessation of the currents there is, correspondingly, an initial exponential decline governed by the time constant of the membrane to an overshoot from which recovery again occurs in about 100 msec. Evidently these time courses of membrane potential result from two overlapping processes, there being, in addition to the membrane time constant, some accommodative change partially restoring the membrane potential. With currents well below threshold for initiating impulses, depolarizing and hyperpolarizing currents give mirror image responses. Fig. 43 C shows that these membrane potentials, drawn as dotted lines, are exactly matched by the plotted points giving the simultaneous changes in excitability, which in part were earlier reported by FRANK and FUORTES (1956b), and by COOMBS, CURTIS and ECCLES (1959).

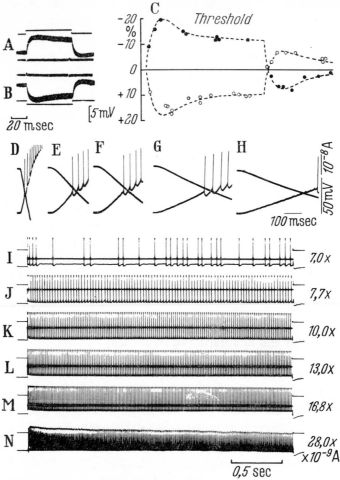

Fig. 43 A—N. Accommodation of neurones. A, B show depolarized and hyperpolarized membrane potentials of a cat motoneurone produced by intracellular application of rectangular current pulses as indicated, the extracellular records being shown immediately below and above the intracellular respectively. C shows the increase and decrease of another motoneurone threshold as tested by brief pulses during and after conditioning by depolarizing (filled circles) and hyperpolarizing (open circles) currents of 93 msec duration. The changes in potential produced by these currents are shown by the broken lines and correspond to A and B (ARAKI, ITO and OSHIMA 1961). D—H. Lower traces show intracellular potentials of a cat motoneurone to slopes of depolarizing current of various steepness (the downward slopes) (SASAKI and OTANI 1961). I—N are the intracellular responses of a rat motoneurone to prolonged (2.5 sec) rectangular depolarizing currents applied through the same electrode. Strengths of currents are indicated to the right as multiples of 10^{-9} A (GRANIT, KERNELL and SHORTESS 1963)

There have been several incomplete investigations on the action of a steady depolarizing current in evoking discharge of impulses from motoneurones (BROCK and MCINTYRE 1953; COOMBS, CURTIS and ECCLES 1959; BRADLEY and SOMJEN 1961; FRANK and FUORTES, unpublished observations), but no systematic study until the recent work of GRANIT, KERNELL and SHORTESS (1963) on both rat and cat motoneurones. The significance of this type of investigation will be appreciated when it is recognized that a continuous depolarizing current entering a neurone through an intracellular micro-electrode has virtually the same action on the impulse-generating mechanism as has the depolarization produced by a steady synaptic bombardment (cf. FUORTES and MANTEGAZZINI 1962). Otherwise expressed, in both cases the initial segment is subjected to continuous action of depolarizing currents, which in the one is due to integrated action of the individually brief (Figs. 14, 15) depolarizing currents at activated synapses, and in the other to the continually applied current through the microelectrode. Apart from the hazard of cell damage by the microelectrode, the only difference would arise in respect of the ionic injections by which the synaptic and the direct depolarizing currents are applied.

Fig. 43 I—N shows a remarkable series of responses of a rat motoneurone to currents of 2.5 sec duration and with a four-fold range of intensity. After the first two impulses the discharge frequency settles down to a slowly declining level until after about 1 sec it reaches a well maintained plateau which endures for 2.5 sec in Fig. 43 and even for 25 sec in later tests on this same motoneurone. Over a wide range (mean values, 22 to 64/sec) these adapted frequencies are linearly related to the current strengths. Similarly, some cat motoneurones also exhibit a well maintained frequency during prolonged depolarizing currents, but the frequencies are lower than with the rat and there is a more restricted range of frequency (mean values 10 to 37/sec) that is linearly related to current strength (GRANIT, KERNELL and SHORTESS 1963). Nevertheless even these restricted ranges more than cover the frequency range for motoneurones responding tonically to prolonged synaptic stimulation, where the maximum frequency was no higher than 13 to 25/sec (GRANIT, HAASE and RUTLEDGE 1960). There is thus full justification for the assumptions made in the quantitative treatment of the excitatory and inhibitory synaptic control of frequency (GRANIT, HAASE and RUTLEDGE 1960; GRANIT and RENKIN 1961).

In contrast to these motoneurones exhibiting tonic behaviour, most motoneurones of both cat and rat are phasic in their response to steady currents (GRANIT, KERNELL and SHORTESS 1963), many responding with only a few impulses. Others exhibit a progressively declining frequency with no tendency to stabilize at a particular level of adaptation.

The accommodation of motoneurones to depolarizing currents has been studied by investigating the relationship between the slopes of linearly rising currents and the latencies for initiation of the first discharge (FRANK and FUORTES 1960; KOIZUMI, USHIYAMA and BROOKS 1960; BRADLEY and SOMJEN 1961; SASAKI and OTANI 1961; ARAKI and ITO unpublished observations);

alternatively, the stimulating currents were exponentially rising with varying time constants, and the relationship of threshold depolarization to latent period gives a measure of accommodation (ARAKI and OTANI 1959; OTANI 1960). By this latter procedure the time constant of accommodation is 25 to 70 msec for the initial segment of toad motoneurones. With linearly rising currents SASAKI and OTANI (1961) find that the accommodation of the initial segment of cat motoneurones is relatively fast, with the consequence that slowly rising currents often initiate impulses in the soma-dendritic membrane instead. For example in the series of Fig. 43 D—H, the first spike is generated at about 20 mV depolarization by the steepest current slope (D) and at 37 mV for the least slope (H). At some intermediate slope the site of impulse generation changes from the IS to the SD membranes, as revealed by differentiation of faster records. In other motoneurones slope of current has little effect on the threshold of spikes being generated in the IS segment by all slopes of current. Since the threshold level of depolarization is only 6 to 12 mV, it seems likely that this latter type of response characterizes motoneurones depolarized by the impalement, which may likewise account for the similar findings of FRANK and FUORTES (1960). Rat motoneurones exhibit an accommodation to linearly rising currents that is virtually complete in 40 to 80 msec (BRADLEY and SOMJEN 1961) as compared with about 200 msec for cat motoneurones (cf. Fig. 43 D to H).

However, there is much uncertainty in the precise significance of these measurements because of the complex character of the stimulated structure, as has been pointed out by GRANIT, KERNELL and SHORTESS (1963). Adopting the simplest picture, a low threshold initial segment joins a high threshold soma-dendritic membrane, and the former has a faster accommodation than the latter so that with long currents the site of impulse initiation is transferred. Alternatively, between the IS and SD types of membrane there may be a zone with transitional properties. However it seems safe to conclude from these investigations that motoneurones have a much slower accommodation than motor axons, and that two classes of motoneurones may be distinguished: phasic motoneurones that rapidly adapt to a steady depolarizing current and tonic motoneurones in which such adaptation is negligible. The eccentric cell of the Limulus eye resembles the tonic motoneurone in having the ability to discharge indefinitely in response to a continuous depolarization. The various factors controlling its frequency of discharge have been studied by FUORTES and MANTEGAZZINI (1962). There is as yet no satisfactory explanation of the very different tonic and phasic behaviour of motoneurones.

C. The generation of impulses by prolonged synaptic excitation

ADRIAN and BRONK (1929) and DENNY BROWN (1929) were the first to show that individual motoneurones would discharge rhythmically, usually at 10 to

50 per second, when subjected to continuous and asynchronous synaptic bombardment of a sufficient intensity. Under such conditions it can be assumed that spatial and temporal summation of the EPSPs produced by the individual presynaptic impulses will build up the motoneuronal depolarization to threshold intensity and so generate the discharge of an impulse. Following the spike potential of this impulse the membrane will be repolarized as a consequence both of the destruction of the existing EPSPs (CURTIS and ECCLES 1959) and of the after-hyperpolarization (BROCK, COOMBS and ECCLES 1952; ECCLES, ECCLES and LUNDBERG 1958). The next discharge will be initiated when the threshold level of depolarization is again attained, which is effected by the passing off of the after-hyperpolarization and by the rebuilding of the EPSP. It was shown (ECCLES 1953) that this postulate would account not only for the normal rhythmic discharges of motoneurones and the effect of intensity of synaptic bombardment in determining frequency, but also for the disturbances of rhythm occurring when one or two antidromic impulses were fired into a motoneurone during its rhythmic response (ECCLES and HOFF 1932).

Rhythmic discharges of motoneurones are produced or accelerated when motoneurones are subjected to a steady depolarizing current (Fig. 43 I—M), while a hyperpolarizing current slows or blocks a repetitive discharge (BARRON and MATTHEWS 1938; ALVORD and FUORTES 1953; FUORTES 1954). Evidently a steady depolarizing action of sufficient intensity generates a rhythmic discharge (FUORTES 1954) in just the same way as occurs with the generator potential of sensory nerve terminals (cf. GRANIT 1955; KUFFLER 1960). Normally this depolarizing action would be produced by asynchronous synaptic bombardment, but experimentally an applied current can be substituted in part or in whole for the synaptic action (GRANIT, KERNELL and SHORTESS 1963). Such rhythmic discharges can be satisfactorily explained by the same hypothesis. The depolarization produced by the applied current would also be destroyed at the time of the spike potential and subsequently would have to be rebuilt just like the EPSP (cf. HODGKIN 1948).

This postulated mechanism of rhythmic discharge has been investigated by intracellular recording from motoneurones during continued synaptic bombardment (KOLMODIN and SKOGLUND 1958). When the depolarization decreased the membrane potential to -51 mV from the resting level of -58 mV (Fig. 44A), a motoneuronal impulse was generated and followed by the predicted repolarization, the next discharge being produced when the depolarization was again built up to -51 mV, and so on for the successive responses of the rhythmic series. When the intensity of synaptic bombardment was raised, the frequency of discharge was increased, but also a higher level of depolarization (up to -49 mV) was required to initiate discharges (Fig. 44 B—E). Evidently there was some cumulative depressant action;

possibly it derived from the high potassium conductance during the after-hyperpolarizations. As pointed out by KOLMODIN and SKOGLUND, a comparable relationship between firing threshold and frequency was observed by EYZA-

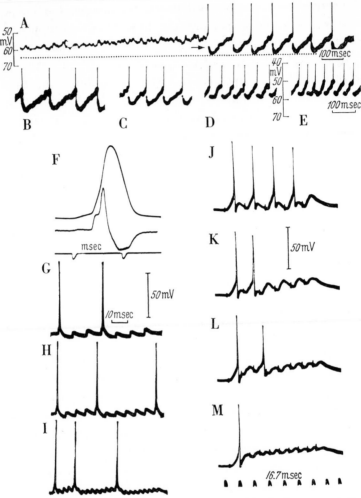

Fig. 44 A—M. A—E. Membrane potential changes during prolonged asynchronous synaptic excitation of a cat motoneurone. In A depolarization from an initial level of − 58 mV to the rhythmical firing level of − 51 mV. B—E, same motoneurone illustrating a wider range of frequency variations, the firing levels and frequencies being − 52 mV and 8.5/sec for B; − 51 mV and 13/sec for C; − 49.5 mV and 19.5/sec for D; − 49 mV and 26/sec for E (KOLMODIN and SKOGLUND 1958). F—I. Intracellular recording from cat gastrocnemius motoneurone, showing in F monosynaptic excitatory action at fast sweep speed with EPSP, IS and SD spikes and differentiated record, as in Figs. 40 B—D and 41 B, and in G—I the responses to maximum group I a volleys at 108, 157 and 330/sec respectively. Note the repetitive EPSPs with spikes produced when a critical depolarization was attained (ECCLES, ECCLES and LUNDBERG, unpublished observations). J—M repetitive synaptic activation of a toad motoneurone as in G—I with frequencies of 44, 56, 70 and 90/sec respectively (ARAKI and OTANI 1959).

GUIRRE and KUFFLER (1955a) in the crustacean stretch receptor cell. The effect of asynchronous synaptic bombardment in producing discharges has also been studied with intracellular recording from retinal ganglion cells (WIESEL 1959; BROWN and WIESEL 1960). Interesting problems are raised by the finding that some motoneurones respond to continuous synaptic activation by a long continued discharge, others merely by a brief initial burst (GRANIT, HENATSCH and STEG 1956; GRANIT, PHILLIPS, SKOGLUND and STEG 1957). Possibly there are differences in the intensity of synaptic activation as well as in the degree of adaptation.

A related investigation on the effect of repetitive synaptic bombardment is illustrated in Fig. 44 G—I, where a gastrocnemius motoneurone is responding to maximum group I a volleys that are set up in gastrocnemius nerve at various frequencies. The first volley always evokes a discharge, as illustrated in the fast record (F), and for 20 to 40 msec later the after-hyperpolarization prevents a subsequent volley from producing a depolarization that attains the firing threshold (G). In Fig. 44H, I, it is seen that the falling off of EPSP size with repetitive stimulation (cf. Fig. 31A) prevents high frequencies of afferent volleys from evoking a commensurate build up of EPSP after each discharge, hence there is little increase in frequency of motoneuronal discharge. With amphibian motoneurones there is a negligible after-hyperpolarization following the discharge of an impulse (FADIGA and BROOKHART 1960), yet in Fig. 44 J to M ARAKI and OTANI (1959) show that raising the frequency of synaptic bombardment is associated not with an increase but rather with a decrease in the number of discharges. In part this would arise from the diminished EPSPs evoked at the higher frequencies, but inspection of Fig. 44 J—M reveals that there is also an increased threshold for initiation of impulses, which presumably is due to an accommodative process in the initial segment (ARAKI and OTANI 1959).

In contrast to motoneurones most other investigated neurones of the central nervous system follow high frequencies of synaptic activation, as for example the cells relaying primary afferent volleys up the spinocerebellar tracts (HOLMQVIST, LUNDBERG and OSCARSSON 1956; OSCARSSON 1957), and the interneurones relaying I a and I b afferent impulses (ECCLES, ECCLES and LUNDBERG 1960). Repetitive synaptic activation of a large invertebrate ganglion cell *(Onchidium)* failed to evoke a corresponding series of spike discharges, just as with the motoneurone of G—M (KUSANO and HAGIWARA 1961). After each discharge summation of successive EPSPs was required before a spike was again initiated. Comparable observations have been made on neurones in the abdominal ganglion of the crayfish (WATANABE 1958).

Fig. 45 A—D illustrates the usual responses evoked by single afferent volleys in neurones relaying cutaneous impulses (MACINTYRE, MARK and STEINER 1956; FRANK and FUORTES 1956a; LAPORTE, LUNDBERG and OSCARSSON 1956; KOLMODIN and SKOGLUND 1958; HUNT and KUNO 1959; WALL 1959; ECCLES, ECCLES and LUNDBERG 1960; MACINTYRE and MARK 1960). The first responses in Fig. 45 A—D are so early that they must be generated monosynaptically. The subsequent discharges could be due either to a prolonged transmitter action or to delayed synaptic bombardments. HUNT and KUNO (1959) show that the timing of the successive impulses of such repetitive responses is correlatable with the underlying EPSP, which rises relatively slowly to a maximum and then slowly declines. Evidently there must be a considerable dispersion of synaptic bombardment, which in part may be due to repetitive bombardment through interneuronal pathways. WALL (1959) attempted to disturb the phase

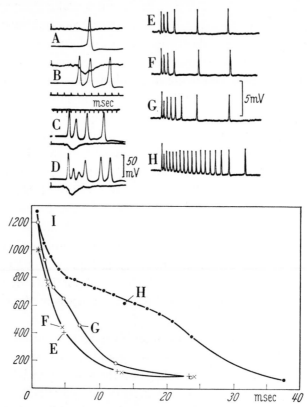

Fig. 45A—I. A—D, intracellular recording from a tract neurone in the dorsal horn of cat spinal cord with membrane potential of −60 mV. Responses evoked by a superficial peroneal (cutaneous) volley of progressively increasing size from A—D. Note different time scales for A, B and for C, D (ECCLES, ECCLES and LUNDBERG 1960). E—H, partial intracellular recording from a Renshaw cell in the cat spinal cord with excitation by maximal antidromic volleys in the motor nerves to plantaris, soleus, medial gastrocnemius and lateral gastrocnemius muscles respectively. In I the responses of E—H as indicated by the symbols are plotted with response intervals calculated as frequencies plotted as ordinates against time of onset of response as abscissae (ECCLES, ECCLES, IGGO and LUNDBERG 1961)

of the rhythmic discharges by injecting an impulse during the discharge. The injected impulse is initiated by a brief stimulating current applied to the interneurone through the microelectrode. Since the phase of the rhythm is only temporarily disturbed, it will be agreed with WALL that this rhythm is impressed on the neurone by the phasing of a relatively synchronous synaptic bombardment. On the other hand the briefer repetitive discharges often observed in such neurones display little evidence of such rhythmic driving, the rhythm being determined both by the level of the EPSP that is maintained by prolonged transmitter action and by the intrinsic properties of the neurone (HUNT and KUNO 1959; McINTYRE and MARK 1960).

The repetitive responses of Renshaw cells provide a remarkable example of the prolonged action of an EPSP produced by a single synchronous synaptic bombardment (RENSHAW 1946a; ECCLES, FATT and KOKETSU 1954; FRANK and FUORTES 1956a; ECCLES, ECCLES and FATT 1956; ECCLES, ECCLES, IGGO and LUNDBERG 1961). As shown in Fig. 45E—H a single antidromic volley in the alpha motor fibres of a muscle produces a repetitive response which always exhibits a progressive slowing of frequency after the initial responses. This progressive decline is seen when the frequency of the successive cycles of the response is plotted against time (Fig. 45 I). Even with weak synaptic stimulation (E, F) the first response interval is about 1 msec, but the decline is then rapid, in contrast to the fairly well maintained discharge at an intermediate level in H. A good correlation is possible between the observed EPSP (Fig. 14F) and the rhythmic discharges of Renshaw cells (ECCLES, ECCLES, IGGO and LUNDBERG 1961).

CHAPTER VIII

THE PRESYNAPTIC TERMINALS OF CHEMICALLY TRANSMITTING SYNAPSES

In the conventional description of the mode of operation of presynaptic terminals it is stated that the nerve impulse invades the terminal, and that as a consequence of the depolarization of the spike potential there is a brief jet-like release of transmitter. This account ignores experimental demonstrations that at least some types of presynaptic nerve terminals have specialized physiological and pharmacological properties, which is a procedure that could be defended on the grounds that these properties are without functional significance. This defence is no longer valid. Presynaptic inhibition has been shown to be due to specialized responses of some types of presynaptic terminals (Chapter XV) and undoubtedly it is of great functional importance. Here there will be an account of other investigations suggesting that presynaptic nerve terminals have special physiological and pharmacological properties. The physiological investigations have been mainly on motor nerve terminals, but the pharmacological work has been intensively pursued also on the presynaptic terminals of sympathetic ganglia.

In two of the sites where synaptic transmission has been most thoroughly studied, neuromuscular junctions and sympathetic ganglia, there is now convincing evidence that the chemical transmitting system is more complex than the simple model hitherto envisaged. Indeed KOELLE (1961, 1962) has developed the remarkable concept that the ACh released from presynaptic terminals to a considerable extent functions as a positive feed-back, evoking further ACh release therefrom, so that an amplification factor is introduced into the transmitter release. In part this conceptual development arises from the demonstration that in ortho-sympathetic ganglia acetylcholine esterase (AChE) is located on the presynaptic terminals (KOELLE and KOELLE 1959; McISAAC and KOELLE 1959), and not on the postsynaptic membrane, as is the case with the neuromuscular junction (COUTEAUX 1958), but KOELLE has also assembled experimental evidence, both with the sympathetic ganglion and the neuromuscular junction, which suggests that the presynaptic terminals are not simply secreting structures, as has been assumed in the standard simplified theory of chemical transmission. More detailed treatment of both physiological and pharmacological investigations on these two types of chemical transmission is therefore necessary in order to assess the significance of this new development.

A. Physiological properties of presynaptic terminals

The propagation of nerve impulses to the presynaptic terminals has been investigated in three different types of chemical transmitting synapse. Since impulses always propagate into close proximity to the presynaptic terminals, intracellular recording does not give information sufficiently discriminative for establishing whether active propagation occurs into these terminals or whether they are passively depolarized by electrotonic spread. A better discrimination can be made if it is possible to record selectively the current that a presynaptic impulse causes to flow across the membrane of the presynaptic terminal. For this purpose it is necessary to apply the recording microelectrode within a few microns from the outer surface of the terminal membrane, and to have a remote indifferent electrode. The interpretation of potentials so recorded from the surface of a linearly extended core conductor is based on the propositions developed by BROOKS and ECCLES (1947b) and by LORENTE DE NÓ (1947) from more general considerations (KATZ 1939; RENSHAW, FORBES and MORISON 1940; BISHOP and O'LEARY 1942). The essential proposition is that, when a current is flowing through the membrane of a linearly extended core conductor, a focal electrode on its surface will record a potential in direct proportionality to the current density, the potential being positive for outward current and negative for inward.

If an impulse propagates at full size along a presynaptic fibre right to its terminal end, an electrode in close proximity to that end will pick up an initial positive potential during the whole rising phase of the impulse, reversing to a negativity during the decaying phase. Theoretically the current across the membrane at the terminal end should be the first derivative of the intracellularly recorded spike potential, as shown in Fig. 46A (dotted line). This relationship would be expected to obtain even when there is a large increase of exposed surface area as the presynaptic fibre expands to form the synaptic terminal, which would be the case particularly with an unmyelinated terminal arising from a myelinated fibre. Under such conditions the current density across the membrane of the terminal would be proportionately lower during both its outward and inward phases.

If the presynaptic impulse fails to propagate into the expanded synaptic terminal, it might be expected that there would be an outwardly directed current across this non-invaded membrane throughout the whole duration of the presynaptic spike potential, the surface electrode consequently picking up a simple positive potential with the time course of the presynaptic spike. However this inference ignores the effectiveness with which electrotonic transmission would produce depolarization ahead of an impulse that probably is blocked just at the terminal expansion of the presynaptic fibre (Chapter II). As illustrated in Fig. 46B (broken line), the presynaptic terminal may be

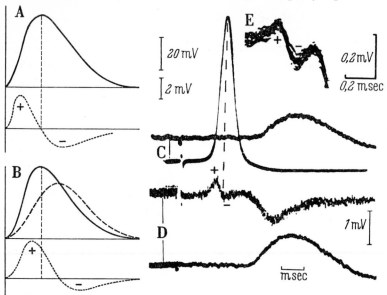

Fig. 46A—E. A, B show diagrammatically monophasic spike potentials (continuous lines) with in A the first derivative (dotted line). In B the broken line gives the intracellular potential that would occur because of electrotonic transmission some distance beyond a blocked spike, and the dotted line gives the potential difference between the continuous and broken lines, which can be regarded as an approximate time course of the potential driving flow of current across the membrane at this site beyond the block. In C are simultaneous presynaptic and postsynaptic intracellular records of orthodromic activation of a giant synapse in the squid stellate ganglion, the latter being at much higher amplification than the former. In D the presynaptic electrode was withdrawn to a just extracellular position and the orthodromic activation was repeated. The vertical broken line allows an accurate comparison of the intracellular and extracellular potentials evoked by a presynaptic impulse. Note high amplification for the extracellular record. Same time scale for C and D (TAKEUCHI and TAKEUCHI 1962). In E is diphasic spike potential recorded by a microelectrode in close proximity to a nerve terminal in a rat diaphragm, and the later EPP that also is in the negative direction (HUBBARD and SCHMIDT 1963). Note + and − signs on all extracellular spike records

depolarized almost to the full extent of the spike potential; and as a consequence the outward current across the terminal membrane would decline towards zero early in the falling phase of the spike potential. Subsequently a phase of reversed current would be expected on account of the rapid repolarization of the activated membrane by the potassium current (HODGKIN 1958; FRANKENHAEUSER 1962a, b, c). Fig. 46B thus shows that, even if an impulse does not invade a presynaptic terminal, an electrode in contact with this terminal would pick up a diphasic (positive-negative) potential (dotted line), which would differ from the invasion potential (Fig. 46A, dotted line) mainly by its later reversal and by the smaller negative phase. If impulse blockage occurred more remotely from the presynaptic terminal, the terminal potential may be almost a purely positive wave, though its phase would still be more rapid than an inverted replica of the intracellular spike potential. From this brief theoretical treatment it will be realized that extracellular recording does not give as discriminative evidence as has been usually supposed on the propagation of impulses into presynaptic terminals.

Fig. 46 C, D illustrates the only experiment in which there has been both extracellular (upper trace of D) and intracellular recording (lower trace of C from the same presynaptic terminal (TAKEUCHI and TAKEUCHI 1962). In the extracellular record from the giant synapse of the squid stellate ganglion (Fig. 46 D), a presynaptic impulse produces a brief initial diphasic wave (a positivity followed by a low negativity) and a later large negative wave due to the postsynaptic depolarization, which is also seen with postsynaptic intracellular recording in C and D. In Fig. 46 D the negative component of potential is much lower than for a first derivative of the intracellularly recorded presynaptic potential (cf. Fig. 46 A), so it appears that the presynaptic terminal is not fully invaded by the impulse. As shown by the vertical broken line the extracellular potential reverses as early as the first derivative of the spike, which indicates that the impulse actually propagates into at least part of the presynaptic terminal close to the recording electrode. In some preparations TAKEUCHI and TAKEUCHI (1962) find that the presynaptic spike produces only a purely positive potential extracellularly at the synaptic region; presumably, as they suggest, this may be due to local injury.

With the isolated rat diaphragm preparation HUBBARD and SCHMIDT (1963) have employed the extracellular recording of min. EPPs as the criterion establishing that the microelectrode tip is in very close proximity to a presynaptic nerve terminal. In such circumstances an impulse in that motor nerve fibre evokes two quite distinct electrical potentials. An initial all-or-nothing diphasic (positive-negative) wave is followed by a much larger and longer negative potential (Fig. 46 E). The former is generated by the presynaptic impulse, the latter by the postsynaptic depolarization, the endplate potential. Usually the presynaptic potential indicates that the terminals have been fully invaded, for it exhibits the characteristic diphasic character with a well-developed negative component. Sometimes the negative component is less prominent, indicating that partial failure of invasion may be occurring as a consequence of injury inadvertently produced in applying the microelectrode in such close proximity. Impulse propagation into the nerve terminal is also suggested by the invariable finding that a current pulse applied through the microelectrode initiates a nerve impulse that is conducted antidromically along the motor fibre (HUBBARD and SCHMIDT 1961, 1963).

In contrast, presynaptic spike potentials suggest that in crustacean neuro-muscular junctions the presynaptic impulse usually does not fully propagate into the terminals. There is sometimes a purely positive presynaptic spike potential, but often it is diphasic with a small negative component that is specifically depressed by presynaptic inhibition or by a topically applied solution of GABA and related substances (DUDEL and KUFFLER 1961 c; DUDEL 1962a, b). Evidently transmission to these presynaptic terminals has a very low safety factor, and normally there may be only a partial invasion. Disability in respect of impulse conduction is further shown by the invariable failure of applied current pulses to set up impulses antidromically conducted away from the nerve terminals (DUDEL and KUFFLER 1961c), which is in contrast to the nerve terminals in the rat diaphragm.

In one other chemical transmitting synapse, the ciliary ganglionic synapses of the chick (Fig. 7C), there is indirect evidence that the presynaptic membrane facing the synaptic cleft is not fully invaded by the presynaptic impulse (MARTIN and PILAR 1963a). As will be argued later (Chapter IX), the observed electrical transmission from the presynaptic to the postsynaptic elements (Fig. 54) could occur only if a large part of the presynaptic membrane facing the cleft is not invaded.

Comment

Several factors would be expected to contribute to the low safety factor for propagation of impulses into presynaptic terminals so that transmission may normally be blocked over the whole or part of the membrane. Consider first the essential process of membrane depolarization ahead of the advancing impulse. With myelinated presynaptic fibres there is transition to the relatively large area of the presynaptic terminal uncovered by myelin (cf. Fig. 1A), and as a consequence invasion is impeded because it requires that a large membrane capacity be discharged through the adjacent nodes. With all types of presynaptic terminals the area fronting the synaptic cleft of ca. 200 Å width would have the disability that the depolarizing current has to flow through the relatively high resistance of this cleft (cf. ECCLES and JAEGER 1958); this factor would be particularly significant with large areas of cleft as in the chick ciliary ganglion (Fig. 7C). Other areas of the presynaptic terminals are also closely ensheathed by Schwann cells and glial cells (Chapter II). In addition to these physical disabilities the invasion of the presynaptic terminal may be impeded by intrinsic properties of the presynaptic membrane; for example, either a higher threshold for impulse initiation, or even complete electrical inexcitability. The areas of dense staining revealed by electron microscopy, the active zones (Figs. 2, 3, 4) may well be so specialized as to be electrically inexcitable. In addition the receptor sites for the transmitter effecting presynaptic inhibition (Chapter XV) possibly are electrically inexcitable in the same way as seems to occur with postsynaptic receptor sites (Chapter VII). The failure of transmission into the nerve terminals on crustacean muscle may thus be attributed to the coverage of these nerve terminals by receptor sites for GABA and related substances (DUDEL and KUFFLER 1961c; DUDEL 1962a, b). On the other hand there is no evidence to suggest that in the central nervous system there is failure of transmission into presynaptic terminals that are subject to presynaptic inhibitory action (Chapter XV). The cholinoceptive receptor sites responsible for specific pharmacological properties of the presynaptic terminals at neuromuscular junctions (Chapter VIII, Section B) may also contribute to the areas not invaded by the presynaptic impulse.

Evidently different types of chemically transmitting synapses exhibit wide variations in the effectiveness with which presynaptic impulses invade the nerve terminals. Probably the depolarization produced by electrotonic spread over the last few microns is in any case so effective that there is no appreciable deficiency in transmitter release if impulse transmission fails.

B. Pharmacological properties of presynaptic terminals

1. The neuromuscular junction

After intravenous injection of prostigmine into cats MASLAND and WIGTON (1940) observed in motor nerve fibres repetitive discharges which apparently originate in the nerve terminals and which are causally related to the well known twitching produced by substances such as eserine and prostigmine that inactivate AChE. They confirmed the finding of LANGLEY and KATO (1915), as also did FENG and LI (1941), that curare abolishes both the twitching and the nerve discharges at a dose much lower than that required for blocking neuromuscular transmission. Since rather massive intra-arterial injections of ACh also evoke repetitive discharges in the motor nerve fibres during the prolonged twitching contraction of the muscle, it was concluded that the nerve terminals are directly excited by ACh and that anti-AChEs may excite nerve terminals secondarily on account of the accumulation of ACh that occurs when the AChE is inactivated. Under the influence of anti-AChEs motor nerve volleys evoke a repetitive discharge from motor endplates (BROWN, DALE and FELDBERG 1936; BROWN 1937a), and there is an associated discharge in the motor nerve fibres (MASLAND and WIGTON 1940; FENG and LI 1941). However ECCLES, KATZ and KUFFLER (1942) showed that the repetitive discharge from motor endplates often occurs in the absence of any discharge from the nerve terminals (Fig. 47A) and that the nerve discharge sometimes occurs at a time that precludes its initiation by muscle impulses (Fig. 47B,C). It was therefore necessary to postulate that, under the influence of anti-AChEs, the

ACh liberated from motor nerve terminals can generate impulses both at the motor endplate and at the nerve terminals, though of course in addition the nerve impulses would also be likely to generate some of the later discharges from motor endplates. It was furthermore shown that under such conditions there could be reversed synaptic propagation — muscle impulses evoking impulses in motor nerve fibres, possibly by electrical transmission at the region of the neuromuscular synapse.

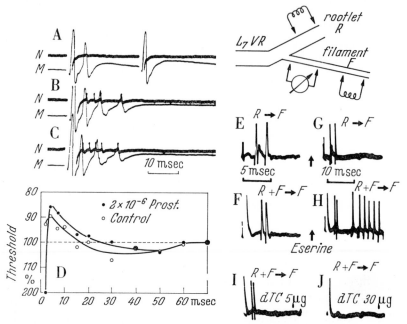

Fig. 47 A—J. Responses of presynaptic nerve terminals to mammalian muscle. A—C. Cat after 0.3 mg eserine per kg with simultaneous recording monophasically from the *chronically* deafferented nerve to peroneus tertius muscle (N) and from the endplate zone of the muscle (M). Two nerve volleys were set up at intervals of 24 msec (A), 1.2 msec (B) and 1.6 msec (C). The initial nerve spikes are not seen as amplification was too high. Note delayed back-response of 4 or 5 discharges of same nerve fibre in B and C, also intense repetitive muscle responses in B and C and with initial response in A (ECCLES, KATZ and KUFFLER 1942). D. Stimulation of a single motor nerve terminal by an accurately placed microelectrode in a rat diaphragm preparation. Threshold values after a single conditioning stimulus are plotted as percentages of control against the stimulus intervals as abscissae. Open circles give control values on muscle paralysed by excess magnesium (11 mM); filled circles after 2×10^{-6} prostigmine (HUBBARD and SCHMIDT 1961). E—J. Stimulation either of rootlet (R) or rootlet plus filament (R + F) of L_7 VR of cat and recording from filament as in the diagram and as specified for each trace. Controls, E, F, are at faster sweep than G—J. Note that after intraarterial eserine injection there is no change in the early back-responses in G, but have late back-response in H. Intra-arterial dTC (5 μg/kg) removed only late back-response in I, but early also removed in J by 6 times larger injection (WERNER 1961)

It has now been established that there are two quite independent ways by which activation of muscle causes the generation of impulses at motor nerve terminals (WERNER 1960b, 1961). Firstly, these terminals are stimulated electrically by the large synchronized muscle spike potential, giving the so-called short latency back-response (LLOYD 1942; LEKSELL 1945; BROWN and MATTHEWS 1960). This short latency back-response is dependent merely on the intensity of electrical stimulation provided by the muscle spike potential and occurs irrespective of whether the motor nerve fibre has been actively concerned in evoking the muscle spike or not (Fig. 47E—G). Secondly, there is a longer latency back-response which is usually repetitive, 100 to 250/sec for up to 50 msec, and which is specific to the initially activated motor nerve fibre. As described above, this secondary back-response is observed only at neuromuscular junctions treated by anti-AChEs (Fig. 47H). The first response of the repetitive series has a latency at least 1 msec (usually about 4 msec) longer than the short latency back-responses.

Two procedures potentiate the production of long latency back-responses, shortening the latency, increasing the frequency and duration and overcoming the ineffectiveness of single impulses. Firstly, there is a large facilitating effect between two impulses at a few milliseconds separation (Fig. 47B, C) (ECCLES, KATZ and KUFFLER 1942; WERNER 1960a, 1960b). This brief facilitating interaction is followed by a prolonged depression of the response to a second impulse — up to 100 msec after a single conditioning impulse. Secondly, a prolonged conditioning tetanus of a motor nerve fibre is followed for several minutes by an increased reactivity of the terminals of that fibre, even in the absence of treatment by anti-AChE (FENG and LI 1941; WERNER 1960a).

In addition to these physiological properties the long latency back-response is remarkable for its pharmacological characteristics, which undoubtedly relate it to the ACh transmission system of the neuromuscular junction. This response is evoked from nerve terminals under the influence of a wide variety of anti-AChE agents: prostigmine, eserine, 3-hydroxy phenyltriethyl ammonium, 3-hydroxy phenyltrimethyl ammonium; 3-hydroxy phenyldiethyl ammonium, and tensilon (MASLAND and WIGTON 1940; FENG and LI 1941; ECCLES, KATZ and KUFFLER 1942; RIKER, WERNER, ROBERTS and KUPERMAN 1959a, b; WERNER 1960a, b, 1961), and it is suppressed by d-tubocurarine and flaxedil in doses too small to depress neuromuscular transmission of single nerve volleys (Fig 47I, J; cf. FENG and LI 1941; RIKER et al. 1959a; WERNER 1961). It is also readily suppressed by drugs that are general depressants of nerve excitability; pentobarbital, cyclopropane and procaine (RIKER et al. 1959b).

The physiological properties led WERNER (1960a) to propose that the long latency back-response is generated by an enhanced after-depolarization of the activated motor nerve terminal. This postulate has not as yet been tested by intracellular recording from these fine terminals, but HUBBARD and SCHMIDT (1961, 1963) have obtained indirectly confirmatory evidence by measuring the excitability changes following activity of motor nerve terminals in the excised rat-diaphragm preparation (Fig. 47D). When the stimulating electrode is placed within a few microns of the nerve ending on the motor endplate, the refractory period passes over to a phase of hyperexcitability indicative of the after-depolarization, and this phase is followed at 10 to 20 msec by a prolonged subnormal excitability indicative of after-hyperpolarization. Prostigmine causes an increase and prolongation of the phase of hyperexcitability (Fig. 47 D, filled circles), and d-tubocurarine has a depressant action. It can be concluded that these excitability tests show that the changes in after-depolarization probably provide an adequate explanation of the long latency back-responses. Furthermore, after a severe conditioning tetanus, there is a prolonged after-hyperpolarizing action (HUBBARD and SCHMIDT 1963) during which a test impulse would be expected to evoke a much larger and longer after-depolarization (ECCLES and KRNJEVIĆ 1959a); hence the effect of a conditioning tetanus in enhancing the long latency back-response can be explained.

As already stated, the pharmacological properties of this response indicate that, superimposed on the physiological process of after-depolarization, there is a depolarizing action related to the ACh transmission system. KATZ (1962) suggested that, with inactivation of AChE, the ACh released by a nerve impulse may cause an intense local efflux of potassium from the muscle fibre, which would in turn depolarize the nerve terminals, so generating the back-response. However, there is overwhelming experimental evidence against this attractive suggestion. If the postulated potassium-induced depolarization is adequate to generate the discharge of impulses from the nerve terminals, close intra-arterial injection of KCl would be expected to evoke a powerful discharge, but FENG and LI (1941) reported a negative result even when the potassium injection produced a contraction as large as a maximal twitch in the cat soleus muscle. Again, if anti-AChEs cause a sufficient accumulation of potassium to excite the discharge of impulses from the terminals, there would also be expected to be a very large increase in the frequency of min. EPPs (LILEY 1956b); yet this is not observed (FATT and KATZ 1952b; LILEY 1956a). Furthermore, electrophoretic application of ACh in very close proximity to the outside of the motor endplate does not significantly increase the frequencies of min. EPPs either of frog or mammalian muscle (FATT and KATZ 1952b; KATZ 1958a; CURTIS and HUBBARD, unpublished observations).

It seems that the most satisfactory explanation is that originally proposed by MASLAND and WIGTON (1940), namely that there are some cholinoceptive sites on the presynaptic terminals in addition to the dominant ACh receptivity of the postsynaptic endplate membrane (Chapter V). The increased after-depolarization of nerve terminals treated by anti-AChEs (Fig. 47D) is thus explained. However, in order to explain the twitching produced by anti-AChEs under resting conditions, it is necessary to postulate that at these receptor sites anti-AChEs also exert a depolarizing action, as was first suggested by FENG and LI (1941), just as they do at postsynaptic cholinoceptive sites. Curarizing agents would of course act by competitive occupation of both the presynaptic and postsynaptic cholinoceptive sites (MASLAND and WIGTON 1940; FENG and LI 1941). It should be mentioned that RIKER et al. (1959a, b) proposed a much more radical hypothesis in which many of the characteristic postsynaptic responses of the neuromuscular junction are transferred to a site "intermediate between the axon and the endplate", but in functional continuity with the nerve.

As discussed in the next section the presynaptic endings at another type of cholinergic synapse, that in sympathetic ganglia probably do not exhibit normally properties that are indicative of cholinoceptive sites. However, these sites can be detected in ganglia infected by pseudorabies virus, the preganglionic terminals being then excited by ACh and anti-AChEs and depressed by dTC.

2. The sympathetic ganglion

Before attempting to account for the observations of KOELLE and his associates (cf. Introduction to this Chapter), it will be convenient to consider a series of pharmacological investigations on the slow potential waves of sympathetic ganglia. Preganglionic volleys evoke in the curarized superior cervical

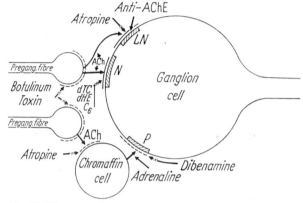

Fig. 48. Diagrammatic representation of the postulated production of the N, P and LN waves of ganglion cells by transmitter released by preganglionic impulses. The receptor sites are shown on the surface of the ganglion cell. The postulated pathways of the transmitter substances, ACh and adrenaline, are shown by arrows and the postulated sites of action of the various pharmacological agents are indicated by arrows, the arrows with crosses signifying depressant actions. Further description in text. Modified from R. M. ECCLES and LIBET (1961)

ganglion of both turtles and rabbits a complex sequence of waves (LAPORTE and LORENTE DE NÓ 1950; R. M. ECCLES 1952), which have been further investigated and interpreted in the light of the hypothesis diagrammed in Fig. 48 (R. M. ECCLES and LIBET 1961; LIBET 1962a, b). When synaptic transmission is blocked by a sufficient concentration of d-tubocurarine (dTC) or dihydro-β-erythroidine (DHE), a preganglionic volley still evokes a depolarization of a ganglion cell (Fig. 40 P, Q), which resembles the EPSPs recorded intracellularly from other types of nerve cells (Figs. 13, 14, 15, 17). In Fig. 49A the initial wave (N) is produced by such an EPSP of the ganglion cells, but is recorded extracellularly between two leads, one on the surface of the ganglion and the other on the distal end of the isolated postganglionic trunk. This N wave of about 100 msec duration is followed by a slight P wave that is soon terminated by a later negative wave (LN) more than 2 seconds in duration. The N wave is greatly depressed at a deeper level of curarization (B), but the LN wave is even increased. Repetitive preganglionic volleys also evoke comparable potentials when the N component is selectively depressed by tubocurarine so that the P and LN waves become more prominent (Fig. 49D, E, I). The P and LN waves can be seen to be concurrent during the tetanus (E), with the LN wave eventually dominant after the tetanus. These potentials are not observed with the leads placed so as to record from the presynaptic terminals in the ganglion; hence generation postsynaptically in the ganglion cells may be assumed (R. M. Eccles and Libet 1961).

Pharmacological investigation reveals very discriminative properties for these three components. As shown in Fig. 49C and F—H for prostigmine, anticholinesterases diminish, delay and eventually, with sufficiently high

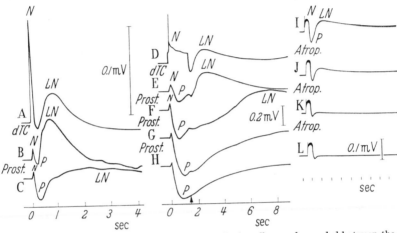

Fig. 49A—L. Postganglionic potentials set up by preganglionic volleys and recorded between the ganglion and the postganglionic trunk of the isolated superior cervical ganglion of rabbit. A—C potentials evoked by single preganglionic volleys in concentrations of dTC of 2.5×10^{-5} M in A, and 8×10^{-5} M for B, C, with also 3×10^{-6} M prostigmine in C. D—H similar series but with repetitive stimulation, 20/sec for 1.4 sec, end of tetanus being marked by arrow below: D and E in dTC 1.6×10^{-5} M and 8×10^{-5} M respectively: in addition progressive prostigmine in F—H, 3×10^{-7} M, 3×10^{-6} M and 6×10^{-6} M (R. M. Eccles 1952b). I—L, similarly evoked potentials, but for repetitive stimulation of 40/sec for 0.5 sec, and with ganglion curarized by 10 μg/ml of dihydro-β-erythroidine. Atropine concentrations were 0.1 μg/ml, 0.5 μg/ml, and 8.0 μg/ml for J, K and L respectively. Many N, P and LN waves are labelled. (R. M. Eccles and Libet 1961)

dosage, suppress completely the LN wave, leaving the N and P waves apparently unchanged (R. M. Eccles 1952). On the other hand reserpine selectively depresses the P wave (Libet 1962a) and atropine very effectively depresses both the P and LN waves and has no action in very much higher concentration on the N wave (Fig. 49I—L). Since botulinum toxin has the very selective action of depressing the release of acetylcholine from cholinergic nerve terminals (Burgen, Dickens and Zatman 1949), its depressant action uniformly exerted on the N, P and LN waves is a key observation (R. M. Eccles and Libet 1961). Finally dibenamine depresses the P wave and also the LN wave to a lesser extent, while the N wave is little changed.

The P and LN responses are prominent only when the N response is greatly depressed by curarizing agents so that it no longer sets up a spike potential and the associated after-potential, which would mask the P and LN waves.

However, by comparing the action potentials and excitability changes produced after maximal antidromic and maximum orthodromic excitation of ganglia and observing the changes produced therein by atropine, dibenamine and reserpine, LIBET (1962a, b) demonstrates that the P and LN responses also occur with orthodromic excitation of normal ganglia. Thus there are three types of synaptic action distinguishable by pharmacological analysis; and, furthermore, these three types of action are not distinguishable by threshold grading of the preganglionic stimulus.

It is assumed in Fig. 48 that all three types of response are produced by the one cell and that separate fibres are concerned in P-wave production, but this latter assumption is not an essential part of the hypothesis. The principal action of the ACh released from the presynaptic fibre is to depolarize the ganglion cell at the sites marked N and so generate the discharge of an impulse. If this action is greatly depressed by curarizing agents, as indicated, the two other actions of ACh become obvious, though previously largely submerged by the large potentials generated as a consequence of the N response, namely the spike and after-potential: in the one the ACh diffuses to a more remote site (LN), where it depolarizes the cell to give the LN wave, atropine and anti-cholinesterases being competitive inhibitors (cf. ECCLES 1957, p. 183); in the other, generation of the P-wave is linked to the observations that adrenaline exerts an inhibitory action on sympathetic ganglion cells, possibly by hyperpolarizing them (MARRAZZI 1939; LUNDBERG 1952), and that the chromaffin cells in the ganglion probably are responsible for the output of adrenaline produced by preganglionic volleys (BULBRING 1944). However, the depressant action of botulinum toxin and atropine on the P wave shows that, as indicated in Fig. 48, cholinergic synapses are concerned in the activation of the chromaffin cells, which in turn secrete the adrenaline that gives the P wave by action at receptor sites (P) that can be blocked by dibenamine.

When an anticholinesterase, diisopropyl phosphofluoridate (DFP) or eserine is applied to the superior cervical ganglion by intra-arterial injection, it evokes a prolonged postganglionic discharge (VOLLE and KOELLE 1961; VOLLE 1962a; TAKESHIGE and VOLLE 1962). Since this discharge does not occur in the chronically denervated ganglion, and since AChE is located on the presynaptic terminals of the ganglion (KOELLE and KOELLE 1959), it has been proposed that this discharge is initiated by the anti-AChE action on the presynaptic terminals, the ACh liberated therefrom evoking the postganglionic discharge (VOLLE and KOELLE 1961). It is important to note that there is no associated preganglionic discharge under these conditions; nor does it occur when postganglionic discharges are evoked by ACh injection as in Fig. 50 (BRONK 1939; DOUGLAS, LYWOOD and STRAUB 1960) or after prolonged tetanization with AChE inactivation (ECCLES 1944; VOLLE and KOELLE 1961). However pharmacological investigation (VOLLE 1961a) shows that the postganglionic discharge has properties which are virtually identical with those characterizing the LN response of ganglion cells (R. M. ECCLES and LIBET 1961), and very different from those observed for synaptic transmission through the ganglion and for the discharge evoked by injected ACh, as may be seen in Table 3, which summarizes the experimental investigations described below.

Table 3. *Pharmacological investigations on the postganglionic responses evoked from sympathetic ganglia by various procedures*

— — severe depression; — depression; 0 no action; + potentiation; NT, not tried

Drug	Synaptic transmission and N wave	Intra-arterially injected ACh		Late firing after tetanus	Prolonged discharges evoked by anti-AChEs	LN response of ganglion cells
		early discharge	late discharge			
dTC, d-Tubocurarine	— —	— —	0	0	+	+ or 0
C₆, hexamethonium	— —	— —	NT	0	0	0
MCA, Mecamylamine hydrochloride	— —	NT	NT	0	0	NT
Atropine	0	0	— —	— —	— —	— —
Procaine	NT	NT	NT	— —	— —	NT
References	LAPORTE and LORENTE DE Nó (1950); R. ECCLES (1952); R. ECCLES and LIBET (1961)	VOLLE (1962a); TAKESHIGE and VOLLE (1962)		VOLLE (1962b); TAKESHIGE and VOLLE (1962b); EMMELIN and McINTOSH (1956)	VOLLE and KOELLE (1961); VOLLE (1962a); TAKESHIGE and VOLLE (1962)	R. ECCLES (1952); R. ECCLES and LIBET (1961); LIBET (1962a, 1962b)

It is further of significance that anti-AChEs very effectively suppress the LN response (Fig. 49C, F—H; R. M. ECCLES 1952), presumably acting as competitive antagonists of ACh on the LN sites (Fig. 48). If this combination of anti-AChEs with the LN sites produces depolarization of the ganglion cells, the production of postganglionic discharges by anti-AChEs would be explained. Moreover the absence of these discharges in chronically denervated ganglia may be correlated with the finding that the excitation of ganglia by carbachol is greatly depressed by denervation, and there is then also a considerable depression of ACh excitation, particularly under the influence of anti-AChEs (VOLLE and KOELLE 1961). Intra-arterial injection of ACh into normal ganglia gives a bimodal discharge, the later component being particularly potentiated by an anti-AChE, so that it is selectively evoked by very small ACh injections (Fig. 50A; TAKESHIGE and VOLLE 1962).

Prolonged preganglionic stimulation is followed by postganglionic after-discharges (LARRABEE and BRONK 1937; ECCLES 1944), and VOLLE (1962b) has shown that the discharge is greatly enhanced by intra-arterial injections of ACh (Fig. 50B), carbachol and tetramethylammonium (TMA). This prolonged discharge has pharmacological properties resembling that evoked by anti-AChEs, being blocked by procaine and atropine (TAKESHIGE and VOLLE 1962), and not affected by hexamethonium (C_6). VOLLE (1962b) has suggested that the injected ACh, carbachol and TMA are evoking the enhanced discharge by acting on presynaptic terminals and causing them to release ACh. Alternatively, a more satisfactory explanation may be that, following the tetanization, the prolonged depolarization of the LN sites by surviving ACh is causing the after-discharge (cf. BRONK 1939) and that this is enhanced by the increased depolarization produced by the action of the injected substances on the LN sites (cf. TAKESHIGE and VOLLE 1962). Fig. 50B illustrates the pharmacological specificity of the bimodal discharge evoked by an ACh injection during post-tetanic conditioning; dTC and atropine act as specific blockers of the early and late discharge respectively (TAKESHIGE and VOLLE 1962).

VOLLE (1962b) recognized that EM-MELIN and MacINTOSH (1956) had made

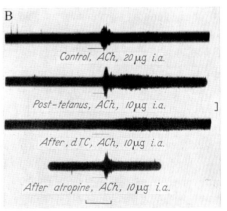

Fig. 50A and B. Postganglionic discharges of cat superior cervical ganglion in response to intra-arterial injections of acetylcholine in the quantities indicated; and at the times shown by the horizontal lines. In A an intra-arterial injection of 100 µg of eserine greatly increases the effectiveness of ACh in evoking a delayed discharge. In B after conditioning by a tetanus (60/sec for 10 sec) there is in the second record an increase in the delayed discharge. The third and fourth records show selective depression of the early and delayed discharges by dTC and atropine respectively. Time scales 1 sec; Voltage scales, 10 µV. (TAKESHIGE and VOLLE 1962)

comparable observations on after-discharges of superior cervical ganglia under the influence of an anti-AChE: eserine, prostigmine, DFP or TEPP. At the end of a repetitive preganglionic stimulation, the nictitating membrane relaxes almost as rapidly as in the absence of the drug, but later there is a second contraction of many minutes duration. This contraction is not modified by

the curarizing agents, dTC and hexamethonium, but it is suppressed by procaine, which is known to depress cholinoceptive sites (DEL CASTILLO and KATZ
1957a; CURTIS and R. M. ECCLES 1958b; CURTIS and PHILLIS 1960); hence it
seems probable that here again is a response due to the activation by ACh
of LN receptor sites on ganglion cells. BIRKS and MACINTOSH (1961) have
detected a small output of ACh from ganglia treated by anti-AChEs, which
could be adequate for the prolonged excitatory action in view of the high
sensitivity for ACh (TAKESHIGE and VOLLE 1962). It might be thought that
this interpretation is contradicted by the suppressor action of anti-AChEs on
the depolarizing action of ACh acting at LN sites (Fig. 49C, F—H); but, as
suggested above this suppression could be due to the competitive depolarizing
action of the anti-AChEs, and it is not unreasonable to suppose that this
depolarization would be increased by the large excess of ACh produced by the
prolonged tetanization, so that the delayed after-discharge would be generated.
Correspondingly it has been found that the delayed after-discharge is suppressed
by atropine (Fig. 50B, TAKESHIGE and VOLLE 1962).

This general concept of two kinds of cholinoceptive sites on ganglion cells
has also been developed in relation to other pharmacological investigations by
AMBACHE, PERRY and ROBERTSON (1956), and by ROSZKOWSKI (1961).

In the alternative explanations of these phenomena, VOLLE and KOELLE
(1961) and KOELLE (1961, 1962) suggest that ACh acts directly on the presynaptic terminals as well as postsynaptically. This concept was developed
originally in relation to the presynaptic location of the AChE in ganglia, and
it has been shown by them to explain the responses of normal and denervated
ganglia to ACh and related substances and to anti-AChEs. Unfortunately it
suffers from a difficulty in relation to this assumed primary action of ACh
and anti-AChEs on presynaptic terminals, for no associated generation of
preganglionic impulses has been observed. As a consequence the release of
ACh from these terminals has to be attributed to localized depolarizations of
the presynaptic terminals, which have not been observed in normal ganglia,
the slow LN potentials being restricted to the postsynaptic membrane.

However in sympathetic ganglia infected by pseudorabies virus there are
periodic bursts of impulse discharge, which are generated presynaptically
(DEMPSHER, LARRABEE, BANG and BODIAN 1955; DEMPSHER and RIKER
1957) by prolonged depolarization of the presynaptic terminals (DEMPSHER
and ZABARA 1960). Until the onset of postsynaptic degeneration in a late
stage of the infection, the presynaptic discharges produce postsynaptic discharges by ordinary synaptic transmission. Since the presynaptic depolarizations and spike discharges are depressed by dTC and increased and prolonged
by eserine and ACh (DEMPSHER and RIKER 1957; DEMPSHER and ZABARA
1960), it seems that under the influence of pseudorabies virus the presynaptic
terminals in the ganglia develop properties resembling those observed with

normal neuromuscular junctions, as described above. At an early stage of the infection, discharges were restricted to the postganglionic fibres, yet a presynaptic origin is indicated by the suppression of such discharges when synaptic transmission is blocked by calcium removal, and by their absence in ganglia with degenerated preganglionic fibres (DEMPSHER and RIKER 1957).

Evidently the infection results in the development of properties of ganglionic presynaptic terminals resembling those postulated by KOELLE (1961, 1962) for normal ganglia, but further investigation is required in order to determine how far the responses of normal ganglia are due to these assumed properties of presynaptic terminals, and how far to the specialized LN receptor sites on the ganglion cells. For example VOLLE and KOELLE (1961) find that, contrary to CANNON and ROSENBLUETH's (1949) denervation hypersensitivity and also to recent observations of MURRAY and THOMPSON (1957), denervated ganglia are much less sensitive to carbachol and even to ACh in the presence of anti-AChEs. This effect of denervation may be due either to the normal prepotent action of these substances on presynaptic receptor sites (VOLLE and KOELLE 1961; KOELLE 1961, 1962); or as here postulated, to the decreased responsiveness of the LN sites in denervated ganglia. In denervated ganglia the anti-AChE, DFP, causes the same large increase in sensitivity of ganglia (11 fold) whether tested by discharges evoked by injections of ACh or of carbachol. Evidently this sensitization is not due to anti-AChE action, a conclusion that is in line with the loss of virtually all AChE after denervation (KOELLE and KOELLE 1959). According to the hypothesis developed above, the DFP causes this sensitization on account of its depolarizing action on the LN postsynaptic receptor sites at which ACh and carbachol produce the depolarization that leads to impulse generation. This explanation may be correlated with the competitive depression that anti-AChEs have on the depolarization generated by the action of pre-synaptically released ACh on LN receptor sites (Fig. 49C, F—H; R. M. ECCLES 1952; R. M. ECCLES and LIBET 1961), and also with the increase that injected ACh produces in the prolonged postganglionic discharge induced by DFP (VOLLE 1962a). A comparable action of DFP and other anti-AChEs in sensitizing ACh receptor sites has been demonstrated by COHEN and POST-HUMUS (1955) on the isolated frog rectus, where it is to a considerable extent independent of anti-AChE action.

In summary it can be stated that the pharmacological investigations have shown that at the neuromuscular junction the presynaptic terminals have cholinoceptive receptor sites that are also sites for the depolarizing action of anti-AChEs. It is doubtful if such presynaptic receptor sites have been de-monstrated for normal sympathetic ganglia, but, their existence, at least at a rudimentary level, is indicated by their development during infection by pseudorabies virus.

CHAPTER IX

EXCITATORY SYNAPSES OPERATING BY ELECTRICAL TRANSMISSION

As provisionally defined in the Introduction, a synapse is a structure anatomically differentiated and functionally specialized for transmission between excitable cells. The present chapter includes a wide variety of electrically transmitting synapses, beginning with the simplest and least differentiated type, the septal synapse. In all cases the transmission is effected by the depolarizing action of an electric current that is generated either by impulses or by synaptic potentials in the presynaptic component. In the most differentiated type, the giant motor synapses of the crayfish, the synaptic membrane is a very efficient electrical rectifier, so one-way transmission is ensured just as effectively as with a chemically transmitting synapse. Nevertheless, even in this synapse the functional arrangements are much simpler than for chemically transmitting synapses, where there are of necessity in the transmitting element the complex phenomena of manufacture, mobilization and release of the transmitter substances, and in the recipient element there are the specialized receptor sites with the associated ionic permeability mechanisms (Chapters IV, V and VI). Because of this greater simplicity it seems likely that the electrical synapses represent the most primitive mode of communication between excitable cells, as for example in coelenterates. There are fascinating fields for investigation on the comparative physiology of synaptic transmission in these primitive organisms.

A. Septal synapses of giant axons

The longitudinal nerve cords of some forms of *Annelidae* and *Crustaceae* contain giant axons that are segmented by transverse septa. Impulses propagate in either direction along these giant axons at a relatively high velocity, which shows that the septa have little influence on the flow of current longitudinally along the core of the giant fibres (ECCLES, GRANIT and YOUNG 1932; BULLOCK 1945; RUSHTON 1945; KAO and GRUNDFEST 1957; KAO 1960).

Evidently the septa have not the rectifying properties of the synaptic membrane between crayfish giant axons and motor giant fibres (FURSHPAN and POTTER 1959a). When employing microelectrode techniques for more precise investigations on the electrical properties of septal membranes, the earthworm giant fibres are unsuitable because the segmental length is too short relative to the length constant of the fibres (KAO and GRUNDFEST 1957; KAO 1960); hence the significant investigations have been on the crayfish septate axons (KAO 1960; WATANABE and GRUNDFEST 1961).

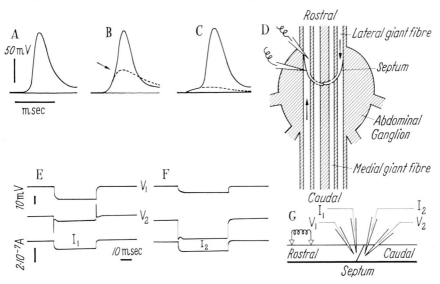

Fig. 51 A—G. Responses of septal and commisural junctions of crayfish lateral giant axons. The intracellular responses of A—C were recorded under conditions shown diagrammatically in D. The rostrally travelling impulse in the left lateral giant fibre is recorded by a microelectrode just below (A) and just above (B) the oblique septum, the latter microelectrode also recording the commisural transmission of the caudally travelling impulse on the lateral giant fibre (C). The dotted lines in B and C show the approximate time courses of the potentials when impulse transmission was blocked by hyperpolarizing the postsynaptic fibre. The experimental conditions for the records in E and F are shown in G with the electrodes for current passing (I) or voltage recording (V) shown on either side of an oblique septum of a lateral giant fibre such as in D. In E hyperpolarizing current pulses through the I_1 electrode (lowest trace) produce the voltage changes recorded with V_1 and V_2 electrodes in the two upper traces. Similarly with the hyperpolarizing current through the I_2 electrode in F (WATANABE and GRUNDFEST 1961)

When as in Fig. 51 D an impulse is propagating rostrally in a lateral giant fibre, intracellular recording immediately below a septum gives a simple spike potential (Fig. 51 A); whereas immediately above there is an inflection on the rising phase as in B, which resembles the IS-SD spike generated by antidromic invasion of a motoneurone (Fig. 41 A). Evidently the septum offers an appreciable impedance to the transmission of the impulse along the fibre. As a consequence there is a delay, usually of 0.1 to 0.2 msec, and blockage of transmission can be effected at the septum when the post-septal segment is hyperpolarized or injured; the post-septal potential is then a small spike (dotted line in Fig. 51 B) due to electrotonic spread from the preseptal segment with perhaps a local response superimposed (WATANABE and GRUND-FEST 1961).

Since the same potential changes are observed across a septum when transmission is in the reverse direction, it would be expected that, when tested by applied currents, there would be no sign of any rectifying properties in the septum. For example in Fig. 51 G two microelectrodes were inserted just rostral to a septum and two just caudal, one of each being for the current application, the other for recording. In E a rectangular current pulse between I_1 and an indifferent electrode causes, after initial capacitive distortion, a steady potential change about 2.7 times larger in the cis-septal record than in the trans-septal. In F, with current similarly applied through I_2, there is approximately the same ratio (2.4) of the cis- to trans-potentials. Since the length constant of the giant fibre is at least 20 times longer than the separation of the cis- and trans-recording electrodes in G, the attenuation factor can be attributed entirely to the septal resistance. There is always the virtual symmetry of septal resistance illustrated in Fig. 51 E, F, which contrasts with a ratio of over 50 for the rectifying synapses between the lateral giant and the motor giant fibres in the crayfish (Figs. 55, 56; FURSHPAN and POTTER 1959a). For investigations such as that of Fig. 51 E—G the resistance of the septal membrane has been found to be 0.2 to 0.4 MΩ, which is considerably larger than for the surface membrane of a segment of the axon; and it can be shown to account for the initial phase of attenuated spike transmission in Fig. 51 B. Thus, in the propagation of an impulse along a septate axon, each septum functions merely as a resistance that is added onto the core resistance. In this way it attenuates the electrotonic spread of depolarization that is responsible for the propagation.

Preliminary experiments (KAO 1960) indicate that, in the septate giant axons of annelids (STOUGH 1926), the septa have a resistance much lower than the membrane resistance of a segment of the axon. Consequently trans-septal transmission would be attenuated much less than in crayfish, which would account for the fast transmission despite the close spacing of the septa. For example BULLOCK (1945) finds that the conduction time is only 0.1 to 0.05 msec per segment of about 2 mm length for the large median giant fibre of annelids, so septal delay must be negligibly small, and in fact has not been measured.

Electron-microscopic examination of the septa of the annelid giant fibres (HAMA 1959) shows a structure corresponding to the physiological properties. The membranes of each segment are in very close apposition with no intercalated tissue, so that the total thickness is approximately 200 Å; furthermore the membrane exhibits a symmetrical structure corresponding to the absence of rectification.

B. Synapses formed by electrically transmitting bridges between septate giant axons

As shown in Fig. 51 D there are commissural branches connecting the two lateral giant axons at each segment both in crayfish and annelids. It is generally assumed as in Fig. 51 D that septa break the protoplasmic continuity of the commissural branches between the two lateral giant fibres, though such septa have not been demonstrated histologically. These very fine connections between the lateral giant fibres (STOUGH 1926) are surprisingly efficient in transmitting impulses (BULLOCK 1945; RUSHTON 1945; WATANABE and GRUNDFEST 1961; WILSON 1961). For example in Fig. 51 C the small initial depolarization is produced by the spread from a spike potential in the other lateral giant via a commissural connection, and it is seen to generate a spike after a delay of almost 0.5 msec. The dotted line shows the commissural potential when it fails to generate a spike in a hyperpolarized axon.

It has so far proved impossible to record from the commissural branches by microelectrodes, but the efficiency of transmission indicates that it is effected by the propagation of impulses along both segments of the commissure, with, presumably, transmission across the septum between them (RUSHTON 1945; WATANABE and GRUNDFEST 1961; WILSON 1961). The impulse propagating down the commissural branch appears directly to spread from this branch to the adjacent part of the giant axon, hence the spike in that axon appears to be initiated at a much lower level of depolarization in Fig. 51 C, than with septal transmission in B. Hyperpolarizing rectangular currents, as in Fig. 51 E to G, block transmission of impulses and reveal the small electrotonic transmission between the two lateral giant fibres via the commissural connection, the attenuation factor, about 12, being much larger than for the septum (see dotted traces in B and C).

The commissural transmission between the lateral giant fibres of annelids is much more efficient. WILSON (1961) estimates that the attenuation factor is about 3 both for spikes and for imposed voltages. Correspondingly there is normally no measurable latency for transmission.

The commissural transmitting mechanism usually operates identically in either direction both for impulses and for electrotonus (RUSHTON 1945; BULLOCK 1945; WATANABE and GRUNDFEST 1961; WILSON 1961). However, if transmission across one commissure becomes unidirectional for impulses, there is opportunity for developing repetitive activation due to continued circulatory propagation of an impulse through the two lateral giant fibres and their commissural connections (KAO 1960; WATANABE and GRUNDFEST 1961). This phenomenon is dependent on local injury, and presumably has no functional significance (WILSON 1961).

C. Synapses formed by electrically transmitting bridges between neurones

There are now known to be transmitting bridges between neurones that have been shown to have some mechanism for synchronizing discharges (HAGIWARA and BULLOCK 1957; BENNETT, CRAIN and GRUNDFEST 1959b). The following descriptions of the various types show that they may with propriety be classified as synapses.

In the most thoroughly investigated structure, the lobster cardiac ganglion, the large follower cells are connected together by pathways that are very

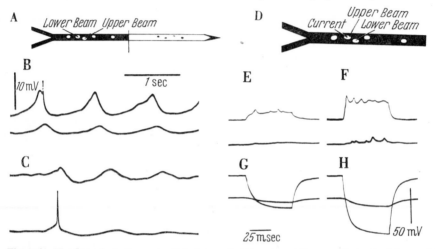

Fig. 52A—H. Spread of slow potential changes between two follower cells in the lobster *(Panulirus japonicus)*. As shown diagrammatically in A the pacemaker cells were inactivated with 0.1 % procaine-sea water. In B are simultaneous recordings from two follower cells, and similarly for C in order to show the transmission of slow potential changes (WATANABE 1958). In E, F, the membrane potential of one cell (the upper trace) was depolarized by a rectangular current pulse that was much stronger in F. Similarly in G and H for a rectangular hyperpolarization (HAGIWARA, WATANABE and SAITO 1959)

effective for electrotonic spread, but not for transmission of brief potential changes such as spikes (WATANABE 1958; HAGIWARA, WATANABE and SAITO 1959; WATANABE and BULLOCK 1960). In this respect these cell bridges differ from the commissural connections between lateral giant fibres.

In Fig. 52A (HAGIWARA 1961) the activity of the four small pacemaker cells to the right was suppressed by procaine. Under such conditions, the large follower cells may exhibit synchronized potential waves as illustrated in B and C, the potential change in one being uniformly much larger than in the other. A likely explanation of this synchronized activity is that there is an electrotonically conducting bridge between the two cells. The possible existence of such a bridge was tested for, as in Fig. 52D, where rectangular depolarizing (E, F) and hyperpolarizing (G, H) current pulses applied through a microelectrode in one follower cell are seen to evoke smaller potential changes in the other follower cell. The attenuation factor in Fig. 52E—H has about the same order of magnitude as that required to account for the spread of the spontaneous potential changes in Fig. 52B and C.

In contrast to this relatively effective transmission of slow potentials, there is a negligible transmission of the brief spike potentials, which as in Fig. 52 are always small with intracellular recording because they are restricted to the axon (BULLOCK and HAGIWARA 1957). For example in Fig. 52E, the small spikes produced by the depolarizing pulse are not transmitted; and in Fig. 52F the transmitted depolarization evokes small spikes (lower trace) that are quite unrelated to the spikes of the upper trace. The explanation is apparent when the attenuation factors are measured for alternating currents at various frequencies: about 3 at 20/sec, and as high as 25 at 250/sec (HAGIWARA 1961). The resistance of the bridge between the large follower cells is measured as 5 to 16 MΩ for D.C. currents (HAGIWARA, WATANABE and SAITO 1959). In addition, depolarization of follower cells spreads electrotonically to pacemaker cells, presumably by similar intercellular bridges, and has been shown to exert in this way an effective positive feed-back control on the cells

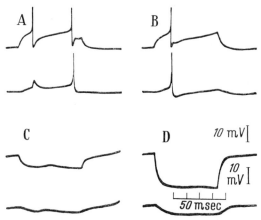

Fig. 53A—D. Potential changes recorded simultaneously by microelectrodes in two giant cells of the segmental ganglion of the leech. Rectangular current pulses were applied through the microelectrode in one (upper traces), the currents being outward (depolarizing) in A, B and inward (hyperpolarizing) in C, D. Currents in A were larger than B and in D larger than C. Time 50 msec and voltage scale, 10 mV (HAGIWARA and MORITA 1962)

initiating the bursts of activity that activate the heart beat (WATANABE and BULLOCK 1960).

In each segmental ganglion of the leech there are two giant cells that have also been shown (HAGIWARA and MORITA 1962; ECKERT 1963) to be connected by some electrotonic pathway. When a membrane potential change is produced in one by a rectangular current pulse, there is developed synchronously a smaller potential in the other (Fig. 53 C, D). The attenuation factor of 2 to 4 is similar for depolarizing and hyperpolarizing currents, there being thus no trace of rectification. However, the electrotonic pathway is also seen in Fig. 53 A, B to transmit spike potentials, so producing either a large depolarization (first response in A); or more usually a spike. From observations such as those of Fig. 53 C, D it is calculated that the resistance of the electrotonic pathway is up to 30 MΩ, being about double that of the cell membrane. The factors involved in electrotonic transmission of the spike potential are complicated because the impulses of these giant cells are restricted to axons, the soma being merely passively depolarized, hence the small sizes of the spikes in Fig. 53 A, B; furthermore the electrotonic bridges probably link the axons and not the somas. As a consequence the electrotonic transmission of the spike potential is more effective than would be anticipated from the attenuation factor for brief pulses applied to the soma (HAGIWARA and MORITA 1962).

Similar investigations have shown that there is electrotonic transmission between the supramedullary neurones of the puffer fish (BENNETT, CRAIN and GRUNDFEST 1959a, 1959b; BENNETT 1960). The attenuation factor is 6 or higher, and no trace of rectification is observed. Again the connecting bridges are apparently established between the axons of the cells, and are specially effective for transmission of slow potential changes such as synaptic potentials. In this way they mediate the synchronization of the constituent neurones of the cluster to synaptic stimulation applied individually.

Recently a very complete study of electrotonic transmission between neurones has been reported by BENNETT, ALJURE, NAKAJIMA and PAPPAS (1963) for the spinal electromotor neurones of Mormyrid electric fish. The evidence for electrotonic transmission resembled that of Fig. 53, and in addition the electron-micrographs showed a most convincing structural correlate; there were large areas in which the dendrites of neurones were not separated by the 200 Å cleft, there being an actual fusion of the adjacent surface membranes. At these presumed electrical transmitting areas there was none of the special features of chemical transmitting synapses — vesicles or mitochrondria. However, elsewhere on the same dendrites there were chemical transmitting synapses.

This evidence for electrotonic transmission between nerve cells in a vertebrate is a warning that such interaction may be the cause of puzzling phenomena that have been attributed to a conventional excitatory synaptic action. For example, if it is arranged that the axon of a frog spinal motoneurone is not excited by a stimulus evoking an antidromic volley, more than half of such motoneurones exhibit a prolonged depolarization that even may be adequate to generate the discharge of an impulse by that motoneurone (KUBOTA and BROOKHART 1962; KATZ and MILEDI 1963). This depolarization is graded in size; it has a central latency of 2 to 2.5 msec, a rapid rise and a much slower decay; and it is associated with an increased excitability to direct stimulation that has a comparable time course. The generation of this potential by conventional synaptic excitatory action on the soma or on dendrites adjacent thereto is regarded as unlikely because it is not changed by polarizing currents through the intracellular electrode, nor does it depress the antidromic spike potential (KUBOTA and BROOKHART 1962). Hitherto the transmission has been attributed to a synaptic excitatory action by motor-axon collaterals onto the motoneuronal dendrites, but it seems that a more probable explanation is that proposed by WASHIZU (1960) in order to explain a rather different transmission between frog motoneurones, namely that it is due to electrotonic linkage between the dendrites of motoneurones. If dendritic depolarization produced by the antidromic spike potential were to spread by electrical coupling to adjacent dendrites of another motoneurone, it could produce in that moto-neurone just such a depolarization. The central latency would be attributable to dendritic conduction time (cf. Chapter VII). Discrimination between these alternative explanations should be possible pharmacologically, for synaptic transmission via axon collaterals would be expected to exhibit the pharma-cological properties of a central cholinergic synapse (KIRALY and PHILLIS 1961; MITCHELL and PHILLIS 1962).

The transmission between motoneurones reported by WASHIZU (1960) differs in that there is only a small brief spike-like potential when transmission fails, not the slow depolarization; also the latency is briefer. It is possible that this transmission occurs between contiguous sites of injury produced by the microelectrode.

Electrotonic bridges are also indicated by the passive electrotonic spread between adjacent neurones in the abdominal ganglion of *Aplysia* (ARVANITAKI and CHALAZONITIS 1959; TAUC 1959). There is transmission not only of passive electrotonus, but a spike potential in one causes a passive depolarization of the other.

D. Conjoint electrical and chemical transmission of the same synapse

When a single presynaptic fibre of a chemically transmitting synapse makes a very extensive synaptic contact, a considerable fraction of the electric current generated by the presynaptic impulse may pass through the post-synaptic element, and excite it, just as occurs with a septal synapse (Fig. 51). MARTIN and PILAR (1963 a, b) have shown that both orthodromic and anti-dromic electrical transmission often occurs with the very large caliciform synapses in the ciliary ganglion of the chick (Fig. 7 C), and that there is always only one synapse on a ganglion cell.

In the intracellular records of Fig. 54 A—C from a ciliary ganglion cell, pro-gressive hyperpolarization first delays, then blocks the origin of the spike from the EPSP, just as occurs with the frog sympathetic ganglion cell in Fig. 17 A. In another ciliary ganglion cell (Fig. 54 D—F) blockage of the spike by hyper-polarization shows that there are two depolarizing responses, and that at an intermediate stage of block (E) the generation of the impulse is displaced from the first spike-like component to the second component that resembles the EPSP of Fig. 17 A. Three criteria establish that the initial brief component is due to direct electrical current flow just as with a septal synapse, being consequently called a "coupling potential" by MARTIN and PILAR (1963 a), while the second is an EPSP generated by chemical transmission. There is no appreciable synaptic delay for the first and a delay of 1.5 to 2 msec for the second. The first is not affected by membrane hyperpolarization, while the second is increased as in Fig. 17A in accordance with a null-point of 0 to —15 mV. The first is not affected by dTC, the second is abolished reversibly (dotted lines in Fig. 54C and F), as would be expected for a cholinergic synapse (cf. Fig. 40 M—Q). The functional significance of this double transmission was demonstrated by the recording of a double spike potential at about 2 msec interval from the postganglionic nerve trunk (MARTIN and PILAR 1963 b).

Electrical transmission in the reverse direction is shown by the series of Fig. 54 G—I, where hyperpolarization first greatly increases the slow depolarization that follows the antidromic spike potential (H), but, when the

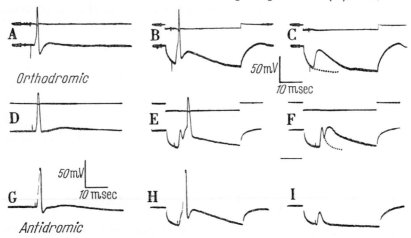

Fig. 54A—I. Intracellular recording from the ganglion cells of the chick ciliary ganglion. A and D show all-or-nothing potentials of two ganglion cells produced by orthodromic activation by an impulse in the presynaptic fibre. B and C illustrate effect of conditioning the orthodromic response A by a hyperpolarizing current pulse through the microelectrode, as shown by the upper traces, and similarly for E, F and the orthodromic response, D. The dotted lines in C and F show the approximate time courses after blockage of chemical synaptic transmission by dTC. G—I are responses of another ciliary ganglion cell to antidromic invasion by an impulse in its axon. In H and I there was conditioning by a hyperpolarizing current pulse applied to the ganglion cell through the microelectrode as in B and C (MARTIN and PILAR 1963a)

antidromic spike fails to invade the soma (I), slow depolarization is absent. It is also removed reversibly by the application of dTC. Evidently, the slow depolarization is generated because the antidromic impulse excites a spike in the presynaptic terminals that then releases the transmitter to give the EPSP. This postulated electrical transmission antidromically across the synapse is directly observed when intracellular recording is made from the presynaptic terminals (MARTIN and PILAR 1963 a).

The recording of volley transmission from both the preganglionic and postganglionic nerves shows that about half of the caliciform synapses normally transmit electrically in the orthodromic direction and most of these also transmit antidromically (MARTIN and PILAR 1963 b), which is in good agreement with the intracellular investigations; hence the electrical transmission cannot be dismissed as an artefact resulting from injury of the impaled ganglion cells. In the simplest explanation of electrical transmission across the caliciform synapse, the flow of current is regarded as similar to that across the septal synapse. Presumably the conductance of the synaptic cleft, as is shown by the dotted line in Fig. 56F, shunts some of the current that otherwise would contribute to the transynaptic depolarization; hence the safety factor is lower than with septal synapses, where there is no cleft. It will be appreciated that the flow of current to give the simple depolarization of Fig. 54F (dotted line) will occur only in so far as the presynaptic membrane fronting the synaptic cleft fails to be invaded by the presynaptic impulse. Conversely, antidromic transmission requires that the postsynaptic membrane fronting the cleft be not invaded by the antidromic impulse. A further requirement is that these two membranes of the synaptic cleft have a relatively low impedance, and this has been observed (MARTIN and PILAR 1963 a, and personal communication).

On theoretical grounds it would be expected that in the basket type of synapses on ciliary ganglion cells (DE LORENZO 1960; SZENTÁGOTHAI 1963 c) the synaptic cleft would have a much higher shunting conductance, and hence these synapses would be very ineffective in electrical transmission, as is observed in Fig. 54A—C. However, it is not yet known whether the property of electrical transmission is exclusive to the caliciform structure, and the absence of electrical transmission to the basket type of synapse.

The club endings on Mauthner cells provide a second example of conjoint electrical and chemical transmission (FURSHPAN, personal communication). However, the electrical transmission is often weak and rarely fires impulses.

E. Electrically transmitting synapses designed for one-way transmission

Giant motor synapses of the crayfish

As shown in Fig. 55A the giant motor fibre of the third root passes across the surface of the lateral giant fibre making a synaptic contact with the one-way conduction (WIERSMA 1947) that is typical of chemically transmitting synapses, i.e. transmission only from lateral giant (presynaptic) to motor fibre (postsynaptic). However, precise investigation (FURSHPAN and POTTER 1959a) with simultaneous intracellular recording from the presynaptic and postsynaptic fibres has shown that transmission occurs with virtually no latency, about 0.1 msec for the onset of postsynaptic depolarization in Fig. 55B, C, which contrasts with the latency of 1 to 2 msec that is recorded by similar procedures in the giant synapse of the squid stellate ganglion (Figs. 8B, 12, 46C). The postsynaptic response may simply have the typical form of an EPSP (Fig. 55D), or a spike potential may arise from the EPSP (Fig. 55 B, C), just as with other excitatory synapses (Figs. 40B—D, I—K, 41B, 44F). Fig. 55 E shows that a spike potential of 77 mV in the postsynaptic fibre produces only an extremely small depolarization (less than 0.3 mV) in the presynaptic fibre, thus illustrating the irreciprocity of transmission across the synapse.

Even during the early part of the rising phase of the presynaptic spike there is a considerable postsynaptic depolarization (Fig. 55 B), and in Fig. 55 D

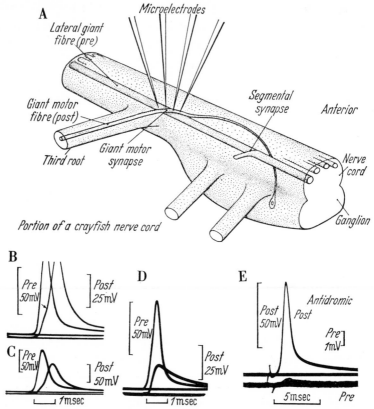

Fig. 55 A—E. Semidiagrammatic drawing of a portion of a crayfish abdominal nerve cord, containing one ganglion. The course of one motor giant axon is shown from its cell body in the ventral part of the ganglion until it leaves the third ganglionic root on the opposite side of the cord. Only its junction with the lateral giant pre-fibre is shown; but its synapses with the two medial giant fibres are located just centrally, where the fibres cross the motor axon. A septal synapse between two segments of the lateral giant fibre is also shown. B—D. Orthodromic nerve impulse transmission at giant synapse shown in A with simultaneous intracellular recording from pre- and post-fibres, the pre-fibre potential being recorded in the upper traces. B and C were recorded from same synapse at different amplifications, post-spike origin being indicated by arrow in B. In E upper trace is post-fibre antidromic spike potential which produces a negligible potential in pre-fibre (lower trace). Note separate potential scales for pre- and post-fibre records in B—E (FURSHPAN and POTTER 1959a)

the rising phase of the EPSP is virtually concurrent with the rising phase of the presynaptic spike; hence it seems likely that there is a direct electrical spread of depolarizing current from the presynaptic to the postsynaptic fibre just as with septal synapses (Fig. 51). As would be expected from Fig. 55 D, the passage of depolarizing current through a microelectrode in the presynaptic fibre has a powerful depolarizing action on the postsynaptic fibre (Fig. 56 G, H), but there is extremely little spread of depolarization in the reverse direction

(Fig. 56I, J). Evidently the membrane between the presynaptic and post-synaptic fibres functions very efficiently as a rectifier, passing current from the former to the latter much more readily than in the reverse direction, as would be expected from Fig. 55 E. According to this simple rectifier postulate, a hyperpolarizing current should be transmitted across the synaptic junction in the reverse sense, i.e. from postsynaptic to presynaptic fibre. This prediction has been experimentally confirmed (Fig. 56I, J); hence the passage of currents through the synaptic membrane between the presynaptic and postsynaptic fibres can be diagrammatically shown as in Fig. 56A to D. Incidentally, it will be noted that, with testing by a wide range of strengths of outward current from the postsynaptic fibre across the synaptic membrane (Fig. 56B, C), there is no trace of a phase of increased membrane conductance such as would be associated with the generation of an impulse.

A very complete study of the synaptic rectifier has been made as in Fig. 51 E—G by simultaneous potential records from the presynaptic and post-synaptic fibres when rectangular currents of various strengths are passed in either direction through additional electrodes in the presynaptic and post-synaptic fibres (FURSHPAN and POTTER 1959a). Some potentials recorded in this investigation are illustrated in Fig. 56G—J, and show that current passes effectively across the synapse only in conditions Fig. 56A and D. Hence the results of this investigation are in conformity with the rectification hypo-thesis; and, when plotted, the curves express the remarkable rectifying pro-perties of the synaptic membrane. It was possible even to account quanti-tatively for the unidirectional spread of depolarization across the synaptic membrane that is illustrated in Fig. 55 B—E. It may therefore be accepted that synaptic transmission in this synapse is entirely attributable to the flow of electrical current.

Efficient operation of electrical synaptic transmission through a synapse can occur only if there is close apposition of the presynaptic and post-synaptic membranes with a negligible synaptic cleft. The conditions for maximum efficiency are almost the opposite from the requirements for a chemi-cally transmitting synapse. With the latter the current depolarizing the postsynaptic membrane has to flow through the synaptic cleft as shown in Fig. 56E (cf. Fig. 14A, inset); whereas, with the former, current flowing through the synaptic cleft is lost for the purpose of postsynaptic depolarization, as shown in Fig. 56F (dotted line).

Investigations by electron-microscopy (ROBERTSON 1955, 1961; DE LO-RENZO 1959) have shown that the synaptic cleft is narrower than with chemical transmitting synapses, for it ranges from 150 Å down to a negligible amount, as against values of 200 Å or more for chemical synapses. Of even more significance are the patches with complete elimination of the synaptic cleft and probably even partial or complete membrane fusion (ROBERTSON

1961). Such areas of membrane would pass current from the pre- to the post-element of the synapse with no loss of current into the synaptic cleft, just as occurs with the septal synapses. These patches of membrane contact with

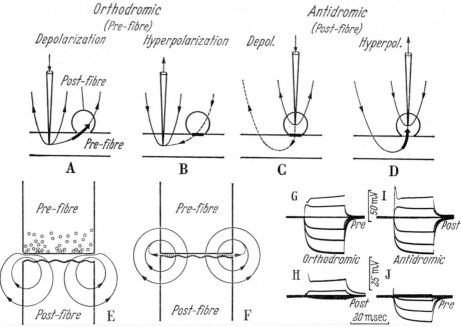

Fig. 56 A—J. A—D illustrate the synaptic rectifier hypothesis for the synapse illustrated in Fig. 55. The post-fibre is shown in transverse section at the point where it crosses the pre-fibre (cf. Fig. 55 A). The junction is indicated by a dotted line or a heavy bar, representing a low or high synaptic resistance, respectively. The arrows give the direction of (positive) current entering or leaving the current-passing micro-electrode, a series of observations being illustrated in G—J; dashed lines indicate negligible current flow due to high synaptic resistance, as shown by downward directed deflections in H and upward in J. Diagrams A and D, corresponding to the two situations in which large transynaptic effects were observed (upward directed deflections in H and downward in J), show that in both cases current would cross the junction in the same direction (indicated by the heavy arrows) (FURSHPAN and POTTER 1959a). E. Diagram of synapse operating by chemical transmission and represented as an end to end contact between two cylinders separated by a synaptic cleft which opens into interstitial spaces so that the postsynaptic currents can flow freely as in inset of Fig. 14A. The vesicles are shown in the presynaptic fibre (cf. Figs. 1—4) and the postulated electrically inexcitable membrane is shown as a wavy line on the postsynaptic side of the synaptic cleft. Other membranes are assumed to be electrically excitable. F. Diagram of synapse operating by electrical transmission and similarly represented as an end to end contact, but, in accordance with electron-microscopic observations, the synaptic cleft is shown much more constricted, the postsynaptic membrane being again represented by a wavy line to indicate that it is electrically inexcitable (see text). Lines of current are drawn at time of transmission, a small current being drawn passing out through cleft (see text) (KUFFLER, personal cummunication 1960)

elimination of the synaptic cleft can be regarded as the active zones for electrical transmission. As yet there is no structural correlate of the rectification property.

F. Discussion

Some of the electrically transmitting synapses have a high safety factor for impulse transmission, as for example the septal synapses of giant axons and the giant motor synapses of the crayfish. These synapses serve merely as rapid transmitters of impulses, having an obligatory character in their operation. Practically the situation with the septal synapse is little different from transmission along a continuous nerve fibre. Presumably the one-way transmission in the giant motor synapse is functionally important.

It is doubtful if electrical transmission has functional meaning in the chick ciliary ganglion, where it occurs only in about half of the synapses and in them with a low safety factor. Furthermore, there is always a very effective chemical transmission to generate an impulse about 1.5 msec later if electrical transmission should fail. Perhaps electrical transmission is merely an accident of the large synaptic contact.

The electrotonic bridges between neurones have usually such a low safety factor for brief potential changes that impulse transmission never occurs; yet, as noted above, such bridges may be of functional importance in transferring a fraction of the depolarization of one neurone to other closely related neurones, so helping to synchronize the activity of a group of neurones. This synchronization would be of particular importance in the lobster cardiac ganglion (HAGIWARA 1961). Such electrotonic bridges can be said to function in a facilitatory manner, adding to excitatory synaptic actions and so tending to generate impulses, which contrasts with the obligatory character of the septal synapse.

CHAPTER X

THE POSTSYNAPTIC ELECTRICAL EVENTS PRODUCED BY CHEMICALLY TRANSMITTING INHIBITORY SYNAPSES

Activation of chemical inhibitory synapses always produces an increased electrical conductance of the subsynaptic membrane, which is the principal agent in suppressing impulse generation. With the vertebrate central nervous system there is in addition an associated increase in the resting membrane potential; but in invertebrates there is usually no hyperpolarization, the increased conductance alone effecting inhibition by tending to stabilize the membrane potential close to its resting level. Nevertheless it will be seen that the ionic mechanisms responsible for the increased conductances in all these chemical inhibitory actions belong to a category that is distinguished both by exclusion of sodium ions and by a high conductance for chloride and/or potassium ions (Chapter XI). The potential changes that eventuate are, of course, merely a resultant of the net movements of potassium and chloride ions down their electrochemical gradients. It is therefore justifiable to classify all these postsynaptic inhibitory actions together. Just as with excitatory synapses it has become customary to designate inhibitory synaptic action by the potential it produces, the inhibitory postsynaptic potential, IPSP, rather than by the less easily demonstrable inhibitory postsynaptic current that produces the potential. It is important to recognize that the IPSP may be in either the hyperpolarizing or the depolarizing direction in accord with the electrochemical gradients, or, of course, it may be virtually zero.

A. Time courses of inhibitory postsynaptic potentials

1. Neurones of vertebrate central nervous system

It is convenient to commence with an account of the postsynaptic potential changes produced in a cat motoneurone, which have been extensively studied since the original investigation (BROCK, COOMBS and ECCLES 1952). Intracellular recording reveals that inhibitory synaptic action by a Ia afferent volley causes a brief hyperpolarization of the motoneuronal membrane (Fig. 57A—F). The microelectrode must be filled with a salt having a large anion such as sulphate or citrate, else this inhibitory postsynaptic potential (IPSP) is likely to be distorted by intracellular changes in ionic composition, as will be seen later (Chapter XI). Variations in the size of the group I a afferent volley cause alterations is the size of the IPSP, but not in its time course, which has characteristically a brief rising phase and a slower, approximately expo-

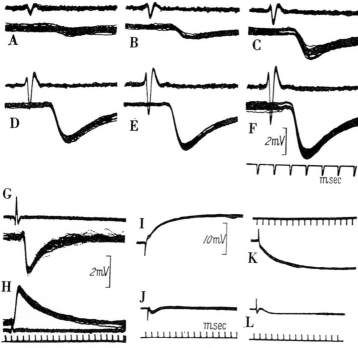

Fig. 57A—L. Lower records give intracellular responses (IPSPs) of a biceps-semitendinosus motoneurone to a quadriceps volley of progressively increasing size, as shown by the upper records, which are recorded from L_6 dorsal root by a surface electrode, downward deflections signalling negativity. All records are formed by the superposition of about 40 faint traces (ECCLES 1958a). G shows IPSPs similarly generated in another biceps-semitendinosus motoneurone, the monosynaptic EPSPs of this motoneurone being seen in H. I to L show changes in potential produced by an applied rectangular pulse of 12×10^{-9} A in the depolarizing and hyperpolarizing [directions, I and K being intracellular and J and L extracellular (CURTIS and ECCLES 1959)

nential, decay; hence it can be assumed that the IPSP is produced by a virtually synchronous action of inhibitory impulses, and that each impulse produces an IPSP having the same time course as those illustrated in Fig. 57A to F for afferent volleys of varying size. The IPSP is approximately a mirror image of the monosynaptic EPSP of the same motoneurone (Fig. 57G, H), but it always has a slightly faster decay with a time constant of decay that is little if any longer than the membrane time constant (compare Fig. 57G, I; CURTIS and ECCLES 1959).

When one comes to consider in detail the synaptic events responsible for the hyperpolarization of the IPSP, it is evident that the increased charge on the motoneuronal membrane must be caused by an electric current outwardly directed across the subsynaptic membrane of the activated inhibitory synapses and inwardly directed across the remainder of the membrane, so hyperpolarizing it, as illustrated in Fig. 58 B. Just as with excitatory synaptic action (Chapter IV) the time course of this inhibitory postsynaptic current can be approximately calculated if the electric time constant of the motoneuronal membrane is known. It will be seen in Fig. 58 A that the current

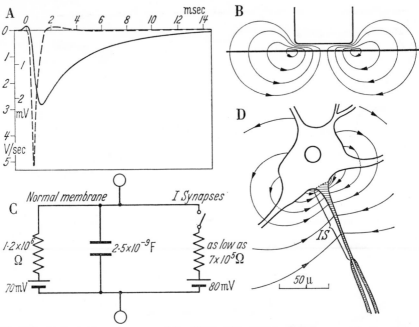

Fig. 58 A—D. In A, the mean curve of the IPSP of Fig. 57 G is plotted as a continuous line, and, on the basis of the electric time constant of the membrane determined from Fig. 57 I to L, it is analyzed to give the time course of the postsynaptic current generating it, as shown by the broken line. In B, the flow of these inhibitory postsynaptic currents is shown. In C there is a formal electrical diagram showing capacity, resistance and battery of the membrane of a standard motoneurone as "seen" by a microelectrode in the soma; on the right side there is in addition a representation of the subsynaptic areas of the membrane that are activated in producing the I a IPSP. Maximum activation of the areas would be indicated by closing the switch (CURTIS and ECCLES 1959). D. Diagrammatic representation of current that flows as the IPSP generated in the soma-dendritic membrane spreads electrotonically to hyperpolarize the initial segment (*IS*) which is the usual site of initiation of impulses discharged from the motoneurone

virtually ceases to flow just after the summit of the IPSP, the decaying phase being almost entirely due to the passive recovery of the membrane potential.

This analysis has been confirmed by a direct recording of the postsynaptic inhibitory current that is produced by activated inhibitory synapses when the motoneuronal membrane is voltage-clamped (Fig. 59; ARAKI and TERZUOLO 1962). As in Fig. 15 the motoneurone is penetrated by two microelectrodes about 10 μ apart, one being employed for recording the voltage (upper trace of B), the other for passing the current that exactly neutralizes the inhibitory postsynaptic current (lower trace of C). In D the postsynaptic inhibitory current as so determined (1) is seen to reach a maximum in about 0.8 msec and to have a total duration of about 2.5 msec. There is no overshoot as in the calculated time course of Fig. 58A because the voltage-clamping eliminates distortion due to electrotonic spread of the IPSP out along the dendrites. If, as will be postulated in Chapter XIII, the inhibitory synapses are concentrated on the soma and dendritic stumps, the record under voltage-clamp conditions (Fig. 59C) will give the exact time course of the postsynaptic inhibitory current.

When, by the application of a steady background current, the motoneuronal membrane is set a sufficiently high level of hyperpolarization, there is reversal

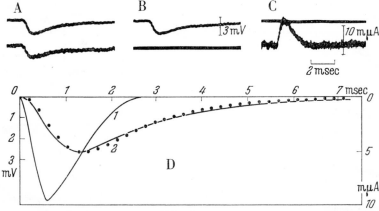

Fig. 59A—D. Membrane current during an IPSP. A: the IPSP set up in a biceps-semitendinosus motoneurone by group Ia afferent volley in the quadriceps nerve, recorded by both microelectrodes. B: the lower beam was switched to record the membrane current. C: the membrane potential was clamped at its resting potential level, as in Fig. 15B, during the IPSP (upper beam). The current is recorded in the lower beam. D: tracings of the IPSP in B (curve 2) and the current in C (curve 1), respectively, the current trace being reversed. The dots show the calculated IPSP. Further explanations in the text (ARAKI and TERZUOLO 1962)

of the inhibitory postsynaptic current, as is shown by the reversed polarity of the IPSPs in the three lower records of Fig. 60A. Plotting of the series partly illustrated in Fig. 60A shows that there is an equilibrium potential of about − 80 mV at which the IPSP is zero, and of course the flow of inhibitory current is then also zero (Fig. 60B). This equilibrium potential for the IPSP (E_{IPSP}) was in Fig. 60B at about 6 mV more hyperpolarized than the normal resting potential. The influence of membrane depolarization in increasing the IPSP and of hyperpolarization in reversing it leads to the postulate that the subsynaptic current flow is due to the net movement of ions down their electrochemical gradients, and that there is no requirement of a supply of metabolic energy to ion pumps. The conditions generating the IPSP are shown in the formal electrical diagram of Fig. 58C, where activation of the I synapses would cause a momentary (for 1 to 2 msec) large decrease of the resistance in the right element of the diagram (COOMBS, ECCLES and FATT 1955b; ARAKI and TERZUOLO 1962).

Fig. 58C suggests that during motoneuronal depolarization there will be a corresponding increase in the size of the voltage that drives the currents produced by activated inhibitory synapses; hence the increased IPSPs of the three upper records of Fig. 60A are accounted for. Similarly there will be potentiation of an IPSP set up during the depolarization of an EPSPs. This is illustrated in Fig. 61, where in the superimposed records of B—K the IPSP is increased

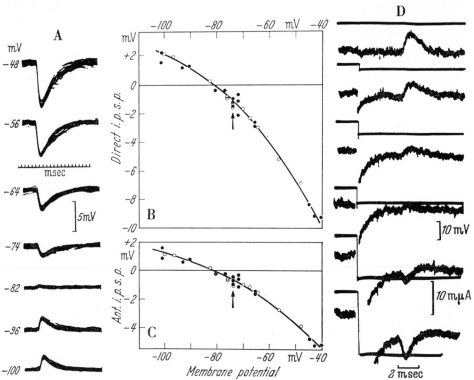

Fig. 60A—D. A. IPSPs recorded intracellularly from a biceps-semitendinosus motoneurone by means of a double-barrelled microelectrode. The records, formed by the superposition of about 40 faint traces, show the IPSPs set up by a quadriceps afferent volley. By means of a steady background current through the other barrel of the microelectrode, the membrane potential has been preset at the voltage indicated on each record, the resting membrane potential being −74 mV. B. Plotting of measurements from series partly shown in A. Abscissae give the membrane potentials and ordinates the sizes of the respective IPSPs. Note that hyperpolarizing IPSPs are plotted downwards and depolarizing upwards. C. Series for same motoneurone, plotted as in B, but IPSPs produced by an antidromic volley (COOMBS, ECCLES and FATT 1955b). D. The upper and lower traces give membrane potential and current respectively for a cat motoneurone that was voltage-clamped as in Fig. 59C. The upper record is control and in lower records, as shown by the upper traces, rectangular hyperpolarizations were applied before the inhibitory post-synaptic currents and continued throughout the records (ARAKI and TERZUOLO 1962)

from its control value of −3 mV to as much as −5.5 mV when the inhibitory currents flow during the maximum of the EPSP. However, when the rising phase of the IPSP precedes the onset of the EPSP (Fig. 61 B—F), there is no potentiation of the later decaying phase of the IPSP, as is well illustrated in the subtracted records of Fig. 61 N. This absence of effect would be expected if the inhibitory current ceased within 2 msec of its onset, as is shown in Figs. 58A, 59D. On the other hand there is potentiation of the IPSP when it is generated at any stage of the declining phase of the EPSP; and, as would be expected from 58C, this potentiation closely follows the time course of the EPSP (Fig. 61 N, O) (CURTIS and ECCLES 1959).

In contrast to EPSPs, it has been reported that no IPSPs could be recorded as a result of electrotonic transmission to the ventral root as it emerged

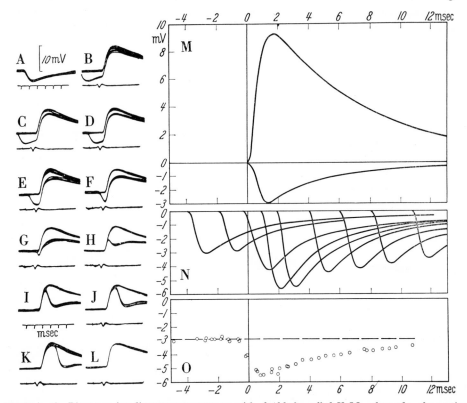

Fig. 61 A—O. Biceps-semitendinosus motoneurone with double-barrelled K_2SO_4 electrode, the resting membrane potential being −70 mV. IPSPs are set up by quadriceps group Ia afferent volleys, and the EPSPs by biceps-semitendinosus afferent volleys. B—K show interaction of IPSP and EPSP at various intervals, the control responses being given in A and L respectively. All records were formed by the superposition of about 40 faint traces, but the quadriceps afferent volley was only turned on for about half the traces, so that the control EPSP was superimposed on all records from B to K. Lower traces show the record from L_7 dorsal root, the quadriceps afferent volley consequently giving a very small spike potential. Same time and potential scales for A—L. M shows tracings of the control EPSP and IPSP, while N shows an analysis of records like those of A—L. It is assumed that the EPSP is unaltered by the superimposed IPSPs, which are themselves greatly potentiated as shown. The peak potentials of the IPSPs so determined are plotted in O against the intervals between their onset and the onset of the interacting EPSP, part of the series being shown in N. Note that same time scale obtains for M, N and O, zero time being placed at the origin of the EPSP (CURTIS and ECCLES 1959)

from the spinal cord (JACK, MCINTYRE and SOMJEN 1959; LLOYD and WILSON 1959). It was therefore postulated that the intracellularly recorded IPSP resulted from the lowering of membrane potential due to impalement by the microelectrode. However, a reinvestigation (ARAKI, ECCLES and ITO 1960) has shown that IPSPs can always be recorded in ventral roots provided that the experimental situation is designed so that it is particularly favourable for the optimum recording of IPSPs and there is a minimum of complication by superposition of EPSPs. For example, in Fig. 62 a quadriceps Ia afferent volley produced the IPSP that may be presumed to be electrotonically transmitted from biceps-semitendinosus motoneurones to the S_1 ventral rootlet. The central latencies of the IPSPs recorded intracellularly (B) and electrotonically (A) are virtually identical; but, as would be expected as a consequence of electrotonic transmission, the IPSP recorded from the ventral root

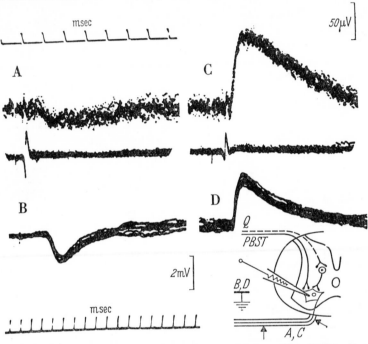

Fig. 62A—D. B and D are intracellular records of IPSP and EPSP evoked in a PBST motoneurone at S_1 segmental level by a Ia quadriceps and a PBST volley respectively as shown in the inset diagram. The upper traces of A, C are the potentials electrotonically conducted from the motoneurones along their motor axons and recorded from an isolated filament of the S_1 ventral root, one electrode being on the filament about 1 mm from its exit from the cord, the other at least 20 mm distally on the isolated filament as shown by the two arrows in the inset diagram. A shows potentials produced by a Ia quadriceps volley, C by a Ia PBST volley (ARAKI, ECCLES and ITO 1960)

has a slower time course. The relative sizes of the EPSPs (C) and IPSPs (A) recorded from the ventral root are not at variance with what would be expected from the means of the intracellular IPSPs and EPSPs produced similarly in motoneurones (ARAKI, ECCLES and ITO 1960). For example the mean sizes of the IPSPs and EPSPs produced respectively by quadriceps and posterior biceps-semitendinosus in lower L_7 or upper S_1 ventral root filaments were 10 and 90 μV respectively. Similarly, with stimulation of the S_3 dorsal root, IPSPs of appropriate size were regularly recorded from the contralateral S_3 ventral rootlets, the mean size being 28 μV.

This demonstration of an IPSP electrotonically propagated to the ventral root establishes that inhibitory synaptic action hyperpolarizes motoneurones that have not had their membrane potential lowered by microelectrode impalement. A similar conclusion may be drawn from the demonstration by ARAKI, ECCLES and ITO (1960) that a residuum of reflex inhibitory action always continues for many milliseconds after the initial brief phase, as will be illustrated below (Figs. 68, 69). We may therefore conclude that, even before impalement by microelectrodes, the membrane potential is more depolarized

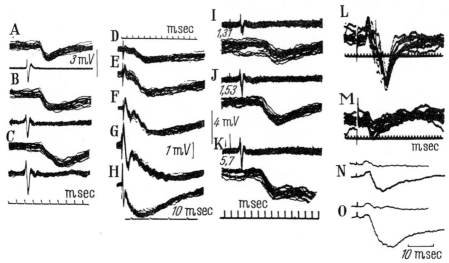

Fig. 63 A—O. Time course of the direct IPSP evoked by I a impulses (A) and the I b IPSP (B and C). Intracellular recording was made with micro-electrodes filled with 0.6 M-K$_2$SO$_4$. A was obtained from a biceps posterior-semitendinosus motoneurone with stimulation of the quadriceps nerve. B and C show the IPSPs evoked in a gastrocnemius motoneurone by group I volleys in the nerves to plantaris and flexor digitorum longus respectively. In the triphasic record of the dorsal root volley, negativity unconventionally is signalled by a downward deflexion (ECCLES, ECCLES and LUNDBERG 1957c). Series D—H show intracellular IPSPs recorded as in A—C, but evoked by antidromic volleys in the ventral root, which were progressively larger from D—G. With G and H the volleys were maximal, but H was recorded at much slower sweep speed (ECCLES, FATT and KOKETSU 1954). I—K show intracellular IPSPs evoked in a gastrocnemius motoneurone by a flexor digitorum longus volley as in C, the stimulus strengths relative to threshold being indicated. I and J show IPSPs evoked by submaximal and maximal I b volleys, while in K there is the later addition due to group II and III impulses (ECCLES, ECCLES and LUNDBERG 1957c). L, M. Intracellular recording from motoneurone in the brachial region of baboon spinal cord, showing that stimulation of the motor cortex evoked a brief initial depolarization and a subsequent hyperpolarization. The latencies indicated that the EPSP was monosynaptic, the IPSP disynaptic. In M a brief anodal pulse of 0.75 mA was applied to the cortex. In L the pulse was several milliseconds in duration and the IPSP shows that it was produced by a repetitive discharge (HERN, LANDGREN, PHILLIPS and PORTER 1962). N, O. Lower traces are intracellular records and upper traces equivalent extracellular records evoked in an extensor motoneurone (cat gastrocnemius) by weak and strong cutaneous volleys respectively (ECCLES 1953)

than the equilibrium potential for the IPSP, i.e. that E_R is less than E_{IPSP}, just as in Fig. 58 C. This conclusion is of importance when considering the ionic mechanism responsible for the inhibitory action (Chapter XI).

The IPSPs produced in motoneurones by primary afferent volleys other than those in group I a fibres often have a more prolonged time course. Thus the IPSPs produced in motoneurones by single volleys in other muscle afferents, I b (Fig. 63 B, C, I, J; ECCLES, ECCLES and LUNDBERG 1957c), or II and III (Fig. 63 K; R. M. ECCLES and LUNDBERG 1959) have slower time courses than the IPSP evoked by Ia volleys (Fig. 63 A), as also the IPSPs evoked from joint or cutaneous afferents. These slower IPSPs are explained more plausibly by temporal dispersion of the activation of the inhibitory synapses rather than by the slower action of individual synapses. The most striking of these prolonged inhibitory actions (Fig. 63 D—H) arises on account of the repetitive discharge which impulses in the motor axon collaterals evoke in special inhibitory cells (Figs. 45 E—I; 82 C, D) now designated Renshaw cells (RENSHAW 1941, 1946a; ECCLES, FATT and KOKETSU 1954; ECCLES, ECCLES, IGGO and ITO 1961). The weakest response (Fig. 63 D) is not very much slower than the Ia IPSP, but the strongest responses (G, H) are greatly prolonged, and show the rhythm of the repetitive discharge of the inhibitory neurones, about 1000/sec (cf. Fig. 82 D). The IPSPs generated in motoneurones by stimulation of the motor cortex have a duration that is comparable with the Ia IPSP (Fig. 63 L, M; HERN, LANDGREN, PHILLIPS and PORTER 1962). IPSPs of long duration are produced in motoneurones by cutaneous volleys, particularly those set up by strong stimulation (Fig. 63 N, O). Undoubtedly this duration is at least in part attributable to repetitive interneuronal discharge as with the inhibitory pathway through Renshaw cells (Fig. 63 D—H). However, it is also conceivable that the transmitter action at the individual synapses may be prolonged in the way that occurs with inhibition at higher levels of the nervous system (Fig. 64 E—L).

The IPSPs recorded from motoneurones of amphibia have the same general features as those of mammalian motoneurones, but are rather slower in time course (ARAKI, OTANI and FURUKAWA 1953; KUNO 1957; FUKAMI 1961; KATZ and MILEDI 1963). As in Fig. 57 G, H there is an approximate mirror-image relationship of IPSP to EPSP, but in the toad both have a time constant of decay (mean 8 msec), which is much longer than the membrane time constant (mean 4.5 msec). It seems likely that just as with the excitatory transmitter there is an appreciable action of the inhibitory transmitter throughout the whole duration of the IPSP. The equilibrium potential of the IPSP is at 10 to 20 mV more hyperpolarization than is the resting membrane potential (FUKAMI 1961).

The IPSPs recorded intracellularly from two types of tract cells in the mammalian spinal cord have approximately the same time course as the motoneuronal IPSPs evoked by the same types of muscle afferents (CURTIS, ECCLES and LUNDBERG 1958; ECCLES, HUBBARD and OSCARSSON 1961; ECCLES, OSCARSSON and WILLIS 1961). The IPSPs produced by quadriceps afferent volleys in a cell of origin of the ventral spinocerebellar tract (Fig. 64 A to C) may be compared with Fig. 63 I—K, as also may the IPSP in a cell of origin of the dorsal spinocerebellar tract (Fig. 64 D).

The earliest intracellular recordings from neurones of the cerebral cortex (ALBE-FESSARD and BUSER 1953, 1955; ALBE-FESSARD 1960) showed hyperpolarizing responses so much longer than motoneuronal IPSPs that there were doubts about their identification as genuine IPSPs. A wide experience of IPSPs intracellularly recorded from cerebral neurones now leads to the recognition that almost all IPSPs have a duration of 100 msec or more; the IPSPs of no more than 20 msec duration that BRANCH and MARTIN (1958) recorded from a cortical neurone are quite exceptional. In our experience the neurones of the cuneate nucleus are transitional, some having IPSPs no longer than motoneurones, while IPSPs of others are as long as 100 msec (Fig. 64E; ANDERSEN, ECCLES, OSHIMA

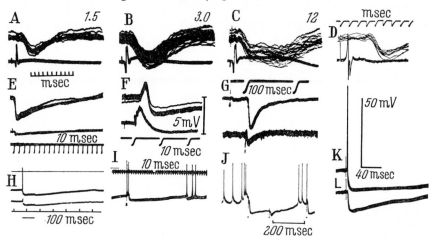

Fig. 64A—L. Intracellularly recorded IPSPs from neurones other than motoneurones in the cat central nervous system. A—C. Upper traces are superimposed traces of IPSPs of a VSCT cell produced by afferent volleys in quadriceps nerve that was stimulated at the indicated strengths relative to threshold (ECCLES, HUBBARD and OSCARSSON 1961). D. IPSP of a DSCT cell produced by a maximum group I volley in the nerve to posterior biceps-semitendinosus muscle (ECCLES, OSCARSSON and WILLIS 1961). E. IPSP evoked in a cell of the cuneate nucleus by a cutaneous volley from the forelimb (ANDERSEN, ECCLES, OSHIMA and SCHMIDT 1963). F, G. Upper traces are IPSPs evoked in cells of the ventro-basal complex of the thalamus by single cutaneous volleys from the fore-limb, there being an initial EPSP in F (ANDERSEN, BROOKS and ECCLES 1963). H, pyramidal neurone of neocortex showing initial EPSP and later IPSP evoked by repetitive stimulation of the pyramidal tract at a strength below threshold for the axon of the cell, the EPSP firing an initial spike in the upper trace. Membrane potential −60 mV. I, as in H but showing initial excitation with spikes and later IPSP produced by stimulation of an adjacent cortical area (PHILLIPS 1961). J, also intracellular recording of a pyramidal cell showing large IPSP generated by stimulation of the ventrolateral nucleus of the thalamus (LUX and KLEE 1962). K, L, large and prolonged IPSPs generated in hippocampal pyramidal cell by stimulation of the fimbria at a strength above and below the threshold for the axon of the cell (KANDEL, SPENCER and BRINLEY 1961)

and SCHMIDT 1963). With thalamic neurones IPSPs are invariably of 100 msec or longer (Fig. 64F, G; PURPURA and COHEN 1962; ANDERSEN and ECCLES 1962; ANDERSEN, BROOKS and ECCLES 1963). There is characteristically a brief rising phase and a very prolonged decay. Even more prolonged and extremely large are the IPSPs observed with intracellular recording of hippocampal pyramidal cells (Fig. 64K, L; KANDEL, SPENCER and BRINLEY 1961; KANDEL and SPENCER 1961; SPENCER and KANDEL 1961c; ANDERSEN, ECCLES and LØYNING 1963), where durations are at least 200 msec. The pyramidal cells of the neocortex have now been intensively investigated and in response to various kinds of stimulation have been shown to develop IPSPs which are comparable with those of the hippocampus (Fig. 64 H, I, J; PHILLIPS 1956, 1959, 1961; LI and CHOU 1962; LUX and KLEE 1962; KLEE and LUX 1962). Prolonged IPSPs have also been observed in Purkinje cells of the cerebellum (GRANIT and PHILLIPS 1956; ANDERSEN, ECCLES and VOORHOEVE 1963).

2. Inhibition of nerve and muscle cells of invertebrates

Since it is often possible to stimulate a single inhibitory fibre in isolation, invertebrate nerve and muscle cells offer very favourable conditions for investigations of the potentials generated by inhibitory synaptic action. As illustrated in Figs. 65 A, 66 A, b these potential changes are often negligible at the resting membrane potential because this is so close to the equilibrium potential for the inhibitory postsynaptic currents. However, when there is sufficient voltage for driving such currents, the IPSPs are seen to resemble the IPSPs of vertebrate neurones in having a relatively rapid rising phase and a slower decay, though the time course may be considerably slower. The IPSPs of the crustacean stretch receptor cells (Fig. 65 A, B) are only 2 or 3 times slower than the IPSPs of Figs. 57 and 60, but with the large ganglion cells of *Aplysia* and *Helix* the IPSPs are respectively about 10 and 30 times slower (TAUC 1958). In all these examples there is evidence that the postsynaptic inhibitory currents are flowing throughout the whole duration of the IPSPs; the decays are much slower than would be expected for a passive process governed by the electric time constant of the membrane; and with the stretch receptor cell the spike potential is depressed throughout the whole duration of the IPSP (KUFFLER and EYZAGUIRRE 1955), indicating a continued high conductance of the subsynaptic membrane (Fig. 65 B).

In the giant neurones of *Onchidium* it is possible to produce large and virtually pure IPSPs, which have an equilibrium potential close to the normal resting potential (HAGIWARA and KUSANO 1961). Both the IPSPs and the inhibitory synaptic currents revealed by the voltage-clamp technique (cf. Fig. 60 D) are linearly related to the membrane potential, as in Fig. 65 A, D, E; hence the IPSP is produced by an increased conductance to one or more ion species. Since the inhibitory synaptic current continues to flow throughout almost the whole duration of the IPSP (Fig. 65 C), a prolonged inhibitory transmitter action seems probable, though, as pointed out by HAGIWARA and KUSANO (1961), in part at least this duration may be an artefact arising because the current is derived by the voltage-clamp technique, and this clamp is applied to the soma, which is probably remote from the location of the inhibitory synapses on the axon. IPSPs with the characteristic quick rising phase and slow decay have been seen with intracellular recording from neurones of the sub-oesophageal ganglia of *Helix*, being either spontaneously occurring (KERKUT and THOMAS 1963 a), or in response to nerve volleys (KERKUT and

WALKER 1962). These potentials are illustrated in relation to the investigation on ionic mechanisms of inhibition in Chapter XI (Fig. 77).

It has been seen that impulses in the lateral and medial giant fibres in the ventral nerve cord of the crayfish produce brief depolarizations of the motor giant fibres (Chapter IX). Other nerve fibres in the ventral nerve cord produce

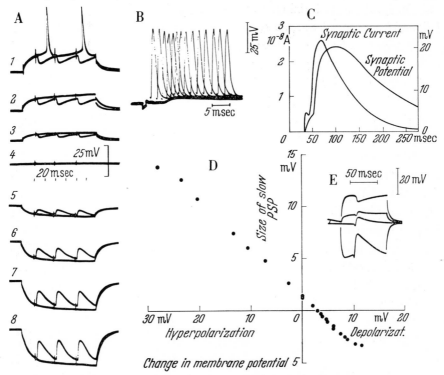

Fig. 65 A—E. A, B. Intracellular records from crustacean stretch receptor cells. In A three inhibitory nerve impulses were fired at intervals of about 40 msec for each record, there being virtually no IPSPs at the resting membrane potential (4). In records 3 to 1 progressively larger depolarizing pulses were applied through the microelectrode, while in 5 to 8 there were progressively larger hyperpolarizing pulses. Microelectrode was filled with K_2SO_4 solution (HAGIWARA, KUSANO and SAITO 1960). In B antidromic spike potentials are superimposed at various positions on a small depolarizing IPSP. Due to superposition of the successive sweeps the single antidromic spike is seen at various positions on the IPSP. The control spike size is seen in the two earliest spikes (KUFFLER and EYZAGUIRRE 1955). C. Inhibitory synaptic responses of a giant neurone of *Onchidium*. The synaptic current is recorded by the voltage-clamp technique (HAGIWARA and KUSANO 1961). D. Plotting of IPSPs at various levels of membrane potential as in E. Depolarizing IPSPs are plotted above the horizontal axis as in Figs. 60 B, C. There was a reversal of size of the IPSP at about 3 mV depolarization. E. Slow IPSPs of crustacean motor axon, which in three of the four traces are superimposed on depolarizing or hyperpolarizing pulses as in A. Note the reversal of the IPSP to a hyperpolarizing response during the largest depolarizing pulse (FURSHPAN and POTTER 1959b)

much longer depolarizing potentials that are reversed by a depolarization of about 7 mV, which suggests they are IPSPs and not EPSPs (Fig. 65 D, E; FURSHPAN and POTTER 1959 b). As would be expected from the level of this reversal potential, such synaptic activity reduces the size of the brief depolarization produced by electrical transmission from the giant axons; hence its inhibitory role is demonstrated. Since this depression occurs only during the rising phase of the IPSP, it appears that very little inhibitory transmitter action survives after the rising phase of the IPSP, just as with some IPSPs of vertebrate motoneurones (Figs. 58A, 59D). However, HAGIWARA (1958) found that there was an appreciable increase in membrane conductance well into the declining phase.

The inhibitory action on crustacean muscle produces very small potentials usually in the depolarizing, but sometimes in the hyperpolarizing direction (Fig. 66Aa, b, c; FATT and KATZ 1953b; HOYLE and WIERSMA 1958b). Displacement of the membrane potential again shows that the E_{IPSP} is very close to the resting membrane potential; and fairly large IPSPs, depolarizing and hyperpolarizing, occur when the membrane potential is appropriately displaced (cf. Fig. 66Aa, c; FATT and KATZ 1953b; BOISTEL and FATT 1958). The IPSP displays the typical time course of postsynaptic potentials, though both the rising and declining phases are considerably slower than for the EPPs recorded through the same electrode (Fig. 66A). Since the IPSP decay is very much slower than would be accounted for by the electric time constant of the membrane, the transmitter action must survive during the declining phase, just as occurs with the stretch receptor cell (cf. Fig. 65 B). During repetitive stimulation there is a progressive potentiation of the IPSPs, and usually investigations have been made on such potentiated IPSPs (cf. Fig. 66B, C), rather than on the very small isolated responses. This potentiation resembles that observed for the EPPs of crustacean muscle and of calcium deficient vertebrate muscle (Fig. 33), and presumably is similarly explicable by mobilization of the transmitter in the presynaptic terminals (Chapter VI).

The effectiveness of the inhibitory synaptic action in controlling the membrane potential is most clearly illustrated in Fig. 66B, where each IPSP is made maximally effective by the summation and potentiation produced by 30 impulses at 150/sec (KUFFLER 1960). The compensation as measured by the return of the membrane towards the equilibrium potential is about 70%, in contrast to a value of about 10% for the IPSPs generated by isolated impulses (Fig. 66Aa—c; FATT and KATZ 1953b). On account of the large potentiation that occurs during repetitive stimulation of the inhibitory fibre to the cardiac ganglion cell of the lobster, there is very effective compensatory action of up to 40% (TERZUOLO and BULLOCK 1958; OTANI and BULLOCK 1959), while again isolated impulses have a negligible action. With the crustacean stretch receptor cell (Fig. 65 A) single inhibitory impulses produce an even higher compensation (up to 90%) than with the repetitive stimulation in Fig. 66B; as a consequence, with repetitive stimulation there can be very little summation of IPSPs (Fig. 67F) (KUFFLER and EYZAGUIRRE 1955). Single inhibitory impulses also have a very effective compensatory action on the membrane potential of the giant motor axons of crayfish (Fig. 65D, E; FURSHPAN and POTTER 1959b), the mean value being about 50%. With the IPSP produced by a single Ia volley in a mammalian motoneurone the compensation rarely exceeds 50 % and is often much smaller, as is shown by the slope of curve in Fig. 60 B (COOMBS, ECCLES and FATT 1955 b).

The potency of the inhibitory action in returning the membrane potential towards the inhibitory equilibrium potential is represented in the formal

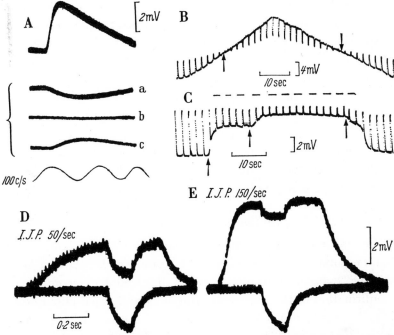

Fig. 66 A—E. Intracellular records from crustacean muscle fibres to show equilibrium potential for the IPSPs and also the conductance changes during IPSPs. A. Upper record is EPP due to stimulation of excitatory fibre. Inhibitory fibre is stimulated in the lower three records. There is negligible inhibition at the resting potential (−73 mV), but in the records above (at −48 mV) and below (at −95 mV) the IPSP is hyperpolarizing and depolarizing respectively (FATT and KATZ 1953 b). B. Intracellular records from crayfish neuromuscular junction. Membrane potential was displaced by passing current through a second intracellular microelectrode. Short trains of inhibitory stimuli at 150 per second, repeated every 2 seconds, set up a depolarization of 5.5 mV at the resting potential of −80 mV. The inhibitory junctional potentials first become smaller at lower membrane potential levels, and eventually they reversed at −72 mV (arrows). Inhibitory stimulation at the full resting potential shifts the postsynaptic membrane to within 70 per cent of the inhibitory equilibrium level. C. Short inhibitory trains at 150 per second for 0.2 second repeated every 2 seconds throughout record. At the resting potential (−85 mV) they cause peak depolarization of 6 mV. Inhibitory equilibrium potential at —77 mV membrane potential (dotted line) was determined as in B. First arrow: 2×10⁻⁵ M GABA depolarizes. Second arrow: 4×10⁻⁵ M GABA causes additional depolarization. Third arrow: washing with normal solution reverses effect. Note, still stronger GABA concentration depolarized to the equilibrium level (not illustrated), completely abolishing inhibitory potentials. D—E. Conductance increase during inhibitory transmitter action. Two intracellular electrodes, one for passing currents, the other for measuring potentials, inserted into a muscle fibre of the crayfish. Resting potential −80 mV. Current pulses of 0.2-second duration, passing 5×10⁻⁹ A, applied during rest and during inhibition. Two exposures superimposed in each record. D. Lower sweep: 2 mV hyperpolarization set up by current pulse. Upper sweep: same current pulse applied during IPSPs set up by stimulation at 50 per second. E. Same as D but higher frequency stimulation (150 per second). Note that during inhibition the hyperpolarizing potential in D is 80 per cent, in E it is 30 per cent, of the control and its time of rise is more rapid, indicating resistance drop across cell membrane (B—E from KUFFLER 1960)

electrical diagram (Fig. 58 C) by the ratio of the conductance of the inhibitory element to the conductance of the membrane in general. The increased conductance during inhibitory transmitter action is very effectively displayed by the difference in the potential change produced by application of a rectangular current pulse (KUFFLER 1960). For example during the IPSPs in Fig. 66D, E, the applied current produced a potential that was smaller and reached its summit much more rapidly than in the control, particularly in E with the higher stimulus frequency to the inhibitory nerve. Both these changes are indicative of an increased membrane conductance, the former being due to the shunting action of the conductance, the latter to the decreased membrane time constant. In Fig. 66E the inhibitory transmitter produced an almost tenfold increase in membrane conductance (KUFFLER 1960).

Interaction between inhibitory and excitatory impulses in the production of postsynaptic potentials of crustacean muscle fibres has been extensively studied by intracellular recording (FATT and KATZ 1953b; HOYLE and WIERS-MA 1958b). However, this interaction is not solely at the postsynaptic level since the additional factor of presynaptic inhibition is also concerned (DUDEL and KUFFLER 1960, 1961c). It is therefore desirable to defer consideration to the section on presynaptic inhibition (Chapter XV).

3. Inhibitory potentials of cardiac and smooth muscle

In 1887 GASKELL reported that repetitive vagal stimulation caused an increase of membrane potential in the quiescent tortoise auricle. After a long period of conflicting experimental observations, intracellular recording provided a final confirmation of the hyperpolarizing action of vagal impulses (BURGEN and TERROUX 1953; DEL CASTILLO and KATZ 1955c, 1957d; HUTTER and TRAUTWEIN 1955, 1956; HUTTER 1957). In Fig. 67A single vagal volleys produce a small hyperpolarization, which is greatly increased by repetitive stimulation (B). A single vagal volley elicited a remarkably slow response, which in the highly amplified response (C) may be seen to have a latency of about 0.4 sec, and a summit some 2 sec later. As would be expected, a local application of ACh produces a still slower response (D). The slow time course of the IPSPs in A and C conform with the time courses of vagal inhibitory action as derived from the action on the rhythmic response of the pacemaker. In the cat after allowing for neural conduction time, the latency for vagal action was about 100 msec and the maximum intensity was attained about 300 msec later (BROWN and ECCLES 1934), which are remarkably long times for transmitter action at a mammalian neuro-muscular junction at 37° C. The latency and time course of the action of the orthosympathetic acceleration (BROWN and ECCLES, unpublished observations) and depolarization of the heart (DEL CASTILLO and KATZ 1957d) are even longer, so the conclusion is that the slow actions (Fig. 67A, C) must be attributed to the transmitter action on the cardiac muscle and not to complications introduced by the ganglion that is interposed on the parasympathetic pathway. No explanation has been offered for these extremely slow transmitter actions, which are several hundred times slower than transmission to mammalian skeletal muscle (Fig. 35) and at least ten times slower than excitatory transmission to mammalian smooth muscle (BURNSTOCK and HOLMAN 1962a).

Fig. 67G, H show intracellular records from smooth muscle fibres of the taenia coli of the guinea pig. Stimulation of nerve bundles in the wall of the intestine is seen to produce discrete hyperpolarizing IPSPs in G, which slow

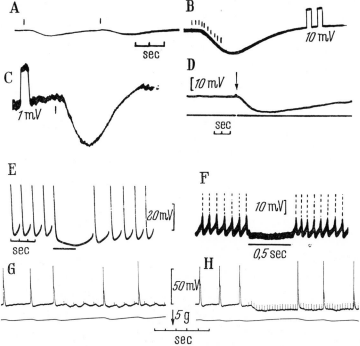

Fig. 67A—H. A—D. Intracellular records of muscle fibres of arrested frog heart. A, B. Hyperpolarizations by two single vagal volleys and by a repetitive train as indicated. Note 10 mV calibrations. C. Hyperpolarization by a single vagal volley at higher amplification. Note latency. D. Hyperpolarization produced by external application of ACh at arrow by a brief current pulse as in Fig. 22 (DEL CASTILLO and KATZ 1957d). E, F. Intracellular records from a heart pacemaker fibre in the sinus venosus of the frog (HUTTER and TRAUTWEIN 1956) and from a crustacean stretch receptor cell (KUFFLER and EYZAGUIRRE 1955). Inhibitory stimuli [20/sec in heart (E) and 100/sec in receptor cell (F)], marked by line, suppress the generator potentials in both tissues, thus preventing conducted impulses from arising. Spike summits are not seen at this high amplification. Note different time scales. G and H. Intracellular records from smooth muscle of guinea-pig taenia coli showing inhibitory junction potentials in response to stimulation of intra-mural nerves. Stimulation frequencies: G, 1/sec; H. 4/sec. Upper trace: membrane potential. Lower trace: tension. Note downwards deflection represents an increase in tension (BURNSTOCK, CAMPBELL, BENNETT and HOLMAN 1963)

the frequency of the spontaneous beats. In H the faster stimulation results in fusion of the IPSPs at a more sustained level of hyperpolarization (BURNSTOCK, CAMPBELL, BENNETT and HOLMAN 1963).

B. Inhibition of impulse generation

1. Neurones of vertebrate central nervous system

It will later be seen that, by the latency test of Fig. 84, the IPSP is precisely fitted to be the initiator of inhibitory action on reflex discharges of motoneurones (ARAKI, ECCLES and ITO 1960; ECCLES 1961 a). The present enquiry is an attempt to see whether this good agreement holds for the whole time course of the inhibitory action.

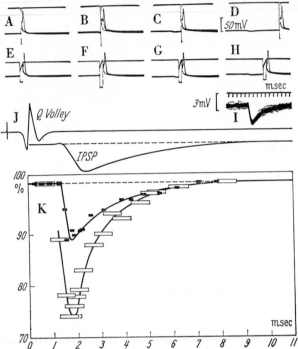

The most direct method of measuring the intensity of inhibitory action is to test excitability by a brief rectangular pulse in the depolarizing direction through the intracellular electrode (ECCLES 1958a; FRANK 1959; ARAKI, ECCLES and ITO 1960). At each testing interval during the inhibition, the pulse is varied in intensity until it evokes a spike potential in approximately one half of the trials (Fig. 68A—H). The time course of the inhibitory action is obtained by plotting the reciprocals of current intensities against the respective intervals after the time of entry of the inhibitory volley into the spinal cord (Fig. 68K). When the current pulse is very brief (0.2 msec), the time course of the inhibitory curve (K, black rectangles) corresponds closely with the time course of the IPSP (I, J). However, when longer

Fig. 68 A—K. In A—H depolarizing rectangular current pulses (the upper records with the pulses recorded downwards) were applied through an intracellular electrode (filled with 2 M potassium citrate) in a biceps-semitendinosus motoneurone and adjusted in strength so that a spike potential was evoked in about half of the trials, as shown in the lower records, there being about 10 superimposed traces in each record. With A—D and E—H the pulse durations were 0.2 and 0.8 msec and the control threshold current strength was 3.3 times larger in A than in E. In B—D and F—H the pulses tested excitability at various times relative to an IPSP set up by a Ia quadriceps volley, which is shown at higher amplification and at the same sweep speed in I, and also plotted in J together with a tracing of the quadriceps volley (Q), as it entered the cord at the upper L_6 level. In K the reciprocals of the threshold current strengths (relative to the control strength) for the series partly shown in A—H are plotted on the same time scale as for J, zero time being measured relative to the entry of the Q volley into the cord. The 0.2 and 0.8 msec pulses are shown as solid and hollow rectangles of appropriate length. In drawing the two inhibitory curves it is assumed that the pulses test the excitability at the mid-point of their duration (ARAKI, ECCLES and ITO 1960)

current pulses (0.8 msec) are employed, there is a much more intense inhibition at brief testing intervals as illustrated in K (hollow rectangles).

Inhibitory curves with a double composition, an initial intense phase and a prolonged tail, are regularly obtained when the inhibition is measured by the depression of a testing monosynaptic reflex (Fig. 69F, H; BRADLEY, EASTON and ECCLES 1953; BROOKS, CURTIS and ECCLES 1957; ARAKI, ECCLES and ITO

1960). However, JACK, McINTYRE and SOMJEN (1959 and personal communication) report that occasionally the inhibitory curve consists only of the brief initial phase, and suggest that this occurs when the spinal cord is in particularly good condition. It should be mentioned that testing for in-

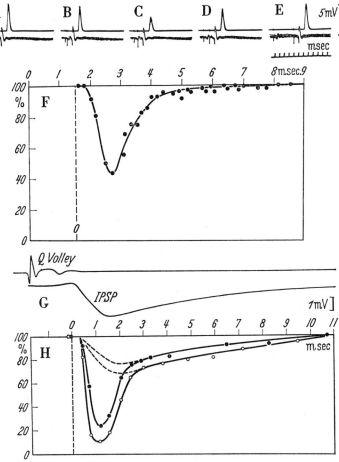

Fig. 69A—H. Reproductions of inhibitory curves in which the inhibitory action of a quadriceps Ia afferent volley is tested by the size of a monosynaptic reflex spike discharged into the ventral root from the PBST motoneurones, as in Fig. 83. A—E show specimen records from which F was plotted. F is the briefest inhibitory curve that we have observed. In G the quadriceps afferent volley and the IPSP are shown on the same time scale as the associated inhibitory curve (H). The approximate time courses of the components of inhibition attributable directly to the hyperpolarization of the IPSPs are shown by the broken lines for each of the two inhibitory curves in H, which were produced by different sizes of the quadriceps Ia afferent volley (ARAKI, ECCLES and ITO 1960)

hibition by the depression of a reflex discharge has the disadvantage, relative to the pulse method of Fig. 68, that the ordinates represent merely the relative population of the discharging motoneurones, and so do not give a direct measure of the intensity of inhibitory action.

The manner in which a Ia inhibitory curve such as Fig. 69F and H is built up from the responses of individual motoneurones is illustrated by determining the range of intervals over which a motoneurone is inhibited by a I a inhibitory volley of constant size. For example with one motoneurone there was complete inhibition of spike generation by a maximal testing volley only over the range from 0.36 to 2.14 msec, i.e. during the period of maximum inhibition in F and H. With weaker testing excitation, the same inhibitory volley produced complete inhibition over the testing range of 0.18 to 5.3 msec.

Any depolarizing action that is exerted on the motoneuronal membrane will be antagonized both by the inhibitory currents and by the membrane hyperpolarization produced by the inhibitory synaptic action (cf. Fig. 58 A). When the stimulating current is as brief as 0.2 msec, it has to be very intense in order to depolarize the membrane to the critical level for impulse generation; and it would not be appreciably antagonized by the flow of inhibitory current. The inhibitory curve would be expected to be virtually identical with the time course of membrane hyperpolarization (the IPSP), as is actually seen in Fig. 68 K (short rectangles). On the other hand a stimulating current of 0.8 msec duration would be of much lower intensity (actually 30 % in Fig. 68), as may be seen by reference to the strength-latency curves for motoneurones (FRANK and FUORTES 1956b; COOMBS, CURTIS and ECCLES 1959), and consequently it is very effectively antagonized by the inhibitory current as well as by the hyperpolarization produced by this current; hence the dual composition of such inhibitory curves (Fig. 68 K, long rectangles). The excitatory synaptic currents generating the monosynaptic EPSP and spike discharge have an effective duration even in excess of 0.8 msec (Fig. 14 A, 15 B; CURTIS and ECCLES 1959; ARAKI and TERZUOLO 1962), so inhibitory current flow would tend to have the dominating influence in preventing the generation of spikes, the hyperpolarization being relatively unimportant, as illustrated in Fig. 69 F, H by the large initial peak of inhibitory action.

The occasional absence of a prolonged phase of inhibitory action that was referred to above has been taken to indicate that under the best physiological conditions the membrane potential is so high that it is at the equilibrium potential for the activated inhibitory membrane, i.e. that $E_{IPSP} = E_R$, the resting membrane potential. As a consequence no IPSP would be produced in the resting membrane and inhibition would be due entirely to the effect of the inhibitory currents in counteracting the depolarizing currents produced by the activated excitatory synapses (JACK, MCINTYRE and SOMJEN 1959, and personal communication). It has not been possible to discover additional instances of the complete absence of a prolonged phase of inhibitory action by a I a afferent volley, though sometimes inhibition could not be detected beyond 7 msec (Fig. 69 F; ARAKI, ECCLES and ITO 1960). Moreover the invariable presence of an IPSP electrotonically propagated to the ventral roots (Fig. 62 A) shows that the summed IPSP for a population of motoneurones has an equilibrium potential at a more hyperpolarized level than the resting potential. It can be concluded that the action of a group Ia afferent volley in suppressing the generation of impulses by a motoneurone is fully accounted for by the inhibitory postsynaptic currents that are caused to flow by the action of the inhibitory impulses. These currents act in two ways; directly in antagonizing the depolarizing postsynaptic currents (Figs. 14 A, 15 B) produced by activated excitatory synapses; and indirectly through the membrane hyperpolarization (IPSP) that they produce (COOMBS, ECCLES and FATT 1955 d).

Though detailed analysis has not been attempted with other postsynaptic inhibitory actions in the vertebrate central nervous system, there is every indication that the suppression of impulse discharge is brought about in the same way. For example the IPSPs produced by action of other inhibitory pathways on motoneurones appear to act in the same manner as Ia IPSPs, the only difference arising on account of their more temporally dispersed character (cf. Fig. 63). The IPSPs of the DSCT and VSCT cells (Fig. 64 A—D) (ECCLES, HUBBARD and OSCARSSON 1961; ECCLES, OSCARSSON and WILLIS 1961) closely resemble the IPSPs of motoneurones. The hyperpolarizing IPSPs of the cuneate nucleus, the thalamus, the hippocampus and the neocortex (Fig. 64 E—L) also doubtless act in the same manner in suppressing the generation of impulses.

2. Invertebrate nerve and muscle cells

Chemical postsynaptic inhibition in invertebrates differs in one important respect from that in the vertebrate nervous system. There is little or no hyperpolarizing action on the resting postsynaptic membrane. There may even be a considerable depolarization. Nevertheless, if the equilibrium potential for the IPSP is at a more polarized level than the threshold for generation of impulses, there will still be an effective suppression of the generation of impulses. Usually the ionic conductance of the activated subsynaptic inhibitory patches is so high (Fig. 65), that a very effective inhibition is secured, as is excellently illustrated with the crustacean stretch receptor cells (Figs. 67 F, 76 B, C) where there is complete suppression of the generator potential that is produced by a stretch stimulus. A comparable suppression is shown in Fig. 67 E for repetitive vagal volleys on a pacemaker of the frog sinus (HUTTER and TRAUTWEIN 1956), and in Fig. 67 G, H there is a temporary suppression of the spontaneous beats of a smooth muscle cell (BURNSTOCK, CAMPBELL, BENNETT and HOLMAN 1963). The inhibitory suppression of impulse discharge is also illustrated in Fig. 65 A, where the repetitive inhibitory volleys produce no potential change at the resting membrane potential, but cause a large hyperpolarization when acting during a depolarizing current pulse, so suppressing the discharge of impulses that otherwise is produced in the uppermost trace.

3. Comment

In all cases that we have considered, the inhibitory impulses diminish the excitatory depolarization by making the subsynaptic membrane highly conductive to certain ions. With the crustacean stretch receptor cell, this conductance is so high that the membrane potential is virtually "clamped" at the equilibrium potential for the inhibitory ionic mechanism (KUFFLER and EYZAGUIRRE 1955). Normally this equilibrium potential is about 5 mV more depolarized than the completely relaxed membrane potential. However, the clamping of the membrane potential at this slightly depolarized level provides a very adequate inhibitory mechanism, for a much larger depolarization of the dendrites (at least 20 mV) is required in order to generate an impulse (EYZAGUIRRE and KUFFLER 1955a, b). With motoneurones and some other vertebrate nerve cells, inhibitory impulses do not produce such a high ionic conductance of the postsynaptic membrane. Their effectiveness in counteracting the excitatory depolarization arises in part because the equilibrium potential of the inhibitory ionic mechanism is about 10 mV more hyperpolarized than the resting potential (Figs. 58C, 60). A larger battery compensates for a lower ionic conductance. The important finding, however, is that inhibition is produced by essentially the same ionic and electrical mechanism in such widely differing examplars of inhibitory action.

CHAPTER XI

THE IONIC MECHANISM GENERATING THE INHIBITORY POSTSYNAPTIC POTENTIAL

The effects produced in the size and direction of the IPSP by varying the initial membrane potential (Figs. 60, 65 and 66 A, B) correspond precisely to the changes that would be expected if the currents generating the IPSP were due to ions moving down their electrochemical gradients. These currents would be caused to flow by increases in the ionic permeability that are produced in the specific inhibitory zones of the subsynaptic membrane under the influence of the inhibitory transmitter substance. The outwardly directed current across the inhibitory subsynaptic membrane (Fig. 58 B) could be due to the outward movement of a cation such as potassium or the inward movement of an anion like chloride or to such a combination of anionic and cationic movements that there is a net outward flow of current.

In this chapter we are concerned firstly to test as rigorously as possible this postulate that the inhibitory postsynaptic current is entirely accountable to increases in the movements of ions down their electrochemical gradients; secondly to determine the relative contributions of the various ion species, such as chloride and potassium, to this current; and thirdly to investigate the nature of the change that the inhibitory transmitter effects in the ionic permeability of the subsynaptic membrane.

The experimental procedure involves altering the concentration gradient across the postsynaptic membrane for one or other species of ion normally present, and in addition employing a wide variety of other ions in order to test the ionic permeability of the subsynaptic membrane. With the inhibitory synapses on invertebrate nerve and muscle cells the investigations are usually performed on isolated preparations. Changes in relative ionic concentrations across the postsynaptic membrane are readily effected by altering the ionic composition of the external medium. This method is not suitable for mammalian motoneurones, and indeed for any neurones of the mammalian central nervous system. Instead, the procedure of electrophoretic injection of ions

173

out of the impaling microelectrode has been employed to alter the ionic composition of the postsynaptic cell. The disadvantage of this procedure is that there is uncertainty about the changes in ionic composition so produced. The cell volume is only approximately known and the passage of the injecting current across the cell membrane results in an ionic exchange between the cell and its environment that can be assessed only very approximately. Nevertheless this method of electrophoretic injection has given very valuable information on the ionic mechanisms concerned in postsynaptic inhibition; and the complication of ionic exchange with the environment can be minimized by the technique of inter-barrel current flow as illustrated in Fig. 74. It also has the great advantage that the cells are being investigated under the excellent physiological conditions provided by a normal blood supply.

A. Inhibition in the central nervous system of vertebrates

Electrophoretic injection of ions has been performed almost exclusively on cat motoneurones (COOMBS, ECCLES and FATT 1953, 1955b; ARAKI, ITO and OSCARSSON 1961; ITO, KOSTYUK and OSHIMA 1962; ITO and OSHIMA 1963; ECCLES, ECCLES and ITO 1964a, 1964b). However, it appears that the same ionic mechanism is responsible for the IPSPs of other central synapses because, like motoneuronal IPSPs, they are readily converted to depolarizing responses by the diffusion of chloride out of an intracellular KCl microelectrode. The following list gives neurones in which the IPSPs are inverted in this manner: the cells of origin of the dorsal spinocerebellar tract (CURTIS, ECCLES and LUNDBERG 1958); hippocampal pyramidal cells (KANDEL, SPENCER and BRINLEY 1961; ANDERSEN, ECCLES and LØYNING 1963); thalamic neurones (ANDERSEN, BROOKS and ECCLES 1963); cells of the cuneate nucleus (ANDERSEN, ECCLES, OSHIMA and SCHMIDT 1963); toad motoneurones (FUKAMI 1961).

This inversion of the IPSP by intracellular chloride injection would be expected if the inhibitory transmitter acted by making the inhibitory zones highly permeable to chloride ions, which under such changed conditions, would exhibit a net flow outward down their electrochemical gradient, so depolarizing the membrane. For example, if the normal flux of chloride ions across activated inhibitory zones could be represented as in Fig. 70G, an increased internal concentration of chloride would cause reversal of the net flux, as in Fig. 70H, hyperpolarization giving place to depolarization.

In the original investigations (COOMBS, ECCLES and FATT 1953, 1955b) it was also found that electrophoretic injection of several other anions (bromide, nitrate and thiocyanate) changed the IPSP to a depolarizing response as in Fig. 70B, while such anions as sulphate (cf. Fig. 70E, F) phosphate, acetate and bicarbonate had no such effect. These observations have now been confirmed and extended to many other anions (ARAKI, ITO and OSCARSSON 1961;

ITO, KOSTYUK and OSHIMA 1962). For example in Fig. 70I the electrophoretic injection of NO_2^- ions by a current of 5×10^{-8} A for 60 sec converts a group Ia IPSP of a motoneurone to a depolarizing potential from which recovery

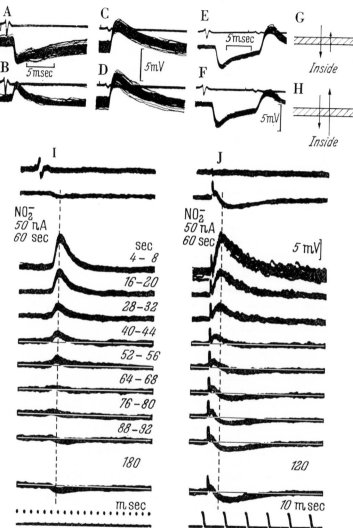

Fig. 70A—J. A and B are IPSPs, C and D are EPSPs generated in a biceps-semitendinosus motoneurone by afferent volleys as in Fig. 57 G and H, respectively. A and C were first recorded, then a hyperpolarizing current of 2×10^{-8} amp was passed through the microelectrode, which had been filled with 3 M KCl. Note that the injection of chloride ions converted the IPSP from a hyperpolarizing (A) to a depolarizing response (B), while the EPSP was not appreciably changed (C and D). Passing a much stronger hyperpolarizing current (4×10^{-8} amp for 90 sec) through a microelectrode filled with 0.6 M K_2SO_4 caused no significant change (E to F) in either the IPSP or the later EPSP. G and H represent provisionally assumed fluxes of chloride ions across the membrane before (G) and after (H) the injection of chloride ions, which is shown greatly increasing the efflux of chloride (ECCLES 1961a). I and J. Effects of electrophoretic injection of NO_2^- ions into motoneurones. I. Ia IPSP in a PBST motoneurone evoked by quadriceps Ia volley. J. Renshaw IPSP in a motoneurone, the innervation of which was not identified, induced by a maximal L7 ventral root stimulation. Records in the top row (lower traces) show control IPSPs evoked before the injection. Records from the second to the ninth row illustrate IPSPs at the indicated times (identical in I and J) after the injection of NO_2^- ions by the passage of a current of 5×10^{-8} A for 60 sec. The bottom records are IPSPs at the end of recovery. Note different time scales for I and J. All records were formed by the superposition of about twenty faint traces (ARAKI, ITO and OSCARSSON 1961)

occurs in an approximately exponential manner with a time constant of about 30 sec. All types of IPSP are similarly affected by ion injections, as may be seen in Fig. 70 J for NO_2^- ion injections on the recurrent (RENSHAW) IPSP in another motoneurone.

It is remarkable that in these very extensive investigations comprising many tests with each one of 34 different species of anions, there is no example

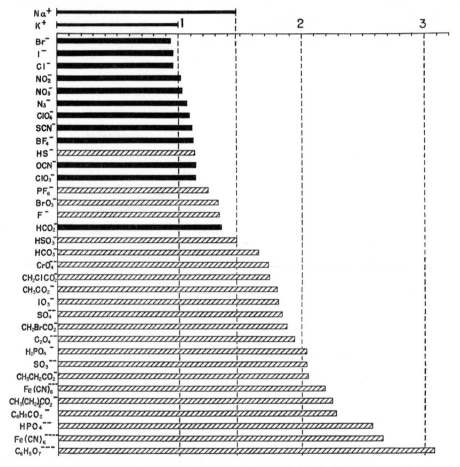

Fig. 71. Diagrammatical illustration of the correlation between the ion size in the aqueous solution and the effects of their injection upon the IPSP. Length of bands indicates ion size in the aqueous solutions as calculated from the limiting conductance in water. The black bands are for anions effective in converting the IPSP into the depolarizing direction, and the hatched bands for anions not effective. Hydrated sizes of K^+ and Na^+ ions are shown above the length scale, the former being taken as unity for representing the size of other ions (ITO, KOSTYUK and OSHIMA 1962)

of an anion with transitional behaviour. Either the electrophoretic injection is without effect on the IPSP, as in Fig. 70E, F, or it is fully effective as in Fig. 70A, B, I, J. This unambiguous separation of anions into two categories is depicted in Fig. 71, where the length of the horizontal band for each ion gives its hydrated ion size relative to the K^+ ion. The bands in black distinguish the species of ions that convert the IPSP to a depolarizing response, while hatched bands signify ineffectiveness.

In Fig. 71 only two species of ions, HS^- and HCO_2^-, lie out of the main sequence in which permeability of the activated inhibitory membrane may be correlated with ionic size in the hydrated state. It is shown by ARAKI, ITO and OSCARSSON (1961, Table 3) that naked ion size is not a factor in determining the penetrability of the inhibitory membrane by an ion species. For example fluoride is impermeable, yet it has a naked ion size that is only about two thirds of the calculated size for such permeable anions as Br^- and I^-. Explanations have been proposed for the anomalous behaviour of HS^- and HCO_2^- with respect to the hydrated ion size in Fig. 71. For example the ineffectiveness of injected HS^- may occur on account of its very rapid binding by protein molecules (ITO, KOSTYUK and OSHIMA 1962), and the permeability of the large HCO_2^- ions may be attributable to an elipsoidal shape (ARAKI, ITO and OSCARSSON 1961).

Despite these apparent exceptions to the main sequence, Fig. 71 provides overwhelming evidence in support of the original suggestion of COOMBS, ECCLES and FATT (1955 b) that the inhibitory transmitter converts the inhibitory subsynaptic membrane into a sieve-like structure that allows small hydrated ions to pass and blocks all larger ones. For all other ion species the critical pore diameter must be less than that of the PF_6 anion (1.24 on the K^+ scale) and larger than the 1.14 on this scale in order to allow penetrability by ClO_3^- ions. Since no large difference can be demonstrated in the relative effectiveness with which each of the twelve anions inverts the IPSP, it is necessary to assume that the inhibitory transmitter converts the inhibitory zones to a sieve-like membrane having pores of a precisely standardized size (cf. COOMBS, ECCLES and FATT 1955 b; ECCLES 1957, p. 219—221, 1961 a, 1961 e; ARAKI, ITO and OSCARSSON 1961). So far as they have been tested the IPSP's of other vertebrate neurones display the same anionic permeability as in Fig. 71, with the anomalous formate permeability. This has been observed for toad motoneurones (ARAKI 1963, personal comunnication) and for Mauthner cells of fish (ASADA 1963).

Chloride is the only permeable anion that normally exists in a concentration sufficient to contribute appreciably to the inhibitory ionic current. But, if the IPSP is produced solely by the movement of Cl^- ions down their electrochemical gradient, the equilibrium potential for Cl^- ions (E_{Cl}) must be at 5 to 10 mV more polarization than the normal resting membrane potential. This value for E_{Cl} could be maintained only if there were an outwardly directed chloride pump (cf. BOISTEL and FATT 1958; FATT 1960). With those nerve or muscle fibres where accurate investigation has been possible, it has not been necessary to postulate such an outwardly directed Cl^- pump (HODGKIN 1958; HODGKIN and HOROWICZ 1959; ADRIAN 1960, 1961; ADRIAN and FREYGANG 1962).

However, as will be discussed below, an inwardly directed Cl⁻ pump has now been demonstrated for the giant axon of *Loligo* (KEYNES 1962a, 1962b), and has also been proposed for motoneurones (ECCLES, ECCLES and ITO 1964b). Such a pump will cause the E_{Cl} to be at a more depolarized level than the normal membrane potential. Particular attention should therefore be given to the possible role of K⁺ ions in contributing to the generation of the IPSP as a hyperpolarizing response, because there is independent evidence from in-

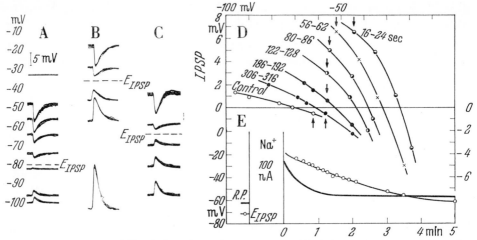

Fig. 72A—E. In A, the IPSPs of Fig. 60A are shown arranged with their membrane potentials on the scale indicated by short horizontal lines to the left of A, and the equilibrium potential for the IPSP is shown by the broken line. B shows the situation 5 to 40 sec after the passage of a depolarizing current of 5×10^{-8} A for 90 sec through the microelectrode (filled with 0.6 M Na₂SO₄); the IPSPs are shown similarly arranged on the same potential scale, the E_{IPSP} being now −35 mV. C shows, on the same scale, the IPSPs obtained during partial recovery at 3 to 4 min after the electrophoretic injection with the E_{IPSP} at −66 mV. D, E. Effect of intracellular injection of Na⁺ on the IPSP. The injection of Na⁺ ions was made from one barrel of a double electrode filled with 1.2 M Na₂SO₄ by a current of 10×10^{-8} A for 120 sec. In D the points on each line were determined by the procedure of recording the IPSPs over a range of membrane potentials as in A—C. The curve furthest to the left obtains for the initial control observations and the other curves were obtained at the indicated intervals in seconds after cessation of the Na⁺ injection. The summits of the IPSPs were plotted as ordinates against the membrane potentials as abscisse, and the E_{IPSP}s can be read off directly as the membrane potentials at which the curves cross the zero IPSP line. Arrows indicate the points obtained when the membrane potential was not displaced by applied current pulses. In E the values for the E_{IPSP}s are plotted before and after the injection, and the resting membrane potential is also shown by the continuous line (ECCLES, ECCLES and ITO 1964a)

vestigations on after-hyperpolarization that the equilibrium potential for K⁺ ions (E_K) is maintained at 20 mV (or even more) polarization above the resting membrane potential of motoneurones. Increased conductance for K⁺ ions appears to be alone responsible for the after-hyperpolarization following an SD spike potential, which has an equilibrium potential of −90 to −100 mV (COOMBS, ECCLES and FATT 1955a; KUNO 1959; ARAKI, ITO, KOSTYUK, OSCARSSON and OSHIMA 1962; ITO and OSHIMA 1963).

In the original investigation of the postulate that the net flux of K⁺ ions contributes substantially to the inhibitory current, COOMBS, ECCLES and FATT (1955b) compared the effects of passing depolarizing currents out of intracellular microelectrodes that were filled either with Na₂SO₄ or K₂SO₄. It was assumed that the current is carried out of the microelectrode largely by the highly concentrated cations therein, Na^+ or K^+ as the case may be, and that it is passed across the cell membrane partly by an outward flux of cations (largely K^+) and partly by an inward flux of anions (largely Cl^-).

An injection out of a K_2SO_4-filled electrode would add K^+ plus Cl^- ions to the cell; and the normal composition of the cell is restored by a net inward movement of water to re-establish osmotic equilibrium and by K^+ and Cl^- ions diffusing out down their electrochemical gradients. The high membrane permeability to these ions accounts for the rapid recovery that occurs under such conditions. On the other hand a much slower recovery occurs after Na^+ injection out of a Na_2SO_4-filled electrode (Fig. 72; COOMBS, ECCLES and FATT 1955 b). This difference is confirmed by alternate injections of Na^+ and K^+ ions into the same motoneurone from a double-barrelled electrode that was charged with K_2SO_4 in one barrel and Na_2SO_4 in the other (Fig. 73; ECCLES, ECCLES and ITO 1964 a). Originally COOMBS, ECCLES and FATT (1955 b) attributed this large and prolonged displacement of the IPSP by the Na^+ injection to the depletion of $(K^+)_i$, which would cause just such an effect if the flux of K^+ ions were importantly concerned in the generation of the IPSP. However this interpretation must now be rejected (ECCLES, ECCLES and ITO 1964 a) because, on the basis of the hypothesis of uniform electric field across the membrane (the Goldman equation), quite different curves would be expected when IPSP size is plotted against membrane potential as in Fig. 60 B, C. On the contrary the family of curves plotted in Fig. 72 D after an Na^+ injection is precisely what would be expected if the internal concentration of Cl^- ions was the determining factor. Hence after a Na^+ injection it appears that the raised $(Cl^-)_i$ recovers with a much slower time constant than its usual diffusional recovery (after Cl^- injections in Figs. 74, 75), being in fact as slow as the recovery from the changes that the Na^+ injection produces in the spike potential and the after-hyperpolarization (COOMBS, ECCLES and FATT 1955 a; ITO and OSHIMA 1963).

When the ionic composition of a motoneurone is modified, as in Figs. 72 to 75, the most significant information about the IPSP is the displacement of its equilibrium potential, not just the changes in the IPSPs as illustrated in Fig. 72 A—C. The E_{IPSP}s are shown in Fig. 72 A—C, but are more accurately determined by the plotted curves of Fig. 72 D, each of which was defined in a few seconds. The points so obtained for the membrane potentials at which the curves of Fig. 72 D cut the zero line for the IPSP, i.e. the E_{IPSP}, are plotted in Fig. 72 E to show the slow time course of recovery of the E_{IPSP} after a Na^+ injection. The points on the E_{IPSP} curves of Figs. 73 to 75 were obtained in the same way as in Fig. 72 E.

The much larger displacement of the E_{IPSP} in the depolarizing direction after the Na^+ injection in Fig. 73 can be accounted for at least qualitatively because the Cl^- ion influx from the environment would be larger than during the K^+ injection (COOMBS, ECCLES and FATT 1955 b, Appendix C). The slower return of the E_{IPSP} after the Na^+ injection in part may be attributed to the larger depolarization of the cell membrane, which would impede the outward diffusion of Cl^- ions, and hence slow the time course of recovery of the E_{Cl} and so of the E_{IPSP}. However, it is regularly observed that, after an Na^+ ion injection, the E_{IPSP} recovers much more slowly than the membrane potential.

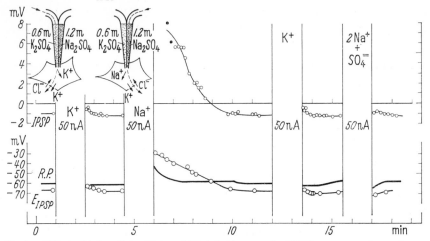

Fig. 73. Effect of intracellular Na^+ and K^+ injections on the IPSP responses of a motoneurone. The ionic injections were given out of a double microelectrode (inset diagrams) by a 90 sec current flow as indicated by the widths of the columns. All the observations are displayed on the time scale that is marked in minutes below the figure. The upper series of plotted points shows the potential measurements (scale on left) for the summits of IPSPs. The IPSP was of the usual hyperpolarizing type (shown by negative sign of voltage scale) at the start of the series, and after recovery from each injection. The two curves in the lower part of the figure are plotted on the voltage scales shown to the left and right, which give the intracellular potential. The thick line shows the membrane or resting potential (R.P.), and each of the plotted points gives a measurement of the equilibrium potential for the IPSP (E_{IPSP}). With the fourth injection the current flowed from the Na_2SO_4-filled barrel to the K_2SO_4-filled barrel, so injecting ($2Na^+ + SO_4^{2-}$). The two filled circles for the IPSP series just after the Na^+ injection indicate that spike potentials were generated by the large depolarizing IPSPs, and these plotted values for the IPSPs were estimated from the steepness of the rising slopes of these IPSPs. Following the Na^+ or ($2Na^+ + SO_4^{2-}$) injections, recording was made through the K_2SO_4-filled barrel, and, subsequent to a K^+ injection, through the Na_2SO_4-filled barrel (ECCLES, ECCLES and ITO 1964 a)

For example, the recovery from an Na^+ injection was very carefully followed in Fig. 72 E, where conditions were exceptionally stable. If the time course of E_{IPSP} recovery also gives the time course for the E_{Cl} recovery, it is not possible to attribute its prolonged recovery time entirely to the action of the depolarized membrane in slowing the outward diffusion of Cl^- ions, since recovery from the membrane depolarization is almost complete at one minute after a Na^+ injection (Figs. 73, 75). Evidently membrane depolarization can be no more than a contributory factor in the slow recovery of the E_{IPSP} which is illustrated in Figs. 72 and 73, and which as stated above requires the postulate that there is a slow decline of the high intracellular level of Cl^-.

Further evidence relating to the effects of ion injections on the IPSP is derived from the injection of salts by interbarrel current flow as illustrated in

Fig. 74. This technique avoids complications arising from the passage of Cl⁻
ions inwards across the membrane during the injection of K^+ or Na^+ by the
depolarizing current. As depicted in the upper diagram, the current passes
from one barrel to the other during the injection and the membrane potential
is unchanged. Comparison of the first and second injections in Fig. 74 reveals
that, as judged by the effect on the IPSP, Cl⁻ ions can be almost as effectively
injected in this way as in the normal procedure of passing current up the
Cl⁻-containing barrel (depicted in the lower diagram in Fig. 74). When Na^+
is injected from one barrel and SO_4^{2-} from the other, the E_{IPSP} is increased,

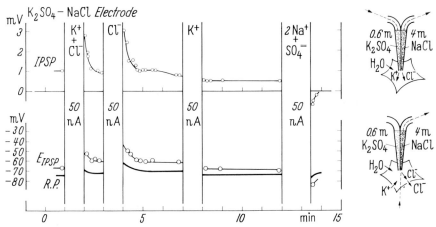

Fig. 74. Effects of various ion and of salt injections on the IPSP responses of a motoneurone. The double
microelectrode had one barrel filled with 0.6 M K_2SO_4 and the other with 4 M NaCl. The plotting is similar
to that employed in the preceding figure, but there were different injections as shown. The upper inset
figure shows the current that is passed when injecting $(K^+ + Cl^-)$ as in the first injection plotted, while
the reverse flow of current would give the fourth injection plotted $(2 Na^+ + SO_4^{2-})$. The lower inset figure
shows the current injecting Cl⁻ ions. The recording of the IPSPs was made through the NaCl-containing
barrel. Further description in text (ECCLES, ECCLES and ITO 1964b)

(last injection of Fig. 74), which contrasts with the large and prolonged decrease when Na^+ alone is injected (Figs. 72E, 73, 75). But of course this
procedure of inter-barrel current flow is an inefficient way of causing K^+ depletion, for the applied current will cause no net outward movement of K^+
ions across the membrane. Diminution of intracellular K^+ concentration is
brought about only by the influx of water that restores osmotic equilibrium.

A systematic investigation has been made with double micro-electrodes
filled with diverse combinations of salts, so that cross-injection between barrels
gives any desired salt injection, and comparisons have been made with the
effects produced when the injection is by current passage through only one
barrel (ECCLES, ECCLES and ITO 1964b).

A particularly significant sequence of injections is illustrated in Fig. 75.
Two injections of Na^+ typically give the prolonged displacement of both the
IPSP and the E_{IPSP} in the depolarizing direction, just as in Figs. 72E and 73,
while after the Cl⁻ injection there is the large depolarizing displacement and

a quick recovery that is almost complete in 1 minute. When $Na^+ + Cl^-$ are injected by inter-barrel current flow, there is a similar fast recovery of both the IPSP and the E_{IPSP}. The ionic composition of the cell after the ($Na^+ + Cl^-$) injection differs in one important respect, the level of $(K^+)_i$, from that after a Na^+ ion injection. In the former case there would be some lowering of $(K^+)_i$ by osmotic inflow of water across the cell membrane, but the decrease of $(K^+)_i$ so brought about would be very much less than after the Na^+ ion injection, which, as we have seen, occurs very largely at the expense of K^+ ion outflow across the cell membrane (right diagram of Fig. 73). Evidently the large

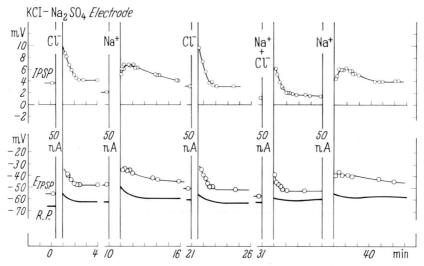

Fig. 75. Effects of various ion and salt injections on the IPSP. The double microelectrode had one barrel filled with 3 M KCl, the other with 1.2 M Na_2SO_4. Following the injections of Na^+ the recording was made through the KCl barrel, and subsequent to the Cl^- and the ($Na^+ + Cl^-$) injections, through the Na_2SO_4 barrel. The effects of the various ion and salt injections are plotted as in Fig. 73, but there are several gaps in the time scale as indicated. Further description in text (ECCLES, ECCLES and ITO 1964b)

decrease of $(K^+)_i$ that eventuates from the Na^+ injection is the crucial factor in causing the slowing of recovery of the E_{IPSP} from its depolarized displacement, and which apparently is due in large part to a slowing in decline of the raised level of $(Cl^-)_i$.

In order to account for all these various effects of ion and salt injections on the IPSP, it has been postulated (ECCLES, ECCLES and ITO 1964b) that at low levels of $(K^+)_i$ there is activation of an inward pumping mechanism, not just for K^+ ions, but for K^+ ions plus Cl^- ions in neutral association, i.e. KCl. Hence at low-levels of $(K^+)_i$, the operation of the pump would maintain $(Cl^-)_i$ above the level at which there is diffusional equilibrium for Cl^- ions across the membrane. The continual influx of Cl^- against the electrochemical gradient thus accounts for the slow decline of the E_{IPSP} that always occurs (Figs. 72E, 73, 75) when an increase in $(Cl^-)_i$ is associated with a large decrease in $(K^+)_i$, and under no other circumstances. It has been possible to develop a mathematical formulation that gives a satisfactory quantitative explanation of the effect of low $(K^+)_i$ in slowing the decline of raised $(Cl^-)_i$ (ECCLES, ECCLES and ITO 1964b, Appendix).

Since the K^+ ions are normally at such a high level in nerve cells, the ion injection procedures can give but a small increase or decrease in relative concentration, and hence have been indecisive in respect of evidence for or against K^+ ion permeability as a contributory factor in production of the IPSP. The K^+ ion contribution could be evaluated experimentally if $(K^+)_o$ could be increased several times, which requires the investigation of an isolated preparation such as the amphibian spinal cord that can be soaked in media of diverse ionic composition. Meanwhile an assessment of a relatively large contribution from K^+ ion permeability can be made on the basis of the following evidence: an E_K value of about 20 mV more hyperpolarized than the resting membrane potential (COOMBS, ECCLES and FATT 1955a; ITO and OSHIMA 1962, 1963); an E_{IPSP} that is similarly in the hyperpolarizing direction, but less so, probably about 6 mV; an E_{Cl} value probably in the depolarizing direction on account of the operation of the inward Cl pump. The value of the E_{IPSP} requires that the permeability of the activated inhibitory membrane for K^+ ions is at least half of that for Cl^- ions. On the basis of these postulates (ECCLES, ECCLES and ITO 1964b) explanations can be offered for all of the changes which the ionic injections produce in the IPSPs. For example, injection of $(2\,Na^+ + SO_4^{2-})$ in Figs. 73 and 74 caused a small hyperpolarizing displacement of the E_{IPSP}, which would be attributable to the reduction of $(Cl^-)_i$ by the osmotic influx of water that results from the salt injection. The simultaneous reduction of $(K^+)_i$ would tend to displace the E_{IPSP} in the opposite direction, hence the small changes actually observed. The effects of other salt injections on the E_{IPSP} can also be explained (ECCLES, ECCLES and ITO 1964b).

B. Inhibition in invertebrates

The ionic mechanism producing IPSPs with invertebrate synapses has been studied with the crustacean stretch receptor cell. The original suggestion that the inhibitory transmitter increases the permeability of the postsynaptic membrane to both K^+ and Cl^- ions (EDWARDS and KUFFLER 1957) is fully substantiated by experiments in which the extracellular potassium and chloride are changed. Removal of extracellular potassium causes the expected increase in the resting membrane potential, but the equilibrium potential for the IPSP is similarly increased (Fig. 76B—C; KUFFLER and EDWARDS 1958; EDWARDS and HAGIWARA 1959). Necessarily, continuous leakage of K^+ from the cell will maintain a small concentration of K^+ ions in the just-extra-cellular position, so this relatively high equilibrium potential for the IPSP under these conditions could be taken to indicate that the flux of K^+ ions alone is sufficient to account for the membrane current that gives the IPSP. However, a substantial contribution from Cl⁻ ion movement is also demonstrated by observing the change produced in the IPSP by substituting sodium monoglutamate for NaCl in the external medium (HAGIWARA, KUSANO and SAITO 1960). Besides the expected decline of the membrane potential, there is an even larger fall in the equilibrium potential for the IPSP (Fig. 76A). Since

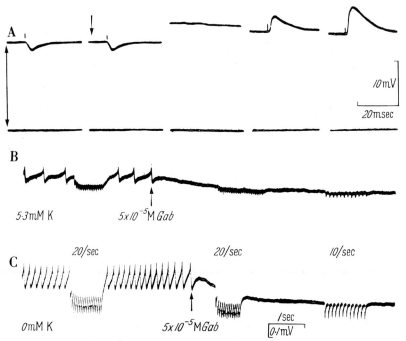

Fig. 76A—C. IPSPs of crustacean stretch receptor cells that are subjected to changes in ionic environment. In A the initial hyperpolarizing response was changed to a large depolarizing response some time after the external NaCl was changed to Na-glutamate at the arrow. Note that at the same time the membrane potential was reduced by about 5 mV (the upward displacement relative to the aligned base lines), hence there was diminution of the E_{IPSP} by at least 20 mV. Intracellular electrode was filled with K_2SO_4. Successive records are at 2 sec intervals (modified from HAGIWARA, KUSANO and SAITO 1960). In B and C external potassium was reduced to zero between the upper and lower traces. Note that the removal of external K⁺ ions in C caused the hyperpolarizing IPSPs produced by 20/sec stimulation to be increased relative to B, and also that 5×10^{-5} M GABA gave a larger hyperpolarization on which the IPSPs still were able to superimpose large hyperpolarizations. Thus removal of external K⁺ ions shifted the E_{IPSP} far in the hyperpolarizing direction (KUFFLER and EDWARDS 1958)

this effect is reversible and is not due to the action of the glutamate ions, it can be concluded that removal of external Cl⁻ ions displaces the E_{IPSP} in the depolarizing direction. This is just the change that would be expected if the inhibitory transmitter increases the membrane permeability to Cl⁻ ions, because removal of external Cl⁻ ions would cause the Cl⁻ ion flux to be preponderantly outwards during the production of the IPSP, i. e. the E_{IPSP} would be displaced in the depolarizing direction. Since an increase of internal Cl⁻ ions produces a similar displacement of the E_{IPSP}, it can be concluded that the IPSP is generated in part by the Cl⁻ flux consequent on an increased permeability of the subsynaptic membrane to Cl⁻ ions (HAGIWARA, KUSANO and

S<small>AITO</small> 1960). Thus the inhibitory transmitter produces an increased permeability to both K^+ and Cl^- ions. The relative conductance increases are as yet unknown, but K^+ ion conductance may be relatively more important than with inhibition of motoneurones.

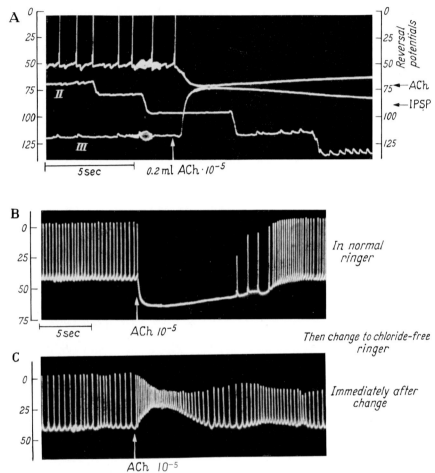

Fig. 77 A—C. Intracellular recording from a cell in the suboesophageal ganglion of a snail. In A the three traces are superimposed so that they have the same membrane potential scales to the left. The upper and lower traces show the effect of application of ACh at the arrow, the upper being at normal potential, the lower during passage of a hyperpolarizing current. Further description in text. In B and C 10^{-5} ACh was applied at the arrow, B being in normal Ringer and C in sulphate Ringer (K<small>ERKUT</small> and T<small>HOMAS</small> 1963 a)

Fig. 77 illustrates the elegant investigations by K<small>ERKUT</small> and T<small>HOMAS</small> (1963a) into the mode of action of inhibitory synapses on a cell in the snail's brain. In the uppermost of the three intracellular records (A) there are initially a random sequence of spontaneous spike potentials and small downwardly directed IPSPs. Externally applied ACh, at the arrow below, hyperpolarizes the membrane to -71 mV and suppresses both types of potentials. In the lowermost trace a steady current through another electrode in the same neurone hyperpolarizes it to -120 mV and consequently suppresses the spontaneous spike potentials and inverts the IPSPs. ACh application at the time of the arrow now causes a depolarization to -73 mV. The indicator ACh-arrow to right shows that the equilibrium potential or null-point for the ACh action in these two traces is about -72 mV. Finally the middle trace displays the effects of successive step-like hyperpolarizations on the IPSPs, which in this way are shown to have a null-point at about -89 mV, as indicated by the IPSP arrow. Comparable differences between these two null-points are regularly observed.

Changes either in the internal or in the external chloride concentrations displace the equilibrium potentials for the applied ACh to a degree indicating that at least 80 % of the increased conductance is accountable to chloride ions. For example, the hyperpolarizing action of applied ACh in Fig. 77 B is changed to depolarization (C) when the external chloride is reduced almost to zero and recovery occurs when the chloride is restored to normal. All gradations of this effect are produced by intermediate variations in the external chloride. Possibly the remaining 20 % of the conductance change is due to potassium ions, but this has not yet been demonstrated.

The IPSPs are affected in the same direction by the variations in external and internal chloride, but to a less extent than the ACh potentials. KERKUT and THOMAS (1963 b) have investigated the permeability of the inhibitory postsynaptic membrane to various species of anions and find that it is very similar to that of vertebrate neurones (Fig. 71). There is the same anomalous permeability to formate ions. In the critical zone there is one difference, namely a very slight permeability to BrO_3^- ions, which would indicate that the calculated diameter of these ions (1.32 times the K^+ diameter) is a precise measure of the effective pore size. There was permeability to ClO_3^- ions and impermeability to F^- ions just as in Fig. 71. Exactly the same anionic permeability was produced by ACh application.

The discrepancy always observed between the equilibrium potentials for the ACh-induced potential and the IPSP can in part at least be attributable to the location of the inhibitory synapses on the axon at some distance from the soma (KERKUT 1963, personal communication). On account of electrotonic decrement the sites for generation of the IPSP would be less influenced by the current applied through an electrode in the soma than is indicated by the membrane potential recorded in the soma as in Fig. 77A. It is thus still possible that at the site of generation the IPSP has an equilibrium potential identical with that for the ACh-induced potential, which of course would be an essential requirement for the hypothesis that ACh is the inhibitory transmitter (cf. Chapter XII).

TAUC (1958) found that the equilibrium potential for the IPSP of the giant ganglion cells of *Aplysia* lies between the equilibrium potential for potassium and the resting membrane potential. Hence he concluded that, as with the motoneurone, the IPSP is generated by an increased permeability to both potassium and chloride ions, and that a high impermeability is maintained for sodium ions.

In contrast to these preceding examples, the inhibitory action on crustacean muscle fibers appears to be produced almost entirely by an increase in chloride permeability (BOISTEL and FATT 1958). The equilibrium potential for the IPSP is almost identical with the normal membrane potential. When the external chloride is replaced by large organic anions, the resting membrane potential falls by 10 to 20 mV, but the equilibrium potential for the IPSP falls by more than 30 mV, the hyperpolarizing response being very small even when the membrane is heavily depolarized by an applied current. Thus, it would appear that the hyperpolarization reaction is dependent on the inward movement of chloride, outward potassium movements making a negligible contribution even under very favourable conditions. This is shown further by the very small changes in the IPSP produced either by removing external potassium or by raising it to several times the normal value.

C. Inhibitory synapses on cardiac muscle

The ionic movements responsible for vagal inhibition of the heart have been studied chiefly by applying the inhibitory transmitter, acetylcholine, or one of its analogues (cf. Fig. 67 D). In this way it has been shown that inhibition is associated with a large increase in the potassium permeability of the cardiac muscle fibres (BURGEN and TERROUX 1953; TRAUTWEIN and DUDEL 1958). Correspondingly, radio-tracer investigations have shown that acetylcholine causes a large increase in the potassium permeability of the sinus venosus of the frog heart (HARRIS and HUTTER 1956). It appears that the observed increase in potassium permeability is sufficient to account for the potential changes (cf. Fig. 67 A—C) and for the increase in the electric conductance of the membrane (TRAUTWEIN, KUFFLER and EDWARDS 1956). There can be little if any increase in chloride permeability.

D. Conclusion

These diverse types of postsynaptic inhibitory response are all effected by an increased permeability to either K^+ or Cl^- ions or to their combination in varying degree. There have been several rigorous investigations of the hypothesis that, when activated by the inhibitory transmitter, the inhibitory subsynaptic membrane functions as a sieve with accurately standardized pores (Fig. 78), being permeable to all ions below a critical size in the hydrated state. If, as suggested by BOISTEL and FATT (1958), it be further assumed that positive electrical charges are distributed along the pore (C), the membrane would exhibit a selective preference for small anions as against small cations, as occurs with crustacean muscle and probably to a lesser extent with mammalian motoneurones and the neurones in the snail's brain. If, on the other hand, the pores are charged negatively (B), the membrane would be selectively permeable to small cations, as occurs with vertebrate heart muscle. The absence of charge would give approximately equivalent anion and cation operation as with the crustacean stretch receptor and the giant ganglion cell of *Aplysia*.

We have seen that there is a sharp separation between the permeable and impermeable species of anions, and that there is virtually the same permeability of the activated inhibitory zones for the largest permeable ion (formate)

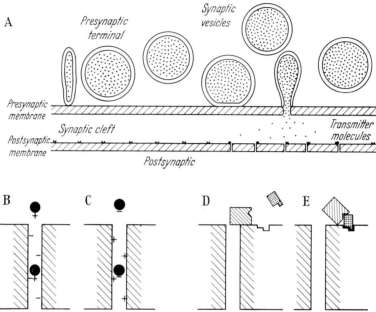

Fig. 78 A—E. Schematic representations of synapse and of pores that are assumed to be the channels for the ionic fluxes through the activated inhibitory patches on motoneurones. A shows diagrammatic representation of a portion of a synaptic cleft with synaptic vesicles in close proximity in the presynaptic terminal, and one actually discharging the transmitter molecules into the synaptic cleft. Some of these molecules are shown combined with receptor sites on the postsynaptic membrane with the consequent opening up of pores through that membrane. In B—E these pores are shown in greater detail. In B the pore is negatively charged and so will be selectively permeable to small cations as shown, while in C it is positively charged and so is selectively permeable to small anions, as occurs with crustacean muscle. D shows diagramatically a way in which an inhibitory pore may be plugged, an inhibitory transmitter molecule being shown free in the environment. In E this molecule is shown in close steric relationship both to the plug and to an inhibitory receptor site on the postsynaptic membrane. As a consequence the plug has been pulled away from the orifice of the pore, which is opened for the ionic flux that occurs during the brief duration of the transmitter action on the subsynaptic membrane

as for the smallest (bromide). It may therefore be assumed that, when the inhibitory transmitter acts on the membrane, it brings into existence pores that have a standardized size. FATT (1961) has suggested that such a happening could readily be envisaged if the pores were permanent structures that were plugged at their external opening and if a transmitter molecule acted by momentarily dislodging the plug. For example the transmitter molecule might form a bridge between two receptor sites to which it was momentarily attached, one on the adjacent membrane and the other on the plug, as has been illustrated diagrammatically (Fig. 78 D, E; ECCLES 1961 e).

CHAPTER XII

INHIBITORY TRANSMITTER SUBSTANCES

A. Postsynaptic inhibitory action in the central nervous system of vertebrates

Though much is known about the central pathways subserving inhibitory action on motoneurones and also about the postsynaptic events responsible for the inhibition of reflex discharges, there is still very little information on the events in the synaptic apparatus between the arrival of an impulse in the inhibitory presynaptic terminals and the initiation of the IPSP. These events occupy a time of about 0.3 msec (Fig. 84), which is comparable with the time involved in equivalent events in excitatory transmitter action (Chapter IV), and it is likewise believed that inhibitory synaptic transmission is mediated by a specific transmitter substance which is released by the presynaptic terminals, traverses the synaptic cleft, and acts on special receptor sites on the postsynaptic membrane (Fig. 78 A). There is no alternative hypothesis for the production of the IPSP.

Hitherto it has not been possible to identify the inhibitory synaptic endings; but, as will be seen in Chapter XIII, there is now very good evidence that the basket cells of the hippocampus are inhibitory cells (ANDERSEN, ECCLES and LØYNING 1963). Since they alone make synaptic contacts with the somas of the pyramidal cells (RAMON Y CAJAL 1911; LORENTE DE Nó 1934), the synapses illustrated in Fig. 4 A (BLACKSTAD 1963) can now be recognized as being inhibitory. It is of great interest to find that these synapses are typical Type 2 synapses as defined by GRAY (1959, 1961 a). There are the usual small clusters of synaptic vesicles at the active zones of the synaptic membranes. It may therefore be assumed that, just as with excitatory synapses, the transmitter is released from a preformed store, presumably in the synaptic vesicles, and traverses the synaptic cleft to act on the postsynaptic membrane for 1 to 2 msec (cf. Figs. 58A, 59) in the case of motoneurones, making it highly permeable to Cl^- ions and also to K^+ ions (Chapter XI). However, there is very little evidence relating to the nature of the inhibitory transmitter substance itself at any synapses in the vertebrate central nervous system.

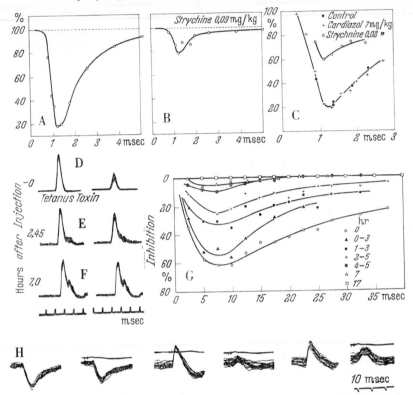

Fig. 79A—H. Pharmacological investigations on postsynaptic inhibition. A, B. Monosynaptic reflexes from biceps-semitendinosus were inhibited by a single Group Ia quadriceps volleys at various testing intervals via an inhibitory pathway as in Fig. 69. The sizes of the test reflexes are calculated as percentages of the control and plotted against the testing interval to give the inhibitory curves. Between A and B 0.09 mg strychnine/kg body weight was injected intravenously (BRADLEY, EASTON and ECCLES 1953). In C are similar inhibitory curves before (●) and after the intravenous injection of cardiazol, 7 mg/kg (+) (pentamethylenetetrazol) and strychnine salicylate, 0.02 mg/kg (O) (CURTIS 1959). D, E, and F show monosynaptic reflex discharges from flexor digitorum longus motoneurones, each giving the control and the reflex at the point of maximum inhibition by the recurrent inhibitory pathway (motor axon collaterals to Renshaw cells, cf. Fig. 82C). D was 0.2 hours before the intraspinal injection of a minute quantity of L61 tetanus toxin; E and F were respectively 2.45 and 7 hours later, by which time the inhibition had almost disappeared. The full sequence of this effect is shown in G, where the recurrent inhibitory curves are plotted for the whole range of test intervals and at various times after the injection, 0.3, 1.3, 2.5, 4.5, 7 and 17 hours, as indicated by the symbols (BROOKS, CURTIS and ECCLES 1957). H. Intracellular recording from a gastrocnemius motoneurone by the centre barrel (filled with 0.6 M K_2SO_4) of a coaxial assembly. The outer barrel was extracellular. The first, second, fourth and sixth records were evoked by stimulation of the peroneal nerve. Strychnine diffused from the 10 mM solution of strychnine hydrochloride in 150 mM NaCl that was in the outer barrel and abolished the IPSPs so that a polysynaptic EPSP remained. Monosynaptic EPSPs evoked by stimulation of the gastrocnemius nerve (third and fifth records) were unaltered (CURTIS 1962)

The only certain findings are derived from the synaptic blockage of postsynaptic inhibitory action (Fig. 79) that is brought about by some convulsant drugs, strychnine (Fig. 79A, B), bruceine, thebaine, 5,7-diphenyl-1,3-diazadamantan-6-ol, but not by others, picrotoxin, pentamethylenetetrazol (Fig. 79C), β-methyl-β ethylglutarimide (BRADLEY, EASTON and ECCLES 1953;

ECCLES, FATT and KOKETSU 1954; FATT 1954; ECCLES 1957, 1962; KUNO 1957; CURTIS 1959, 1962 b, 1963 b; LONGO 1961; LONGO and CHIAVARELLI 1962); and also by tetanus toxin (Fig. 79 D, E, F, G; BROOKS, CURTIS and ECCLES 1957; CURTIS 1959; WILSON, DIECKE and TALBOT 1960). Intravenous injections of strychnine and other anti-inhibitory drugs are rapidly effective (in 30 sec) in depressing both the inhibitory postsynaptic potential and the inhibition of reflexes; and in a subconvulsive dose (0.08 mg/kg) strychnine reduces to less than half all the postsynaptic inhibitory actions in the spinal cord, while monosynaptic excitatory actions are not affected (Fig. 79 B). Larger doses virtually eliminate postsynaptic inhibition.

By taking special precautions to restrain the background diffusion of strychnine out of the micropipette CURTIS (1962 b) has been able to demonstrate its depressant action on postsynaptic inhibition when given by electrophoretic injection (Fig. 79 H). It was furthermore shown that this electrophoretic injection did not affect the postsynaptic membrane potential; hence a direct excitatory action of strychnine is excluded.

Since strychnine does not depress the discharges of the interneurones that are on the inhibitory pathways under test (ECCLES, FATT and KOKETSU 1954; ECCLES 1957, p. 95; CURTIS 1959), it must act directly on the inhibitory synapses. On analogy with the pharmacological blockage of cholinergic excitatory synapses on muscle, in sympathetic ganglia and on Renshaw cells, it can be assumed that such selective blocking drugs are likely to be competitive for inhibitory receptor sites, just as with the curariform drugs on cholinoceptive sites (DEL CASTILLO and KATZ 1957a; THESLEFF 1958). Likewise, on analogy with the action of botulinum toxin at cholinergic synapses (BROOKS 1956; THESLEFF 1960a), it can be assumed that, in its selective depression of inhibitory synapses, tetanus toxin acts by preventing the release of transmitter from the inhibitory presynaptic terminals (BROOKS, CURTIS and ECCLES 1957). Since all the postsynaptic inhibitions that have been investigated in the spinal cord are blocked by strychnine and tetanus toxin, it is likely that they are all produced by the same transmitter substance. Furthermore, this substance would be sterically related to the drugs which are believed to act by competitive occupation of the receptor sites (BRADLEY, EASTON and ECCLES 1953; ECCLES 1957; CURTIS 1959; LONGO 1961; LONGO and CHIAVARELLI 1962).

The blocking action of strychnine and bruceine indicates that the same inhibitory transmitter is responsible for the inhibitory action which impulses in the olivo-cochlear bundle exert on the sensory fibre terminals and on the hair cells of the organ of Corti (RASMUSSEN 1953; GALAMBOS 1956; DESMEDT and MONACO 1960, 1962; DESMEDT 1962; FEX 1962). The presumed inhibitory synaptic endings are of the typical chemical transmitting type with clusters of synaptic vesicles (ENGSTRÖM 1961). Metrazol and picrotoxin even in convulsant dosage are without effect on the olivo-cochlear inhibition (DESMEDT and MONACO 1962). However 5-7-diphenyl-1-3-diazadamantan-6-ol is also with-out action, though it appeared to act like strychnine on inhibition of reflex activity in the spinal cord (LONGO 1961).

On the basis of extractive procedures and pharmacological testing many substances have been proposed as inhibitory transmitters in the central ner-vous system, and have been critically evaluated (CURTIS 1961b; McLENNAN 1961, 1962, 1963). In the most recent attempt to assess the credentials of these substances CURTIS (1963b) has formulated two essential conditions, though of course there are in addition the criteria listed in Chapter V, before a substance can be finally recognized as a synaptic transmitter. Firstly, the substance must induce the same conductance change in the subsynaptic membrane beneath inhibitory synapses as does the transmitter. Secondly, on pharmaco-logical testing, the postsynaptic action of the substance must be identical with that of the transmitter, particularly with respect to the blocking action of strychnine, though it must be recognized that the strychnine depression of postsynaptic inhibition has not been demonstrated at the higher levels of the brain, e.g. in the hippocampus, neocortex, thalamus and cerebellum. On the basis of the criteria CURTIS (1963b) has critically examined the following candidates for the role of transmitter of postsynaptic inhibition in the central nervous system: Factor I, γ-amino-butyric acid (GABA), γ-amino-β-hydroxy-butyric acid (GABOB), an inhibitory substance extracted by LISSAK, ENDROC-ZI and VINCZE (1961), substance P, adrenaline, noradrenaline, 3-hydroxy-tyramine, 5-hydroxytryptamine, acetylcholine. Not one of these substances qualifies on both of the criteria. The development of testing procedures for screening such substances can best be illustrated by considering two that have been most throughly investigated, Factor I and GABA or a chemically related substance.

Extracts from mammalian brain have been purified to give a substance, labelled Factor I, that has powerful inhibitory actions on various tissues, particularly on the discharges from the crustacean stretch receptor cell and on the crustacean heart (FLOREY 1954). Factor I is almost certainly a mixture of several substances, and presumably different samples can vary widely in composition. For example, it has been claimed (BAZEMORE, ELLIOTT and FLOREY 1957) that the inhibitory activity of Factor I on the crustacean stretch receptor cell is entirely due to γ-aminobutyric acid (GABA); but this is certainly not the case with other preparations of Factor I (McLENNAN 1959, 1960, 1961, 1963; FLOREY and McLENNAN 1959).

On account of its potent depressant action on nerve cells it has been suggested that GABA or a related amino acid might be the inhibitory trans-mitter in the vertebrate central nervous system (HAYASHI and NAGAI 1956; BAZEMORE, ELLIOTT and FLOREY 1957). However, these substances have now been shown not to produce a hyperpolarization of nerve cells, as would be expected for the inhibitory transmitter, but to have a general depressant action on all neuronal responses (CURTIS, PHILLIS and WATKINS 1959; CURTIS and WATKINS 1960b), which is strikingly different from the mode of action of inhibitory synapses. By employing the coaxial microelectrode as in Fig. 24 (inset), it has been shown that electrophoretic application of GABA and related substances to the exterior of motoneurones reversibly depresses both excitatory (Fig. 80 G—I), and inhibitory (Fig. 80 J—L) postsynaptic potentials. In

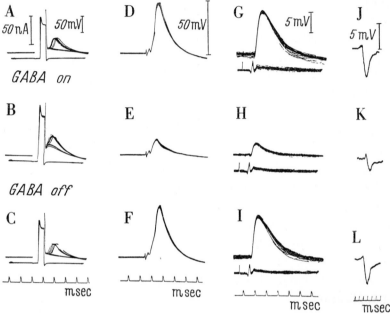

Fig. 80 A—L. A, D, G and J give responses of a motoneurone recorded with a double (coaxial) microelectrode with centre barrel in the motoneurone, being respectively the spike response to a just threshold testing current pulse (shown by 0.5 msec upward deflection on the record of current), the spike response to an antidromic impulse, the monosynaptic excitatory postsynaptic potential (EPSP) and an inhibitory postsynaptic potential (IPSP). The extracellular electrophoretic injection of GABA by a continuous current of 310 mμA depressed the excitability as shown by the increase in threshold current (B), by the partial blockage of the antidromic spike (E) and it also greatly depressed the EPSP (H) and the IPSP (K). There was complete recovery after cessation of the injection C, F, I, L (CURTIS, PHILLIS and WATKINS 1959)

addition there is depression of the spike potential (D—F) and the excitability of the neuronal membrane to applied current pulses (A—C); yet there is no detectable change in the membrane potential. Since intracellular recording from vertebrate nerve cells (Chapter XI) shows that inhibitory synaptic action always produces a membrane hyperpolarization (except after intracellular injection of some anions), a hyperpolarizing action would be expected for the inhibitory transmitter substance. Furthermore, the depressant action of GABA differs from that of the inhibitory transmitter in not being suppressed by strychnine (CURTIS, PHILLIS and WATKINS 1959). Apparently GABA and related substances act by causing a large increase in the conductance of the neuronal membrane, possibly to chloride ions, which would account for the various depressant actions in the absence of a change in membrane potential. Investigations on other types of nerve cells in the spinal cord indicate that GABA acts similarly on them (CURTIS, PHILLIS and WATKINS 1959). However the electrophoretic application of GABA to the Mauthner cell reveals that it exerts a depressant action only when it is applied to the regions of the cell (axon hillock, soma and adjacent dendrites) that have inhibitory synapses (DIAMOND 1963), and that this action is probably due to an increased conductance for Cl^- ions.

Since it is unlikely that GABA and its analogues are the usual postsynaptic inhibitory transmitters in the vertebrate central nervous system, it seems that extractive procedures provide the best line of investigation. It is evident that the blood-brain barrier makes it imperative to test for transmitter activity by direct injection into the environment of nerve cells, as has been done for pharmacological agents by CURTIS, PHILLIS and WATKINS (1959, 1960). However, FLOREY and McLENNAN (1955) and HONOUR and McLENNAN (1960) have found that topical application of Factor I to the cat spinal cord causes a very rapid and effective depression of reflex discharges, and this depression is antagonised by intravenous injection of strychnine in subconvulsive dose. Depressions also were produced by Factor I in other synaptic transmissions both central and peripheral. These results are certainly encouraging (cf. McLENNAN 1963), but progress will be uncertain until pure substances can be isolated from the brain extracts; and far more systematic and detailed investigation is required. There are so many pitfalls in the method of diffuse topical application.

B. Inhibitory action in the peripheral nervous system of vertebrates

In Chapter I reference was made to the fundamental work of LOEWI and DALE in establishing that acetylcholine is the inhibitory transmitter substance to the vertebrate heart. In Chapter V there has been a full treatment of acetylcholine as a synaptic transmitter substance and of the related features of its metabolism. Similarly there has been reference to noradrenaline which is the inhibitory transmitter to many smooth muscles. Since this non-controversial field is marginal to the subject of this review, it will be sufficient to cite references to comprehensive and authoritative accounts (ROSENBLUETH 1950; MINZ 1955; v. EULER 1959). In addition CURTIS (1963 b) has recently reviewed inhibitory transmitter substances to heart and smooth muscle of vertebrates. In Chapter VIII there was reference to the hypothesis that there is an adrenergic inhibition of sympathetic ganglion cells (R.M. ECCLES and LIBET 1961).

C. Inhibitory synapses of invertebrates

There is such a wealth of diversified investigation that a detailed treatment is not appropriate to the theme of this book. There are two emerging stories.

One relates γ-amino-butyric acid (GABA) to inhibitory synaptic action in crustacea; at neuromuscular synapses, on the stretch receptor cell, and on lateral giant axons. The other identifies acetylcholine (ACh) as the inhibitory transmitter at central synapses of *Mollusca*. The evidence for and against these developing hypotheses has been discussed in detail in several recent reviews (ELLIOTT and JASPER 1959; KUFFLER 1960; EDWARDS 1960; VAN DER KLOOT 1960; FLOREY 1960, 1961, 1962, 1963; CURTIS and WATKINS 1960b; FLOREY and HOYLE 1961; CURTIS 1961b, 1963b; McLENNAN 1961; 1963).

1. Inhibitory synapses in Crustacea

Inhibitory synaptic action on the crustacean stretch receptor cells (Figs. 65 A, 65 B, 76) can be investigated so effectively in isolation that it has provided some of the most convincing experiments relating GABA to the synaptic transmitter. The inhibitory action on these receptor cells seems to be similar for a wide variety of crustacea: on crayfish, lobsters and crabs.

It was discovered by BAZEMORE, ELLIOTT and FLOREY (1957) that the inhibitory action of brain extracts on crustacean stretch receptor cells could be duplicated by GABA and that there were large quantities of GABA in the extracts. An intensive study by KUFFLER and EDWARDS (1958) and EDWARDS and KUFFLER (1959) showed that in every respect synaptic inhibitory action on the crustacean stretch receptor cell could be duplicated by GABA or its near relatives, and this resemblance has recently been confirmed and extended by HAGIWARA, KUSANO and SAITO (1960). GABA affects the membrane potential in exactly the same way as does inhibitory synaptic action, the equilibrium potentials being identical. The two actions are also identical when there are changes in either the K^+ or Cl^- concentrations (Fig. 76), so it can be concluded that the similarity extends to the increased conductances for each of these two ion species. Furthermore, GABA action can be as powerful as high frequency tetanization of the inhibitory fibre, 10^{-4} increasing the membrane conductance from five to seven times (HAGIWARA, KUSANO and SAITO 1960). GABA is the most potent amino acid in all these actions, though guanido-acetic and β-guanidinopropionic acids are almost as effective (EDWARDS and KUFFLER 1959; EDWARDS 1960).

There are indications that GABA acts on the region of the receptor cell that is subjected to inhibitory synaptic action. Thus the axon of the cell is more than 1000 times less sensitive than the soma-dendritic region, and picrotoxin similarly diminishes or suppresses both neural and GABA inhibitory action (ELLIOTT and FLOREY 1956; KUFFLER 1960; FLOREY 1960; EDWARDS 1960). A cautionary finding is that GABA also inhibits the excitatory responses of stretch receptor cells that appear to be devoid of inhibitory synapses (KUFFLER and EDWARDS 1958; EDWARDS 1960), which at least suggests that, even when inhibitory receptor sites are present on a cell, GABA may act elsewhere. This situation may be comparable with the excitation of Renshaw cells by the acidic amino acids (Chapter V). The role of GABA as an inhibitory transmitter has also to be considered in relation to the report of an extremely potent inhibitory action (100 times GABA) of 3-hydroxytyramine on stretch receptor cells of a crayfish *(Pacifastacus leninsculus)* (McGEER, McGEER and McLENNAN 1961). However this action could not be confirmed (FLOREY 1963). In any case, this substance is unlikely to be an inhibitory synaptic transmitter because picrotoxin has only a weak blocking action, whereas it is very effective against both neural and GABA-induced inhibition, which suggests that 3-hydroxytyramine acts at receptor sites other than those concerned in neural inhibition.

GABA in relatively low concentration (3 to 5×10^{-7} M) also acts similarly to neural inhibition at the synapses on the giant motor axons of crustacea (Fig. 65 D, E; FURSHPAN and POTTER 1959b). For example the equilibrium potential for GABA action is very close to that of the IPSP (Fig. 65 D), which indicates that the large conductance increases in these two cases involve the same ion or ions.

Inhibitory actions on crustacean muscle exhibit much more variety in their pharmacological properties. In part this is due to the complicating superposition of presynaptic inhibition on postsynaptic inhibition, GABA having in the crayfish actions corresponding to both types of inhibition (DUDEL and KUFFLER 1961 c). In addition it appears that some species are exceptions to the general finding that inhibitory neural action is exactly duplicated by GABA and its near relatives (McLENNAN 1957; BOISTEL and FATT 1958; ROBBINS and VAN DER KLOOT 1958; GRUNDFEST, REUBEN and RICKLES 1959; ROBBINS 1959; KUFFLER 1960). For example HOYLE and WIERSMA (1958b) were unable to demonstrate any inhibitory action of GABA in concentrations up to 10^{-3} on the opener muscles in several species of crabs and crayfish. In the leg muscles of crabs (FLOREY and HOYLE 1961) GABA acts by greatly attenuating the EPPs, while neural inhibition acts later in the chain of events leading to muscle contraction.

Apart from these exceptions there is general agreement that neural inhibition and GABA both cause increased permeability to the same ions (largely Cl^-) with the consequence that there is the same equilibrium potential (Fig. 66 C; BOISTEL and FATT 1958; GRUNDFEST, REUBEN and RICKLES 1959; KUFFLER 1960); and both actions are depressed by picrotoxin, though picrotoxin alone has no action on the EPPs or on the conductance of the postsynaptic membrane (ROBBINS and VAN DER KLOOT 1958; ROBBINS 1959; KUFFLER 1960; VAN DER KLOOT 1960). Strychnine has no action on either the neural or the GABA-induced inhibition of crustacean muscle (GRUNDFEST, REUBEN and RICKLES 1959)—so contrasting with its specific depression of postsynaptic inhibition in the vertebrate nervous system, which complementarily is not affected by picrotoxin (FATT 1954; ECCLES 1957, 1962; CURTIS 1959, 1963 b). These drug specificities certainly indicate a difference between the inhibitory transmitter substances of vertebrates and invertebrates. It is postulated that picrotoxin acts as a competitor both of the inhibitory transmitter substance and of applied GABA by combining reversibly with inhibitory receptor sites on the post-synaptic membrane (ROBBINS and VAN DER KLOOT 1958; VAN DER KLOOT 1960).

These investigations on inhibition of crustacean nerve and muscle cells certainly suggest that GABA could be the inhibitory transmitter substance. It is therefore of prime importance to discover if GABA occurs in the inhibitory nerve fibres. KRAVITZ, KUFFLER and POTTER (1963) have actually isolated long lengths of single inhibitory fibres from the legs of lobsters and by extractive procedures find them to contain GABA in the surprisingly high concentration of 0.5 % (wet weight). In contrast, in extracts from the associated meropodite excitatory fibres, GABA cannot be detected, which signifies that its concentration therein must be less than one hundredth and even less than one thousandth of the concentration (0.5 %) in the inhibitory fibre. In an attempt to reconcile these observations with those of FLOREY and BIEDERMAN (1960) and FLOREY and CHAPMAN (1961), it could be objected that the extractive procedures may have split off the GABA from some larger molecule, which is the actual transmitter substance (cf. FLOREY 1963); but at least this extraordinary exclusiveness in its distribution establishes that GABA plays a specific role in inhibitory axons of crustacea. Before it can be regarded as the actual transmitter, it will have to be shown that, when an impulse reaches the inhibitory terminals, it causes the immediate release of an adequate amount of GABA (KRAVITZ, KUFFLER and POTTER 1963).

It is of interest that when extracts are made from the whole nerve, GABA accounts for only 30 to 50 % of the blocking activity, as assayed on crustacean neuromuscular transmission, taurine and betaine being also very effective (KRAVITZ, KUFFLER, POTTER and VAN GELDER 1963). However, unlike GABA these other blocking substances were distributed uniformly between excitatory and inhibitory fibres, which further emphasizes the specific association of GABA with inhibitory transmission. Furthermore, extracts from the central nervous system of lobsters also contained GABA, taurine and betaine as the principal blocking substances (DUDEL, GRYDER, KAJI, KUFFLER and POTTER 1963), which is additional evidence that GABA may be concerned in the inhibitory action on the lateral giant fibres (FURSHPAN and POTTER 1959 b).

2. Inhibitory synapses in Mollusca

In contrast to *Crustacea* it seems that *Mollusca* utilize at least one of the transmitter substances widely distributed in vertebrates. There is now very good evidence that ACh is an inhibitory transmitter at many synapses.

Fig. 81 B (upper trace) shows that the diffuse application of ACh in a concentration of 10^{-6} causes hyperpolarization of one type of ganglion cell of *Aplysia* (the H-cells) (TAUC and GERSHENFELD 1961, 1962), and detectable actions have been observed with concentrations as low as 10^{-12}. When the membrane is hyperpolarized (Fig. 81 B, lowest trace), ACh causes a depolarization, and at an intermediate level (-63 mV) ACh gives only a very slight depolarization. Corresponding to these potential changes there are increases

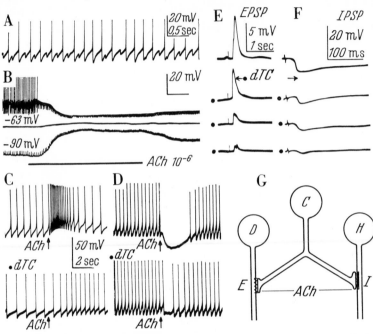

Fig. 81 A—G. Intracellular recording from a ganglion cell of *Aplysia*. A shows fast record of spontaneous discharges and unitary IPSPs randomly interspersed. In B there are slower traces (time, 5 sec) and during each ACh was applied externally in a concentration of 10^{-6} as shown by the horizontal line. The upper trace is at the same membrane potential as A, the lower two during hyperpolarization by an applied intracellular current to -63 and -90 mV respectively, all three traces being superimposed at the same voltage scale (TAUC and GERSHENFELD 1962). C, D. Effect of brief electrophoretic injections of ACh (arrows) on the intracellular records of a D-cell (C) and of an H-cell (D) firing spontaneously. In the lower records the ACh was much less effective after addition of 10^{-4} dTC. E and F show effects of dTC in 10^{-4} concentration (applied at arrows) on the evoked EPSP and IPSP of a D cell (left column) and a H-cell (right column). On removal of dTC the initial potentials were restored (not shown) (TAUC and GERSHENFELD 1961). G shows diagram of D and H cells with a common interneurone (C) that acts by ACh on inhibitory (I) and excitatory (E) synaptic zones

of up to five-fold in membrane conductance. When electrophoretic injection of ACh is employed to give strictly localized application of ACh, the most sensitive areas are found at the region of the synapses on the axon, one or two millimetres distal from the soma (TAUC 1962a, b); nevertheless the soma is itself very sensitive to ACh, despite its absence of synapses (TAUC and GERSCHENFELD 1962). In the faster trace of Fig. 81 A, small hyperpolarizing potentials (spontaneous IPSPs) are interspersed amongst the spike potentials. During suppression of the spikes by hyperpolarization in the uppermost and lowermost traces of B these IPSPs are a prominent feature, and are seen to be reversed by hyperpolarization to -90 mV, and to be zero at -63 mV. Thus the null-points for the ACh-induced potential and the IPSPs are virtually identical, despite the location of the inhibitory synapses on the axon at 1 to 2 mm from the site of current application and recording in the soma. However electrotonic transmission is very effective in these giant axons, the space constant being several millimetres (TAUC 1962a).

Further evidence indicating that ACh is the inhibitory transmitter is illustrated in Fig. 81. In D the blocking agent of cholinoceptive sites, dTC at a concentration of 10^{-4}, very effectively reduces the action of ACh in producing hyperpolarization and the associated depressant action on impulse discharges. In F, dTC similarly depresses the inhibitory synaptic actions, the IPSPs. Atropine is likewise effective on both the ACh action and the IPSPs. Since eserine increases the effect of applied ACh, the presence of AChE may be assumed; and, furthermore, ACh is present in the ganglion in a high concentration (BACQ 1947). Altogether this is an impressive assemblage of evidence that ACh is the inhibitory transmitter on H cells. The only disturbing observation is that eserine does not produce the expected prolongation of the IPSPs, which on the contrary are rapidly diminished (TAUC and GERSCHENFELD 1962). Apparently eserine blocks the cholinoceptive sites.

There are now similarly convincing experiments on the *Aplysia* neurons that are excited by ACh (the D-type cells). The depolarizing action of ACh and the excitatory synaptic action are both depressed by 10^{-4} dTC (Fig. 81 C, E) and by atropine; hence it appears that ACh is the excitatory transmitter substance on the D-cells (TAUC and GERSCHENFELD 1961; STRUMWASSER 1962). This dual role for ACh is surprising enough, but even more remarkable is the discovery (TAUC and GERSCHENFELD 1961; STRUMWASSER 1962) that the impulses discharged from a single interneurone actually exert typical synaptic excitatory actions on D-type neurones and inhibitory actions on H-type neurones; and that, as shown above, both these synaptic actions probably are mediated by ACh, as is shown diagrammatically in Fig. 81 G.

This extraordinary finding provides a further corroboration of DALE'S principle, which is simply that the same transmitter is liberated at all the synaptic terminals of a neurone. The differentiation in this case is provided by the specific properties of the ACh receptor sites on the two classes of recipient neurones. In one the ACh induces an ionic permeability giving depolarization, while in the other it induces the high conductance for Cl^- and/or K^+ ions characteristic of inhibitory synapses (Chapter XI). There are several examples of ACh being the transmitter for each of these actions (Chapters V and XII), but none, hitherto, where the ACh liberated from the same cell has these two diverse actions at different synapses. Evidently the type of synapse, excitatory or inhibitory, in the *Aplysia* ganglion is dependent on specification by the subsynaptic membrane rather than by some specification induced by the presynaptic fibre. Relevant to this postulated specification is the differential action of hexamethonium, which blocks both the synaptic and the ACh depolarizing actions on D-cells, and is without action on the synaptic and the ACh hyperpolarizing actions on H-cells (TAUC and GERSCHENFELD 1962).

Recent investigations by KERKUT and collaborators on inhibitory synapses of some neurones in the snail's brain also suggest that the inhibitory transmitter is ACh. Very discriminative chromatographic and pharmacological tests show that ACh is contained in the brain in a concentration of at least 1 in 10^6 (KERKUT and COTTRELL 1963). Direct applications of ACh to some neurones in concentrations as low as 10^{-8} inhibits them by a hyperpolarization resembling the IPSPs of those neurones, and an increase in conductance to Cl$^-$ ions is principally concerned in both these responses (KERKUT and THOMAS 1963 a). However, as already illustrated (Fig. 77 A), there is a difference of up to 15 mV for the null-points of the IPSPs and of the ACh-induced potentials.

Other sites in *Mollusca* where ACh appears to act as an inhibitory synaptic transmitter are on the hearts of *Venus mercenaria* (PROSSER 1940; WELSH and TAUB 1948), of *Mya arenaria* (HUGHES 1955), and of some lamellibranchs (FLOREY and MERVIN 1961), in all of which inhibition is produced by concentrations of ACh as low as 10^{-11} to 10^{-12}. In contrast ACh has an action resembling inhibitory synapses on the ganglion cells of *Onchidium*, but only at such a high threshold concentration of 5×10^{-4} M, that its role as a synaptic transmitter seems improbable (HAGIWARA and KUSANO 1961), unless access to the receptor sites is blocked by diffusional barriers. In a recent study (OOMURA, personal communication 1963) it has been found that ACh depolarizes some ganglion cells and hyperpolarizes others, just as has been found for *Aplysia* cells (Fig. 81 C—F); however both types of action appear to be due to a increased Cl$^-$ ion conductance, i.e. hyperpolarization or depolarization occur according as the equilibrium potential for chloride ions is above or below the membrane potential. Conceivably a similar mechanism may account for the responses of the H-cells and D-cells of *Aplysia* (Fig. 81 C—G).

CHAPTER XIII

PATHWAYS RESPONSIBLE FOR POSTSYNAPTIC INHIBITORY ACTION

A. Invertebrates

With invertebrates the nerve cell or muscle fibre under investigation is often supplied by only one or two inhibitory fibres, which can be dissected free of the excitatory fibres and stimulated in isolation (HOFFMANN 1914; WIERSMA and VAN HARREVELD 1935; VAN HARREVELD and WIERSMA 1937; ALEXANDRO-WICZ 1951; FLOREY and FLOREY 1955).

This stimulation in isolation establishes that inhibitory nerve fibres are purely inhibitory in their action on crustacean muscle fibres (FATT and KATZ 1953 b; BOISTEL and FATT 1958; HOYLE and WIERSMA 1958 b; KUFFLER 1960; DUDEL and KUFFLER 1961 c), and on the crustacean stretch receptor cells (KUFFLER and EYZAGUIRRE 1955; BURGEN and KUFFLER 1957; KUFFLER 1958, 1960; HAGIWARA, KUSANO and SAITO 1960).

With the cardiac ganglion of the lobster MAYNARD (1955) showed that a single inhibitory axon in the dorsal nerve directly inhibited the ganglion cells. Stimulation of this single fibre was found to produce depolarization of some ganglion cells and hyperpolarization of others (TERZUOLO and BULLOCK 1958), hence it appeared that this axon is an exception to the above generalization. However, a more recent investigation (OTANI and BULLOCK 1959) indicates that the inhibitory axon produces only IPSPs, and that the depolarizations are probably a consequence both of the leakage of chloride out of the electrode (Chapter XI) and of a high level of the membrane potential.

It was first suggested by TAUC and GERSCHENFELD (1961) and later confirmed by STRUMWASSER (1962) that synaptic endings of the same interneurone in a ganglion of *Aplysia* have an excitatory action on some cells (D-cells) and an inhibitory action on other cells (H-cells), acting at both synapses by ACh as the transmitter (Fig. 81 G). It seems likely that this represents the first exception to the generalization that a nerve cell never directly acts in both an excitatory and inhibitory manner though on analogy with Onchidium neurones (OOMURA, personal communication 1963) this may be due to differences in chloride ion concentration in the D and H cells. Probably similar examples will be discovered when the individual neurones of invertebrate nervous systems are analysed and characterized in the systematic manner that is described by KERKUT and WALKER (1962). Another possible example of conjoint excitatory and inhibitory action by single impulses is described by HAGIWARA and KU-SANO (1961) on the same ganglion cell in *Onchidium*. However this is more likely to be an example of electrical transmission preceding an IPSP, just as occurs with EPSPs in chick ciliary ganglion cells.

The occasional examples of a mixed excitatory and inhibitory action exerted by impulses in the one fibre must be weighed against the many examples of pure inhibitory action. It must also be recognized that there is no question of the liberation of different transmitters from the same fibre; there is merely a different postsynaptic action of the same transmitter with blockage by dTC and atropine at both synapses (Fig. 81). The metabolic uniqueness of inhibitory fibres has recently been demonstrated to an amazing degree by chemical analyses of motor and inhibitory fibres isolated from nerves in the meropodite of lobsters (Chapter XII; KRAVITZ, KUFFLER and POTTER 1963). When long lengths of isolated fibres made the analysis most discriminative, the GABA concentration was more than 1000 times larger in the inhibitory fibre.

B. Inhibitory pathways in central nervous system of vertebrates

1. The spinal cord

The simplest inhibitory pathway in the central nervous system of mammals has been the subject of controversy: one view is that the same Ia afferent fibres from muscle act directly in exciting some motoneurones and in inhibiting others; the other that all Ia afferent fibres are excitatory, and that their inhibitory action is mediated by interneurones that are uniquely inhibitory in action. Evidently, this controversy concerns quite fundamental issues, particularly in relation to the chemical transmitter hypothesis. It is proposed, therefore, to consider the evidence in detail, and in the light of new experiments to argue that it can no longer be maintained that group Ia afferent fibres have a direct inhibitory action.

Impulses in the largest afferent fibres (Group Ia from the annulospiral endings) of muscle exert a characteristically brief inhibitory action on moto-neurones supplying antagonistic muscles (LLOYD 1941, 1946a, b; RENSHAW 1942). There is a detectable inhibition of a monosynaptic reflex discharge even when the inhibitory volley precedes the excitatory by a small fraction of a millisecond (cf. Fig. 69). Thus LLOYD (1946a) and LAPORTE and LLOYD (1952) were led to postulate that Ia inhibitory and excitatory actions on motoneurones have identical central latencies; and hence that inhibition of motoneurones is exerted through a monosynaptic central path, the designation direct inhibition being applied. However, these investigations on the latency of central inhibitory action had the defect that the inhibition was being studied indirectly by relating the interval between the volleys entering the cord to the amount of inhibitory action on the monosynaptic reflex discharge. For our present purpose it is important to note that the central latency of inhibitory action was not measured; it was derived from the least volley interval for effective inhibition by a calculation that will be shown to be misleading.

When intracellular recording revealed that inhibitory synaptic action of a group Ia volley on a motoneurone is associated with a hyperpolarization (the inhibitory postsynaptic potential or IPSP; Fig. 57 A—G), which has a time course comparable to the inhibition of reflex discharge (Fig. 69 G, H; BROCK, COOMBS and ECCLES 1952), it was concluded that the IPSP is the cause of the inhibition of reflex discharge, and consequently that its latency provides a direct and accurate value for the latency of the inhibitory action on motoneurones. As measured from the time of entry of the afferent volley into the spinal cord to the onset of the IPSP, the inhibitory latency is almost a millisecond longer than the latency of the monosynaptic EPSP (Figs. 57 G, H; 62 B, D). Longitudinal conduction time of the inhibitory volley in the spinal cord accounts for only a small fraction of the discrepancy, and the remaining differential of 0.8 msec must be otherwise explained (ECCLES, FATT and LANDGREN 1956). Moreover the discrepancy cannot be due to a longer delay in the actual synaptic mechanism concerned in producing the IPSP because there is approximately the same interval (about 0.3 msec) between the onsets of the spike potentials in the respective presynaptic terminals on the one hand and the onsets of the EPSP and the IPSP on the other (Fig. 84 G, H; ECCLES, FATT and LANDGREN 1954, 1956). It was further found by ECCLES, FATT and LANDGREN (1956) and by ECCLES, ECCLES and LUNDBERG (1960) that the Ia impulses selectively excite interneurones in the intermediate nucleus (Fig. 82 A, B); and much evidence indicates that these interneurones have properties that precisely fit them to be interpolated on the Ia inhibitory pathway, and so to be responsible for this additional delay of 0.8 msec. For example they are selectively activated by Group Ia volleys, responding with brief latencies and high frequencies. Moreover, Group Ia afferent volleys produce a potential field in the spinal cord that would be expected if it were generated by intermediate neurones whose axons project towards the motoneurones being inhibited (ECCLES, FATT and LANDGREN 1956). Finally, R. M. ECCLES and LUNDBERG (1958 a) showed that in the anaesthetized preparation there must be summation of several simultaneous Ia afferent impulses before they can produce any IPSP of motoneurones, which can be explained only if there are interpolated neurones that require spatial summation of their synaptic activation (Chapter IV) in order to discharge impulses along the final stage of the inhibitory pathway.

It seemed as if interneurones had been firmly established as essential links in the Ia inhibitory pathway, and hence that the simplest inhibitory

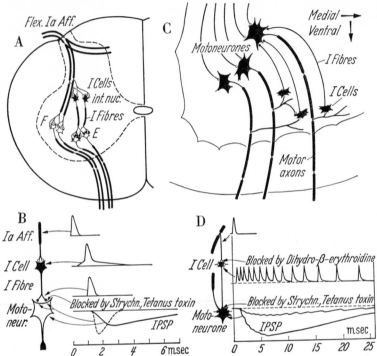

Fig. 82A—D. A. Drawing of monosynaptic excitatory pathway for flexor Ia afferent fibres to flexor motoneurones (F) and the disynaptic inhibitory pathway to extensor motoneurones (E) with a relay on inhibitory neurones (I cells) in the intermediate nucleus. Note that Ia afferent fibres converge on the intermediate neurones making spatial summation possible. B. Schematic drawing of the anatomical and physiological features of the Ia inhibitory pathway. It shows the events in the primary afferent fibre, in its excitatory synaptic connections with an intermediate neurone (I cell) and finally the inhibitory synaptic connection of this neurone with a motoneurone, where the inhibitory subsynaptic current is shown by a broken line and the IPSP by a continuous line (cf. Fig. 58A). C. Drawing of recurrent inhibitory pathway from motor axon collaterals to Renshaw cells (I cells) and thence to motoneurones. D. Diagram summarizing the postulated sequence of events from an impulse in a motor axon to the inhibition of a motoneurone. All events are plotted on the time scale shown below and the corresponding histological structures are shown diagrammatically to the left (note indicator arrows). The four plotted time courses are from above downwards for the following events: the electrical response of impulse in motor-axon collateral; the electrical response evoked in a Renshaw cell by the cumulative effect of acetylcholine at many synapses, showing impulses superimposed on a background depolarization; the IPSP generated in the motoneurone by the Renshaw cell discharge; and the aggregate IPSP evoked in a motoneurone that is bombarded repetitively by many Renshaw cells, which become progressively more asynchronous, so smoothing the latter part of the ripple. The structural diagram to the left shows converging synapses on the Renshaw cell (I cell) and on the motoneurone

pathway is disynaptic as shown in Fig. 82A, B. However, LLOYD and WILSON (1959) and LLOYD (1960a, b) attempted to re-establish the postulate of a monosynaptic inhibitory pathway, and to undermine all the evidence from the intracellular recording by making two postulates: that the intracellularly recorded IPSP is not the primary agent of Ia inhibitory action, but may be a secondary and later manifestation thereof, occurring up to 1 msec later than the onset of inhibition of reflex discharge; that the spike potential recorded intracellularly in the soma cannot be used as a signal of the reflex discharge

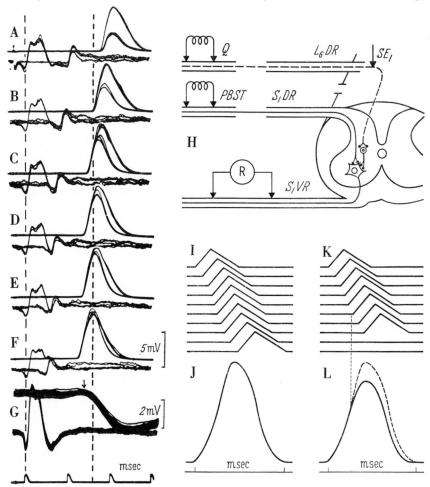

Fig. 83 A—L. The experimental arrangements are shown diagrammatically in H. In A—F a monosynaptic reflex spike response (monophasically recorded from S_1VR [upper traces]) was generated by an afferent volley from PBST, which also produced a diphasic spike in the records from the dorsum of the cord (lead SE_1 in H) at the upper L_6 level (lower traces). This PBST volley reached the cord at various times after a maximum group I afferent volley from quadriceps, which is at a fixed position in A—F, its arrival time at the upper L_6 level being given by the left perpendicular broken line. The superimposed traces for each of the testing intervals A—F were formed by firstly photographing eight traces for the PBST volley alone at 7 seconds interval to give the control reflex spike, and then a further eight traces with quadriceps volley in addition. The second vertical broken line at 1.59 msec from the first passes through the onset of the inhibition as signalled by the reflex spikes for all but record A. In G there is an IPSP produced by the Q volley and intracellularly recorded from a PBST motoneurone at the S_1 segmental level a little later in this same experiment and at the same sweep speed. The manner of production of a record such as C or D is illustrated in the constructions, I—L. In I there are schematic reflex spikes in ten fibres dispersed over 0.5 msec, as in a normal monosynaptic reflex, which is derived as in J by summation. Inhibition beginning at the dotted line in K, delays the onset of the 6th to 8th spikes as shown and suppresses the 9th and 10th. As a consequence the summed reflex potential (the continuous line in L) deviates from the control (the broken line in L) at a point just later than the dotted line (ARAKI, ECCLES and ITO 1960)

of an impulse along the axon. Evidently, in resolving this conflict, it is necessary to measure the latency of inhibitory action, not by intracellular recording, which is disallowed by the first postulate of LLOYD and WILSON, but by tests on the reflex discharge in the ventral roots (ARAKI, ECCLES and ITO 1960).

In Fig. 83 such measurements have been made by taking advantage of the considerable range in the latency of the individual components of the mono-synaptic reflex discharge (cf. Fig. 83I, J). If the inhibitory action is timed to begin during the dispersed reflex discharges from motoneurones, as illustrated in Fig. 83 K, the later components of the complex spike discharge will be delayed or suppressed, so causing a deviation of the inhibited spike from the control, as illustrated in Fig. 83L. The onset of the deviation would be expected to provide an accurate measure of the latency of inhibitory action, and this is illustrated in Fig. 83A—F, where the interval between the entrance into the spinal cord of the inhibitory and excitatory volleys is diminished progressively from 0.85 to 0.28 msec, and correspondingly the deviation point occurs progressively later on the reflex spike. When, as in Fig. 83 A—F, the inhibitory volley is at a fixed position (the first vertical broken line), the deviation points lie close to a second vertical line, which is in this figure 1.59 msec later. This interval gives the central latency for inhibitory action on reflex spike discharge if a small allowance (in this case 0.28 msec) is made for conduction time of the impulse from its origin in the initial segment of the motoneurone to the recording point on the ventral root (as indicated in H), i.e. the central inhibitory latency is 1.31 msec. This value is in good agreement with the latency of the IPSP (1.37 msec in G) intracellularly recorded from one of the motoneurones that contributed to the reflex spike. In a series of six experiments of this type, the latency of the IPSP was sampled in 24 motoneurones and was always within 0.1 msec of the central latency for inhibition of the reflex spike discharge. Similarly, with the contralateral inhibition at S_3 level, which provided the experimental basis for the arguments of LLOYD and WILSON (1959), there is excellent agreement (within 0.1 msec) between the latencies of the intracellular IPSPs and of the inhibitory action on reflex spike discharges.

Thus the experimental evidence refutes the postulate of LLOYD and WILSON (1959) that there is an earlier inhibitory process having no electrical sign, yet causing the inhibition of impulse discharge and somewhat (up to 1.0 msec) later the IPSP with its action in inhibiting the spike potentials that are recorded intracellularly in motoneurones. Incidentally this postulate also is at variance with the evidence that the IS component of the spike recorded in the motoneurone signals the initiation of the impulse discharges into the ventral root (Chapter VII; COOMBS, CURTIS and ECCLES 1957b).

Meanwhile the postulate of an interneurone on the inhibitory pathway was confirmed by directly stimulating these interneurones by brief electrical pulses applied through a microelectrode in the intermediate nucleus (EIDE, LUNDBERG and VOORHOEVE 1961). Such stimuli evoked both IPSPs and EPSPs of motoneurones with a latency of about 0.5 msec. Identification of

IPSPs was secured by taking advantage of the large changes produced by displacement of the membrane potential (cf. Fig. 60). Alternatively the mono-synaptic EPSPs were eliminated by degenerating the dorsal root fibres, the IPSPs being then seen in isolation as in Fig. 84A, B. The briefest latency of the IPSP so evoked by interneuronal stimulation is 0.46 msec and the mean latency is 0.52 msec, which gives a latent period for inhibitory synapses of about 0.3 msec when allowance of 0.2 msec is made for conduction time to the motoneurones. A similar duration had been given for the synaptic delay of IPSPs by ECCLES, FATT and LANDGREN (1956) and it is also the approximate latency of EPSPs (Chapter IV).

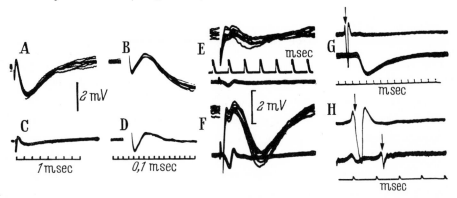

Fig. 84A—H. A, B intracellular records by a K_2SO_4-microelectrode from a motoneurone of a chronically deafferented cat with intact ventral roots, while C, D are the corresponding extracellular records. The stimulus was applied through another microelectrode in the intermediate nucleus at the same segmental level. A and C are at much slower sweep speed than B and D (EIDE, LUNDBERG and VOORHOEVE 1961). E, F. IPSPs recorded in a VSCT cell in response to weak and stronger stimulation of the ipsilateral half of the spinal cord 2.1 cm rostrally (ECCLES, HUBBARD and OSCARSSON 1961). G, H are respectively the IPSP produced in a semitendinosus motoneurone by a Group I quadriceps afferent volley, the volley entering the spinal cord being shown in the upper trace, and the extracellular recording at higher amplification and faster speed just outside that motoneurone to show the spike (lower half of trace) attributed to impulses in the terminals of the inhibitory neurones that evoked the IPSP in G. All records are formed by superposition of about 40 faint traces (ECCLES, FATT and LANDGREN 1954)

Fig. 84E, F illustrates the only other situation where a brief inhibitory latency has been observed in the spinal cord (ECCLES, HUBBARD and OSCARS-SON 1961). A descending volley in the ipsilateral half of the spinal cord pro-duced an IPSP in a cell of the ventral spinocerebellar tract. From the time of stimulation 2.1 cm rostrally to the onset of the IPSP was 0.8 to 0.9 msec, so a monosynaptic inhibitory pathway must be assumed, and the inhibitory synaptic delay would then be little if any longer than 0.3 msec. Only three cells were observed with this monosynaptic inhibitory action from the ipsi-lateral half, but the observations are of interest because they show that in-hibitory cells may have axons at least 2 cm in length. In parenthesis it may be noted that the olivo-cochlear bundle is composed of axons of inhibitory cells (DESMEDT and MONACO 1960, 1962), which also have a length measured in centimetres.

Now that the latency of onset of the IPSP has been conclusively shown to correspond with the latency of onset of inhibition of reflex spike discharges, it is permissible to use the IPSPs generated by other types of inhibitory action in order to measure the latencies of such inhibitions. With all postsynaptic inhibitions generated by primary afferent fibres, the latency of the IPSP has been so long that there is time for at least one interneurone on the central inhibitory pathway. For example the central latencies of motoneuronal IPSPs generated by Ib afferent volleys vary from 1.3 to 3.0 msec (Fig. 63 B, C, I, J; Eccles, Eccles and Lundberg 1957c); even the shortest latencies give time for relay in the intermediate nucleus via neurones that are selectively excited by Ib afferent volleys (Eccles, Eccles and Lundberg 1960). Again the latency of recurrent inhibition via motor axon collaterals (1.1 to 1.8 msec) has precisely the duration that is required for action through the Renshaw cells (Figs. 63 D, E, 82 C, D; Eccles, Fatt and Koketsu 1954). Moreover, the unique features of the high frequency repetitive discharge (Fig. 45 E—H) and of the pharmacology (Fig. 23) are exactly reflected in the IPSPs (Fig. 63 G) which are generated in motoneurones via the recurrent inhibitory pathway, as is shown diagrammatically in Fig. 82 C, D.

At least one interneurone also appears to be interpolated in the inhibitory pathways to motoneurones from Groups II and III muscle afferent impulses, and from cutaneous and joint afferents (R. M. Eccles and Lundberg 1959). When the central latencies for the excitatory and inhibitory actions of Group Ia and Ib muscle impulses on the cells of origin of the dorsal and ventral spinocerebellar tracts are compared (Curtis, Eccles and Lundberg 1958; Eccles, Oscarsson and Willis 1961; Eccles, Hubbard and Oscarsson 1961), there is the same extra delay of about 0.8 msec that is found with the Ia inhibitory action on motoneurones, so likewise it may be inferred that an interneurone is interpolated on the inhibitory pathway.

A descending volley in the pyramidal tract monosynaptically excites motoneurones of the monkey and baboon, and also often has an inhibitory action on the motoneurones (Preston and Whitlock 1960, 1961; Hern, Landgren, Phillips and Porter 1962; Landgren, Phillips and Porter 1962). The latency of the IPSPs is always longer than the monosynaptic EPSPs, the difference of about 1.2 msec suggesting that an interneurone is interpolated in the inhibitory pathway. Preston and Whitlock (1960) further observed interneuronal discharge at the time required for transmission of inhibitory action to the motoneurones, and suggested that the great sensitivity of the inhibitory pathway to barbiturates was attributable to the interneuronal relay. The very thorough and accurate investigation of Landgren, Phillips and Porter (1962) finally establishes the pattern of pyramidal action on the motoneurones to the arm muscles of the baboon, with the dominant monosynaptic EPSP and the interneuronal linkage giving disynaptic IPSPs.

By recording intracellularly from motoneurones of the toad spinal cord at fore-limb level, FUKAMI (1961) observed that dorsal root volleys evoked EPSPs with monosynaptic latency (about 1.5 msec from cord entry at 22°C). The IPSPs had a latency of about 3.0 msec, which is just long enough for a disynaptic pathway. It seems that, just as in the cat, primary afferent volleys cannot directly have an inhibitory action. An interneurone has to be interposed for this purpose.

In summary it can be stated that there is no recorded instance of a central inhibitory action directly produced by impulses in primary afferent fibres. In every case an interneurone is interpolated. Furthermore this is also the case with the pyramidal tract, and possibly also with other descending tracts because, in the three exceptions on VSCT cells (Fig. 84 E, F), the axons of the interneurones were probably being excited. It has been suggested that the interpolation of the interneurone in the inhibitory pathway is necessary in order to change the chemical transmitter mechanism from an excitatory to an inhibitory type (ECCLES, FATT and LANDGREN 1956; ECCLES 1957, 1961 a). This presumed necessity accounts for an anatomical arrangement that in other respects introduces a disability into the inhibitory pathway, namely the hazard of an additional synaptic relay (Fig. 82) and the consequent delay of at least 0.8 msec. Apparently in the course of evolution there was rejection of the alternative solution, namely specialized postsynaptic cells as with *Aplysia* (Fig. 81 G), so that excitation and inhibition are produced by the same transmitter.

A corollary to the hypothesis of inhibitory interneurones is that such interneurones cannot be on a pathway that leads eventually to some excitatory action. Renshaw cells are examples of such inhibitory interneurones, so a problem arises in attempting to account for the excitatory action that activation of Renshaw cells sometimes has on motoneurones (RENSHAW 1941; WILSON 1959; WILSON and BURGESS 1962b). However, there is now convincing pharmacological evidence that, even when facilitating the testing reflexes, Renshaw cells are acting by synaptic inhibitory action, this being exerted on interneurones of a tonic inhibitory pathway to motoneurones (WILSON and BURGESS 1962b); the motoneuronal facilitation would be brought about by a process of disinhibition (WILSON, DIECKE and TALBOT 1960; WILSON and BURGESS 1962a). The synapses made by Renshaw cells are thus reduced to two sets of purely inhibitory synapses, those on motoneurones (Fig. 82C), and those on the interneurones of the tonic inhibitory pathway ; hence in this respect Renshaw cells conform with DALE's principle.

2. *The brain*

The simple and stereotyped organization of synaptic connections onto the pyramidal cells of the hippocampus offers extraordinary advantages when attempting to answer problems relating to excitatory and inhibitory pathways. Histological investigation (RAMON y CAJAL 1911; LORENTE DE NÓ 1934; BLACKSTAD 1956, 1958) shows that presynaptic fibres of a certain type make synaptic contact with restricted parts of the pyramidal cells, which themselves

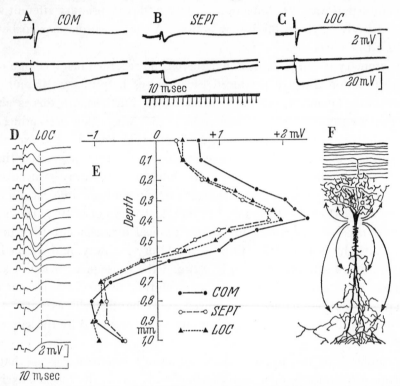

Fig. 85A—F. A, B and C. Extra- and intracellular records from a CA3 hippocampal pyramidal cell in response to commissural (*COM*), septal (*SEPT*) and local (*LOC*) stimulation; upper traces are surface records; lower traces the intracellular records; middle traces the extracellular records taken just outside the cell with the same gain and polarity as the inside recording. D shows responses recorded by a microelectrode penetrating CA3 following local stimulation. E. Graph in which the sizes of the positive waves of the responses to commissural, septal and local stimulation are plotted against depth. The positivities are measured at a time indicated by the stippled line in D, and correspondingly for the other inputs. Same depth scale for D and E. F. CA3 pyramidal cell, semidiagrammatically drawn to scale to facilitate comparison with E. Arrows indicate the extracellular flow of current generated by the inhibitory postsynaptic potential (ANDERSEN, ECCLES and LØYNING 1963)

are arranged with their somas in a single layer and their long axes at right angles thereto (Fig. 85 F).

As shown in Fig. 85 A—C stimulation of three separate inputs regularly produces in pyramidal cells very large and long IPSPs (ANDERSEN, ECCLES and LØYNING 1963), which were originally observed by KANDEL, SPENCER and BRINLEY (1961) and by KANDEL and SPENCER (1961) in response to fimbrial stimulation. In Fig. 85 D are arranged the extracellular potentials produced by local stimulation and recorded at various depths along a track that penetrated to approach the terminals of the apical dendrites of the CA3 pyramidal cells (cf. Fig. 85F). There is an initial negativity at superficial levels probably due to synaptic excitation of the basal dendrites of the pyramidal cells (ANDERSEN 1960b); but the dominant potential down to 0.5 mm is the large positive wave that attains a maximum at about 5 msec after the stimulus. This wave was measured at the fixed interval shown by the broken line, so as to minimize contamination by the initial superficial negativity, and plotted as filled triangles in E. Similarly, measurements for the potentials generated by the other stimulations, commissural and septal, are also plotted in E. There is a remarkable similarity in these three plots of potential fields, which all have a sharp maximum at a depth of 0.4 mm.

The interpretation of such potential fields is simplified by recognizing that because of their length, density and orientation, the pyramidal cells are the only neurones that could generate such large extracellular fields. Furthermore the cell bodies of these neurones are arranged in a sheet at a depth of 0.4 to 0.5 mm below the surface of the alveus, and the electrode track is perpendicular to this sheet and runs along the length of the cells from their basal to their apical dendrites as shown in F. It can thus be concluded that the field potentials of E must be produced by a powerful source of potential at or near the somas of the pyramidal cells, and that, in the extracellular medium, current flows from this source both superficially to the basal dendrites and deeply to the apical dendrites, as indicated by the arrows in F.

The wide distribution of the inhibition and the finding that all three inputs produce inhibitory postsynaptic potentials in virtually all pyramidal cells suggest that there is some mediating cell for this inhibition, an inhibitory interneurone. This suggestion is strengthened by the observation of latency differences of 0.8 to 3.2 msec between the initial depolarizing potential and the inhibitory potential when both are recorded from the same cell. The requirements for this inhibitory neurone based on the physiological findings described would be: 1. its axon should have extensive ramifications and should be distributed to a large number of pyramidal cells; 2. the synaptic terminals of this cell should end on the soma of the pyramids; 3. the inhibitory neurone should be activated by all three inputs employed, either directly, or more likely, indirectly by axon collaterals of the pyramidal cells after these had been excited in the first place. The last type of operation would be another example of recurrent inhibition.

These postulated inhibitory neurones can be identified both anatomically and physiologically. The detailed histological investigations of RAMON Y CAJAL (1911) and LORENTE DE NÓ (1934) reveal a special type of cell, the basket cell (Figs. 86A, 87B) that exactly corresponds to the postulated inhibitory neurone, and there is no alternative. The axon of each basket cell ramifies profusely and distributes itself to the somas of 200 to 500 pyramidal cells, making a dense plexus enclosing the cell bodies of the pyramidal cells in a basket-like structure (Fig. 87A, B) ending in terminal synapses (Fig. 4A).

The physiological evidence of inhibitory cell activity is usually given by a brief high frequency (500—1000/sec) ripple resembling that given by Renshaw cells in the spinal cord. This ripple appears on the initial phase of the positive wave, is largest at a depth of 0.3 to 0.4 mm and is given by all the inputs.

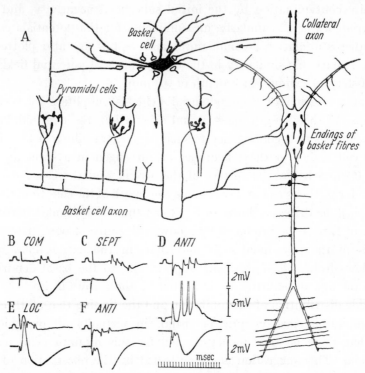

Fig. 86A—F. A. Diagram of a CA 3 pyramidal cell with some of its connexions. The right half is taken from LORENTE DE NÓ (1934) showing the endings of basket cell axons on the soma. Other afferents make excitatory synaptic contacts with the apical and basal dendrites. The left half of the diagram is drawn to illustrate the proposed pathway. Axon collaterals from three of the four pyramidal cells converge on a basket cell, drawn black. The basket cell axon (indicated with an arrow) ramifies and makes synaptic contact on the somas of the pyramidal cells; these are the postulated inhibitory synapses. Additional synapses on the basket cell and other branches of the basket cell axon indicate that the basket cell may receive impulses from and deliver impulses to a great number of hippocampal pyramidal cells. B, C and E, F show the responses of a presumed basket cell to the commissural, septal, local and antidromic afferent volleys. *ANTI* is stimulus applied to axons of pyramidal cells in the fimbria, but it also evokes impulses that are conducted orthodromically towards the hippocampus. This cell fires repetitively during the initial phase of the positive wave at a frequency of about 500/sec, and is not antidromically invaded. Recording depth 0.2 mm. D. Upper trace shows extracellular response to antidromic stimulation (ipsilateral fimbria). Middle trace shows intracellular record with a prolonged excitatory postsynaptic potential giving rise to the repetitive discharge of spikes that are truncated. Lower trace is surface record. The antidromic input is contaminated with orthodromically conducting impulses in the ipsilateral fimbria (ANDERSEN, ECCLES and LØYNING 1963)

Occasionally it is possible to record from one of the rhythmically firing cells (Fig. 86B—F), and it exhibits the properties expected for an inhibitory cell: 1. activation by all the inputs; 2. discharge often just preceding the onset of the positive extracellular wave and continuing during its rising phase; 3. not antidromically invaded when pyramidal cell axons are stimulated; 4. when activated under such conditions (D), it differs from pyramidal cells in showing a prolonged excitatory postsynaptic potential with superimposed spikes and no IPSP. Furthermore, this cell was at a depth of only 0.2 mm, where basket cells but not pyramidal cells may be found.

The proposed inhibitory pathway is shown semi-diagrammatically in Fig. 86 A where a basket cell receives excitatory synapses from axon collaterals of pyramidal cells and itself forms many inhibitory synaptic endings on the

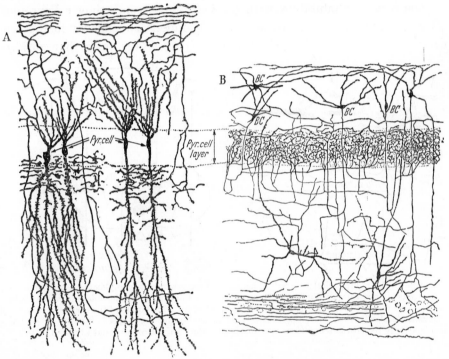

Fig. 87 A and B. Golgi-Cox stain of a section of the hippocampal cortex in a month-old rabbit. In A are four pyramidal cells each with their axon and basal and apical dendrites. Note that the pyramidal cell bodies are arranged in a layer. In B are four basket cells (*BC*) with their axons terminating as profuse ramifications around the somas of the pyramidal cells that are in the same layer as in A, but are unstained. Note the recurrent pathway of the axon collaterals of the *BC* cells that usually pass through the pyramidal cell layer and then return to it. The dorsal surface of the hippocampus is above as in Figs. 85 and 86 (RAMON Y CAJAL 1911, Figs. 473, 475)

somas of pyramidal cells. The inputs employed in Fig. 85 would all excite pyramidal cells and so indirectly activate the basket cells.

In conclusion, it seems possible for the first time to give an example from the mammalian nervous system of a recurrent inhibitory pathway where both the inhibitory neurone (Fig. 87 B, *BC*) and its synapses (Fig. 4 A) are histologically identifiable. It will be appreciated that from strategic considerations inhibitory synapses located on the soma are optimally placed for controlling the generation of impulse discharge, because they would be sited between the excitatory synapses on the dendrites and the axon hillock where the impulse generation probably occurs (Chapter VII). There are several other examples of dense synaptic innervation of the somas of neurones, for example the basket cell endings on Purkinje cells (Fig. 4 B; RAMON Y CAJAL 1911, Figs. 11, 20, 23), and from the pericellular network around cortical pyramidal cells (RAMON Y CAJAL 1911, Figs. 361, 362); probably these, too, are the terminal branches of inhibitory cells. This inference has been corroborated for the basket cells of the cerebellum by an investigation similar to that of Fig. 85 (ANDERSEN, ECCLES and VOORHOEVE 1963).

The recurrent inhibitory pathway via interneurones shown diagrammatically in Fig. 86 A appears to be a very common arrangement in the central nervous system. For example PHILLIPS (1959, 1961) finds that antidromic

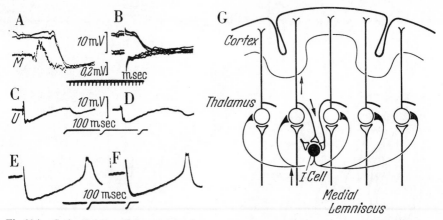

Fig. 88 A—G. A—F, intracellular records of neurones in the ventrobasal complex of the thalamus recorded with a potassium citrate-filled microelectrode. A and C are evoked by single volleys from the median and ulnar nerves respectively, while B and D—F are evoked by stimulation of the cortical terminals of the thalamocortical relay cells. Note that A and B are at much faster sweep speeds than C—F. G shows diagrammatically the postulated pathways for recurrent inhibition (ANDERSEN and ECCLES 1962)

activation of the pyramidal tract evokes large IPSPs in cortical pyramidal cells (Fig. 64 H). Possibly, too, the large IPSPs observed by LUX and KLEE (Fig. 64 J; 1962) and KLEE and LUX (1962) are produced by axon collaterals of cortical cells projecting to the centrum medianum, the ventro-basal complex of the thalamus and the caudate nucleus, though an alternative pathway would be via orthodromic activation of interneurones in the cortex.

The role of recurrent inhibition in controlling the frequency of rhythmic waves has been suggested on several occasions, most notably by SPENCER and KANDEL (1962) in the generation of the theta waves of the hippocampus, but also by VASTOLA (1959) for the rhythmic waves of the lateral geniculate body, and by FESSARD (1962, personal communication) for the alpha rhythm of the cerebral cortex. The decisive role of IPSPs in generating rhythmic waves has been demonstrated with the ventrobasal complex of the thalamus (ANDERSEN and ECCLES 1962; ANDERSEN, BROOKS and ECCLES 1963), and can be explained by means of the diagram of the proposed recurrent inhibitory connections in Fig. 88.

In Fig. 88 it is seen that large and prolonged IPSPs are produced in a thalamic neurone either by an orthodromic volley from a cutaneous nerve and up the medial lemniscus (A, C) or by an antidromic volley set up by stimulation of the cortical terminals of the thalamo-cortical fibres (B, D—F). These IPSPs occur independently of whether or not that particular neurone responds by an impulse (Fig. 88 E, F), and are seen in all thalamic neurones that project to the cerebral cortex from the ventro-basal complex. The postulated inhibitory interneurones (the I cell in Fig. 88 G) are presumably the thalamic neurones that do not degenerate after ablation of the cerebral cortex (SHEPS 1945; CLARK and POWELL 1953; McLARDY 1950; POWELL 1952).

This recurrent inhibition is of interest because it provides the essential mechanism in the phasing of the successive burst discharges that follow a single orthodromic activation of the thalamus (ADRIAN 1941; ANDERSEN and ECCLES 1962; ANDERSEN, BROOKS and ECCLES 1963). By means of the recurrent inhibitory pathway, the discharge of thalamic neurones results in a powerful and widespread inhibition (Fig. 88 G) which suppresses all thalamic discharges for about 100 msec, and so cuts off the recurrent activation of the inhibitory neurones. Hence the IPSP is not sustained, and late on its declining phase post-anodal exaltation or rebound will again cause the discharge of thalamic neurones, perhaps with the aid of a background interneuronal excitation. The resultant activation of the inhibitory cells will cause abrupt termination of this burst discharge by the newly generated IPSP. This is illustrated in Fig. 88 E, F for a thalamic neurone that is activated antidromically either by a volley that invades the neurone (E), or fails to do so (F). It is seen that late on the recovery phase of the IPSP a burst response is generated and then terminated by the consequent IPSP, so starting a new cycle, and so on.

The phasing of the population of thalamic cells so that they respond together in the same rhythmic cycle is envisaged as being implemented primarily by the widespread recurrent inhibition. Moreover, the rhythmic electrical waves themselves are attributed mainly to the postsynaptic electrical currents that generate the IPSPs (Chapter X). In accord with previous suggestions a comparable type of recurrent inhibitory mechanism acting on pyramidal cells may be regarded as being responsible for the alpha rhythm of the cerebral cortex and for the theta rhythm of the hippocampus.

CHAPTER XIV

INHIBITORY SYNAPSES OPERATING BY ELECTRICAL TRANSMISSION

In most species of fish the two large Mauthner cells (M-cells) are the most conspicuous neurones in the brain. As illustrated in Fig. 89 A several distinct types of synapse cover the two large dendrites; but of particular interest is the helicoidal feltwork of fine fibres (s.p.) that is embedded in the so-called axon cap (Bartelmez 1915; Bodian 1937, 1942, 1952; Retzlaff 1954). The axon cap is an approximately spherical structure of glial and nervous elements surrounding the axon of the M-cell from its axon-hillock origin to the beginning of its myelination (see broken line of Fig. 89 A). The axon of each M-cell then expands to about 40 μ in diameter, decussates with its fellow, and runs down the spinal cord (Fig. 97 A).

By a detailed study with intracellular and extracellular recording from M-cells with microelectrodes placed at known locations, it has been established that activation of the fine nerve fibres within the axon cap applies a hyper-polarizing current to the axon hillock, so effecting an inhibition of the M-cell (Furukawa and Furshpan 1963). The essential observations are that, after orthodromic or antidromic activation of a M-cell, the extracellularly recorded spike potential of that cell is followed by a positive wave of about 1 msec in duration; and there is a similar positive wave outside the contralateral un-activated M-cell (Fig. 89 B, F). These extracellular positive waves are of maximum size (10 to 15 mV) in the region of the axon hillock, and are very much smaller when the microelectrode is inserted into the axon hillock (Fig. 89 C, G), which proves that most of the extracellular potential actually is impressed on the membrane of the axon hillock as a hyperpolarization. The hyperpolarization is measured as the difference between the extracellular and intracellular records in B, C and F, G. There is no detectable change in membrane conductance, so there is effectively a passive hyperpolarization of the axon hillock, just as would be produced by the external application of the anode of a current-passing circuit; hence the designation *external hyperpolarizing potential*, EHP. The EHPs generated by an impulse in the axon of an M-cell are larger for the contralateral than for the ipsilateral M-cell.

The superimposed traces of Fig. 89 E show that the brief anelectrotonus of the axon hillock blocks its invasion by the four concurrent antidromic impulses (note arrows), but not the antidromic impulses immediately before or after. These four blocked impulses are seen as the small spikes electrotonically trans-

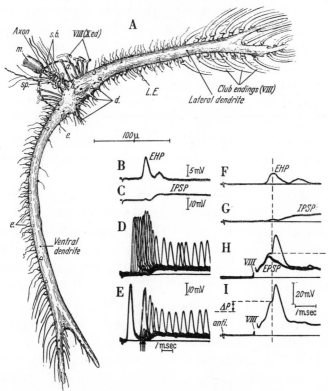

Fig. 89A—I. Semi-diagrammatic drawing of Mauthner cell of goldfish with mid-line to left and dorsal above. The extent of the axon cap is indicated by the circle and within it are seen a few of the spiral fibres *sp.* arising from a fibre bundle *s.b.*, and also the axon hillock (*h*). As described in the text an impulse in the contralateral M-axon evokes respectively potentials B and C extracellularly in the axon cap and intracellularly in the axon hillock. D and E are also intracellularly recorded and show that the EHP and later IPSP produce depression or block of an antidromic impulse invading that M-cell from its axon. F and G correspond to B and C but are from another M-cell and are at a faster time base. In H are superimposed traces of EPSPs of M-cells evoked by gradually increasing stimuli to the ipsilateral eighth cranial nerve, the largest of which generated a spike and so indicated that threshold was at the level of the broken line. In I the threshold level of EPSP is seen to be increased by ΔP because of its superposition upon the conditioning EHP of F (Furukawa and Furshpan 1963)

mitted from the adjacent axon. Only under optimal conditions does the EHP block antidromic impulses. For example there is no block in Fig. 89 D because the EHP is smaller, being generated by the contralateral M-axon only, whereas in E there is summation of the EHPs produced from both M-axons.

The EHP also raises the threshold for synaptic generation of an impulse. For example in Fig. 89, the threshold level of EPSP for generation of a spike (broken horizontal line in H) is seen to be raised considerably (by ΔP in I) when there is a synchronously applied EHP. This EHP is indicated by the extracellular (F) and intracellular (G) records produced by the same conditioning situation, which is antidromic activation of the contralateral M-cell.

The EHP has almost the same amplitude throughout the axon cap, so the hyperpolarizing current applied to the initial segment of the M-axon must be generated by nerve fibres in the axon cap, which presumably are activated by the axon collaterals of the M-cells. The latent period between the arrival of an antidromic impulse at the axon hillock of the M-cell and the onset of the EHP is 1.2 to 2 msec, which would allow for one or even two interneurones in the pathway (N_1 and N_2 in Fig. 97A). The existence of interneurones on the pathway is also indicated by the suppression of EHP that occurs during low frequency stimulation—at about 5/sec. It is suggested that the EHP is produced by the fibres in which the impulse fails to invade the terminal parts in the helicoidal feltwork of the axon cap region, these terminals thus being sources for extracellular current flow to the more proximal excited zones on their fibres.

The intracellular records of Fig. 89 C and G show that, immediately after the small positive spike produced by the current flow generated by the EHP, there is a prolonged positive wave (depolarization). This wave of about 20 msec duration exhibits the properties characteristic of an IPSP (Chapters X and XI), its depolarizing direction being attributable to the diffusion of Cl^- ions out of the microelectrode. In Fig. 89D and E this IPSP depresses the antidromic spike potential. It also depresses the EPSP produced monosynaptically by 8th nerve impulses (Fig. 97 H, I), and the generation of impulse discharges by this EPSP. During the IPSP there is the typical increase in ionic conductance, which is largely attributable to Cl^- ions (FURUKAWA and FURSHPAN 1963). An extensive investigation of the permeability to various anion species during the IPSP has revealed a precise agreement with Fig. 71, even to the anomalous permeability to formate ions (ASADA 1963).

Since there is complete correlation between the experimental conditions producing the EHP and the IPSP, it may be assumed that both are produced by impulses in the same fibres. Fibres of the helicoidal system eventually break out from it to make typical synaptic endings on the region of the axon hillock (BODIAN 1937). Presumably in some collaterals of these fibres in the helicoidal feltwork there is the blockage of impulses that gives the sources responsible for the EHP, while in other branches impulse conduction continues to the inhibitory synapses. The functional significance of the initial brief electrical inhibitory action must be considered in relation to the inhibitory action of the later prolonged chemical inhibition that presumably is produced by the same impulses. On account of its briefer latency the electrical inhibition can be considered simply as a device for procuring an earlier onset of inhibition, which later is continued by the IPSP.

Stimulation of the ipsilateral or contralateral 8th nerve also produces a brief extracellular positive wave (Fig. 97D, F) that resembles the EHP in that it is of uniform size throughout the axon cap (FURUKAWA and FURSHPAN 1963; FURUKAWA, FUKAMI and ASADA 1963a). It likewise causes a brief hyperpolarization of the axon hillock and an associated depression of antidromic invasion; hence it is another example of electrically transmitted inhibition. The fibres producing this hyperpolarization of the axon hillock however have a later chemical transmitting action in the opposite direction producing an EPSP (Fig. 97H, J) and the initiation of impulse discharge. It may therefore be questioned if this initial electrical inhibition is functionally significant, or whether it is merely an inadvertent accompaniment of the blockage of some excitatory impulses in the axon cap.

In their elucidation of the nature of the EHP FURUKAWA and FURSHPAN (1963) have clearly established for the first time that functionally effective inhibition can be produced by electrical transmission from nerve fibres to a nerve cell. Structures resembling the helicoidal feltwork of the axon cap also exist around axon hillocks of other nerve cells (BODIAN 1937), so it seems likely that there may be other examples of this electrical inhibitory mechanism.

CHAPTER XV

PRESYNAPTIC INHIBITION

A. In the vertebrate central nervous system

GASSER and GRAHAM (1933) found that dorsal root volleys produced slow positive potentials (P waves) of the cord dorsum, and that the time courses of these waves corresponded approximately to that of the inhibition of flexor reflexes when one dorsal root volley was employed to condition the flexor reflex evoked by another volley. Consequently, they asked "whether the positive potential may not be connected with the process responsible for inhibition?". In further communications Hughes and GASSER (1934a, 1934b) provided additional evidence supporting this correlation; and later GASSER (1937) attributed the inhibition to a depression of interneurones in a common central pathway that was produced by the positive after-potential that followed their activation by the conditioning volley. BARRON and MATTHEWS (1938) found that dorsal root volleys also gave rise to a depolarization that spread electrotonically along the same or adjacent dorsal roots and postulated that this dorsal root potential (DRP) was produced by the same potential generator that gave the P wave; and this identification has been accepted by all subsequent investigators (BREMER and BONNET 1942; BERNHARD 1952, 1953; KOKETSU 1956a, 1956b; ECCLES, MAGNI and WILLIS 1962; ECCLES, KOSTYUK and SCHMIDT 1962a; ECCLES, SCHMIDT and WILLIS 1963a, 1963b).

BARRON and MATTHEWS (1938) further postulated that the potential generator for the P wave and the DRP had an inhibitory action in the spinal cord because it gave rise to electric currents that caused blockage of conduction in the collateral branches of interneurones. Subsequently there has been additional evidence that inhibitory action in the spinal cord is due to block or depression of presynaptic excitatory impulses (RENSHAW 1946b; BROOKS, ECCLES and MALCOLM 1948; HOWLAND, LETTVIN, McCULLOCH, PITTS and WALL 1955). Particularly convincing evidence of presynaptic inhibition was reported by FRANK and FUORTES (1957) and FRANK (1959) who showed that muscle afferent volleys produce inhibition by diminishing the size of the monosynaptic EPSP of motoneurones without having any other demonstrable action on those motoneurones. There is no associated membrane potential change either at the normal resting potential or when the membrane potential is altered by a background depolarizing or hyperpolarizing current (FRANK, personal communication); hence there can be no change in the ionic permeability of the postsynaptic membrane, such as invariably occurs with postsynaptic inhibition. Furthermore, there is no associated change in motoneuronal excitability, as tested either by the intracellular application of current pulses or by the responses to invasion by an antidromic impulse in the motor axon.

Evidently, it should be concluded that the diminution of the EPSPs is due to a diminished excitatory action of the Ia presynaptic impulses. However, FRANK (1959) in addition proposed an alternative explanation, which attributed the EPSP depression to an action exerted so far out on the dendrites of the motoneurone that no trace of the inhibitory influence itself could be detected by a microelectrode in the motoneuronal soma. Since both of these alternative explanations would locate inhibitory action at a site remote from the motoneuronal soma, FRANK (1959) designated the phenomenon "remote inhibition." However, there is now a wealth of experimental evidence establishing that depolarization of the presynaptic fibres is responsible for the diminution of the EPSP and the consequent inhibition of reflex discharge (ECCLES, ECCLES and MAGNI 1961; ECCLES, MAGNI and WILLIS 1962; ECCLES, SCHMIDT and WILLIS 1962); hence this inhibitory phenomenon will forthwith be called "presynaptic inhibition," which was the term initially used by FRANK and FUORTES (1957).

An intensive investigation during the last three years has revealed that exactly the same type of inhibition is widely distributed throughout the mammalian central nervous system, and that it is more powerful than postsynaptic inhibition in depressing the central excitatory actions of almost all primary afferent fibres. It is proposed firstly to consider experimental investigations on the mechanism of presynaptic inhibitory action, then subsequently the investigations on the various central pathways and on the actions of drugs. Since presynaptic inhibition of the monosynaptic activation of motoneurones by impulses in Group Ia afferent fibres can be more easily and accurately investigated than any other variety, it will provide all of the initial illustrative material (Figs. 90—93). However, as a result of a fairly comprehensive investigation, it has been established that the other varieties have similar properties, so it can be presumed that they are all examples of precisely the same type of central inhibition. The initial description will cover sequentially three aspects of presynaptic inhibitory action: firstly, the depression of monosynaptic excitatory action; secondly, the consequent depression of reflex discharge; and finally, the depolarization of the presynaptic fibres that is postulated to be responsible for presynaptic inhibition. This depolarization of presynaptic fibres is measured directly by an intrafibre microelectrode, and also indirectly by their increased excitability: and of course it gives rise to the dorsal root potential and to a characteristic field potential in the spinal cord with ventral negativity and dorsal positivity, which

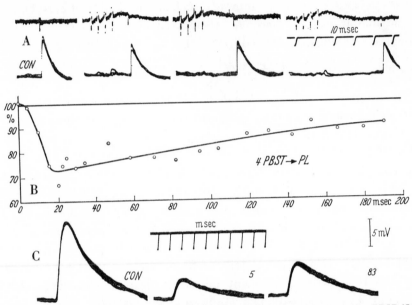

Fig. 90 A—C. Depression of monosynaptic EPSP by presynaptic inhibition. In A the EPSP (CON) in a plantaris motoneurone is seen to be depressed by four group I conditioning volleys in the nerve to the knee flexors, posterior biceps plus semitendinosus (PBST). The timing of the conditioning and testing afferent volleys is shown in the upper traces (positivity upwards in both traces). In B the time course of the EPSP depression (expressed as percentage of control) is shown for the series illustrated in A. In C the control EPSP (CON) of another experiment is seen to be greatly depressed both at 5 and 83 msec after conditioning tetanus of 22 Group I volleys (Eccles, Eccles and Magni 1961)

includes the P wave on the dorsum of the cord first reported by Gasser and Graham (1933).

The most direct evidence of presynaptic inhibition is illustrated in Fig. 90A, where four conditioning Group I volleys from the knee flexor muscle, posterior-biceps semitendinosus, depress the monosynaptic EPSP of a plantaris motoneurone relative to the control (CON) response, but do not produce any appreciable postsynaptic potential, either EPSP or IPSP. The time course of this depression of the EPSP is given by the plotted points of Fig. 90B, there being a latency of about 5 msec, a maximum at about 20 msec and a total duration in excess of 200 msec. Several conditioning volleys at 200 to 300/sec are usually employed as in Fig. 90A, in order to increase the size of the pre-synaptic inhibition by temporal facilitation (Eccles, Schmidt and Willis 1963b). For example in the series of Fig. 90A, one conditioning volley pro-duced a maximum depression of less than 10%, and with two it was less than

20 %. However, the time course of the depression resembled that in Fig.90A,B, except that it was virtually over by 200 msec (ECCLES, ECCLES and MAGNI (1961).

FRANK and FUORTES (1957) and FRANK (1959) reported that with presynaptic inhibition the depression of the monosynaptic EPSP was not

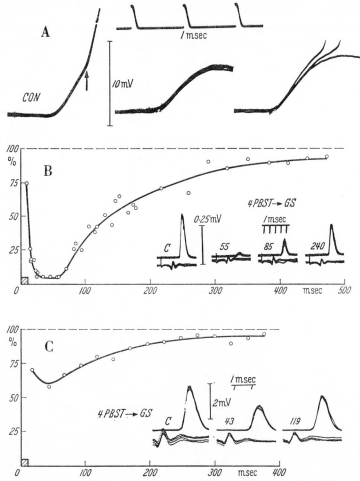

Fig. 91 A—C. Presynaptic inhibition of monosynaptically generated reflex discharges. In A the superimposed control EPSPs (CON) are seen always to generate the discharge of an impulse at the arrow, whereas conditioning presynaptic inhibition causes impulse generation to fail or be delayed. B and C are comparable series of presynaptic inhibition of monosynaptic reflex discharges into the ventral root, B being from an animal anaesthetized by nembutal and with the spinal cord severed, while C is from a decerebrate unanaesthetised preparation. Specimen records of the reflex discharges are shown, c being control and the others at the indicated intervals after the conditioning tetanus of four PBST volleys (ECCLES, SCHMIDT and WILLIS 1962)

associated with any alteration in its time course, which also appears to be the case in Fig. 90A; but there is a more convincing demonstration in Fig. 90 C, where the monosynaptic EPSP of a gastrocnemius motoneurone is greatly diminished in size following conditioning by 22 PBST volleys at 210/sec. The EPSPs at the various test intervals after the tetanus are depressed in size even below 25 %, but have the same time course as the control.

The specimen records of Fig. 91 A show that, as would be expected, the simple diminution of the EPSP may prevent it from generating the discharge of an impulse, or at least delay the discharge. Presynaptic inhibition of mono-synaptic reflex discharge can be observed for a population of motoneurones, as in the specimen records of ventral root discharges in Fig. 91B, which are a part of the plotted series. For the initial 20 msec or so there may be post-synaptic inhibitory or excitatory actions superimposed, but thereafter the

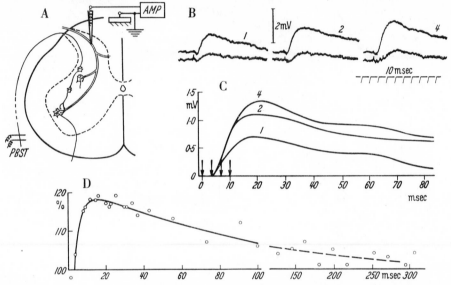

Fig. 92A—D. A shows the experimental arrangement for obtaining the responses B—C. The micro-electrode is inserted into a group I a afferent fibre (GS) from the gastrocnemius-soleus muscle at a depth of 0.6 mm from the cord dorsum, and the potential changes of the upper records of B are produced by 1, 2 and 4 group I volleys in the combined posterior biceps-semitendinosus (PBST) and deep peroneal nerves (PDP). The lower records of B show the potentials similarly produced, but with the microelectrode withdrawn to a just extracellular position. The actual potential changes across the membrane of that group I a fibre are given by the differences between the corresponding intracellular and extracellular potentials, as plotted in C for 1, 2 and 4 volleys, upward deflections signalling depolarization. D shows the time course of the excitability changes which a single PBST volley produces in group I a afferent fibres of gastrocnemius nerve at the region of their synaptic terminals in the ventral horn (cf. ECCLES, MAGNI and WILLIS 1962). Ordinates show excitability values as percentages of the control, while abscissae give test intervals (ECCLES 1963)

depression of the reflexes can be assumed to be entirely due to presynaptic inhibition (ECCLES, SCHMIDT and WILLIS 1962). Such powerful and prolonged presynaptic inhibitions are often observed in preparations under barbiturate anaesthesia (ECCLES, SCHMIDT and WILLIS 1962, 1963d; R. M. ECCLES and WILLIS 1963). In decerebrated unanaesthetized animals the inhibition is always less (Fig. 91 C), but nevertheless is much longer than postsynaptic inhibitions in the spinal cord.

As shown in Fig. 92A intracellular recording from Group I a primary afferent fibres has been possible only in the dorsal region of the cord, where the fibres are rather coarse. Since field potentials are relatively large, it is essential to record potentials both inside the fibre and just outside (92B), the actual membrane potential change being obtained by subtraction, as has been done for the plotted records of Fig. 92C with the depolarizations produced by 1, 2 and 4 volleys in the PBST nerve. The time course of this presynaptic depolarization is in excellent agreement with that of the depression of the EPSP in Fig. 90B, there being a latent period of about 4 msec, a summit at about 20 msec and a duration far in excess of 100 msec and probably at least 200 msec. Comparable depolarizations of Group Ia afferent fibres are regularly produced by volleys in the Group I afferent fibres of flexor muscles (ECCLES, MAGNI and WILLIS 1962; ECCLES, SCHMIDT and WILLIS 1963 b).

An alternative method of displaying depolarization of primary afferent fibres is to test their excitability by brief current pulses applied through a coarse extracellular microelectrode, which is a technique notably developed by WALL (1958). Depolarized fibres are more readily excitable; consequently more fibres are excited by a given submaximal stimulus and there is a larger spike potential antidromically transmitted along the peripheral afferent nerve under observation. The percentage change in excitability is determined by reference to the responses evoked by application of a calibrating range of pulse strengths through the microelectrode (ECCLES, MAGNI and WILLIS 1962). For example the points obtained in this way are plotted in Fig. 92D to give the time course of excitability increase produced by a single PBST volley. If suitably scaled this curve would represent the average time course of depolarization of the Group Ia fibres from gastrocnemius muscle. The latency is about 4 msec, the summit is at 15 msec and the total duration is in excess of 300 msec. Two conditioning PBST volleys caused an excitability increase of almost double size, but with a comparable time course. Evidently this method of testing for the depolarization of a population of Group Ia afferent fibres gives results in good agreement with the depolarizations directly observed by intra-fibre recording (Fig. 92B). The advantage of the method of excitability testing is that it can be applied throughout the whole course of the Group Ia fibres within the spinal cord, and is not restricted to the dorsal segment, as is the case with intracellular recording. This full range of excitability testing is important because it shows that the increase in excitability of Group Ia fibres near their terminals in the motoneuronal nucleus is at least three times greater than at the region where intracellular recording is possible (ECCLES, SCHMIDT and WILLIS 1963b). It can therefore be anticipated that the depolarization at the motoneuronal terminals of the fibre would be correspondingly larger than in Fig. 92C.

The latency of synaptic action is now known not to exceed 0.5 msec in the mammalian central nervous system (Chapter IV), so it is likely that most of the central delay of presynaptic inhibition is occupied in transmission along an interneuronal chain. It has been postulated that this central pathway includes at least two serially arranged interneurones; and interneurones with appropriate properties have been discovered (ECCLES, KOSTYUK and SCHMIDT 1962a).

Under the most diverse experimental conditions the primary afferent depolarization in the spinal cord invariably displays a prolonged phase (10 to 25 msec) of increase to a rounded summit, which is much more prolonged than is generally observed for postsynaptic actions in the spinal cord (Chapters IV and X). The simplest explanation is that there is a prolonged repetitive bombardment of the synapses depolarizing the presynaptic fibres, just as occurs for example with Renshaw cells (Figs. 45E—H; 63D—H); and interneurones showing this postulated repetitive discharge for as long as 20 msec have been frequently observed in the intermediate nucleus (ECCLES, KOSTYUK and SCHMIDT 1962a).

If it be postulated that the *primary afferent depolarization* (PAD) is produced by the action of a chemical transmitter, the long duration (Fig.92C, D) can be attributed either to a prolonged action of the transmitter or to a slow passive decay of the depolarization because of the long electric time constant of the membrane (Chapter IV). The passively decaying component of the PAD should be erased by an impulse propagating down the afferent fibre to its central terminals, exactly as occurs with an antidromic impulse and the EPSP of motoneurones (Chapter IV; CURTIS and ECCLES 1959; ECCLES 1961b).

In Fig. 93 A—E are specimen records showing the effect of superimposing an action potential at various times during the PAD of a nerve fibre. A small after-depolarization (ADP) and later after-hyperpolarization (AHP) follows the spike potential in the control records, F, H, but this single volley produces no detectable PAD. In the superimposed tracings (G) the ADP is reduced in size when superimposed on the depolarization of the PAD, and is even reversed towards the summit of the PAD. The PAD fails to recover to its control level at all intervals after the interpolated action potential, the deficit being larger with interactions close to the summit of the PAD. However, the level of depolarization after the interaction is always larger than for the ADP and the subsequent hyperpolarization in Fig. 93 F and H, so it can be presumed that a considerable proportion of the PAD either survives the propagation of an impulse into the fibre terminals or is rebuilt afterwards. Somewhat comparable observations have been reported for the action of an interpolated afferent volley in partly destroying the DRPs recorded from a frog dorsal root (ECCLES and MALCOLM 1946), but the situation there was more complicated because the interpolated volley itself produced a large DRP.

The simplest hypothesis is that the impulse destroys all the PAD that is preformed in that fibre, and that subsequently the lingering transmitter rebuilds much of the depolarization. As would be expected, the rebuilding is seen to be very effective after the earliest interpolation of the impulse in

Fig. 93G, and to be progressively less effective at longer intervals. Thus it would be envisaged that the transmitter continues to act throughout the whole duration of the PAD; consequently it is not necessary to postulate in addition that a large area of the surface membrane of the primary afferent fibre has a time constant hundreds of times longer than in peripheral medullated nerve fibres. The production of the PAD can therefore be attributed to the prolonged action of a chemical transmitter substance which operates in a manner compa-

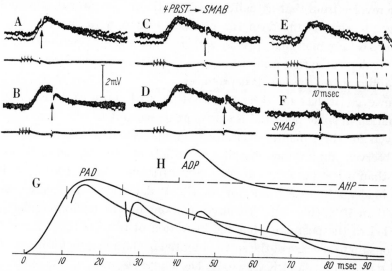

Fig. 93 A—H. Effect of an impulse in a fibre on the primary afferent depolarizatio n (PAD) of that fibre. As shown by the upper traces the PAD produced by four PBST volleys in a SMAB afferent fibre was subjected to the action of an impulse in that SMAB fibre at the times marked by the arrows in A to E, while F shows the response to the impulse alone, only the small after-depolarization (ADP) being seen because the spike was too large and brief at that amplification and sweep speed. Lower traces in A to F give the cord dorsum potentials. Voltage calibration is for the upper traces only, but time scale is common to both. In G are shown traces of the PAD and of the interacting impulse at the four positions of A to D. The control trace of the PAD is the mean of several records and the various other traces in G were adjusted to this record up to the times of the interpolated spikes that are indicated by the short vertical lines. H shows mean potential produced by antidromic volley alone and plotted on the same scales as G (ECCLES, SCHMIDT and WILLIS 1963c)

rable with other depolarizing transmitters, namely, by effecting a high permeability to ions. As mentioned below, the attempt to evaluate the equilibrium potential for this presumed ionic depolarizing process has not been successful. All that can be stated is that it is likely to be at least 30 mV depolarized in relation to the resting membrane potential (ECCLES, SCHMIDT and WILLIS 1963c).

There has been excellent agreement in every respect between the observed depolarizations of the primary afferent fibres and the depression of their synaptic excitatory action (ECCLES, ECCLES and MAGNI 1961; ECCLES, MAGNI and WILLIS 1962; ECCLES, SCHMIDT and WILLIS 1962, 1963 a); yet, it is important to realize that this agreement is only qualitative. This qualitative relationship also obtains for the demonstration that passive depolarization

15*

of primary afferent fibres diminishes their ability to produce EPSPs (Eccles, Kostyuk and Schmidt 1962 c). For example in Fig. 29 the passage of polarizing currents through the spinal cord, as in the diagram, causes a decrease in the monosynaptic EPSP produced by a maximum volley when the presynaptic terminals are depolarized, and an increase when they are hyperpolarized. The currents would of course also polarize the motoneuronal membrane and so change the size of the EPSP (Fig. 17); but this effect would be expected to be the reverse from that actually observed, the motoneuronal spike potentials of Fig. 29 being changed in the opposite direction to the EPSPs. It can therefore be assumed that, just as with the squid giant synapse (Fig. 26), presynaptic depolarization diminishes the size of the presynaptic spike potential and so diminishes the EPSP it produces.

However, it has not been shown that with presynaptic inhibition the diminution in spike potential is sufficient to account for the large diminutions observed for the synaptic excitatory action. When superimposed on PADs, the observed diminutions of spike potentials of afferent nerve fibres are no more than a few per cent (Eccles, Schmidt and Willis 1963 c), which may seem inadequate to account for an EPSP depression that may amount to more than 50% (Fig. 90). Yet investigations on the neuromuscular junction have led to the postulate that the liberation of transmitter has a very steep relationship to the size of the spike potential in the synaptic terminals (Chapter VI; Liley 1956c); and Katz (1962) has suggested that, as a consequence, the relatively small presynaptic depolarization produced in presynaptic inhibition may nevertheless have a large depressant action on transmitter liberation, and so on the EPSP. For example, if every 15 mV depolarization gives a 10-fold increase in transmitter output (Fig. 10B), a diminution of the spike potential by 5 mV would reduce the EPSP to less than 50%. It is important also to allow for the fact that, in all investigations on the depressant action of the PAD on the presynaptic spike potential, the intra-fibre recording has been remote from the presynaptic terminals; and the testing of excitability at these terminals suggests that the depolarization is at least three times larger.

In addition, there would be a further factor besides the mere depression of spike potential by an amount equivalent to the PAD. Since it can be assumed that the PAD is generated by the flow of ionic currents with an equilibrium potential well below that of the spike potential, these ionic currents would be effective in reducing the absolute potential level of the spike summit, as in Figs. 19 and 42L, M; and this factor would be particularly effective when the presynaptic inhibitory synapses are superimposed directly upon the excitatory synaptic knobs, which appears to be the usual location (Fig. 5). Thus it is postulated that the EPSP depression is produced by the combined influence of two factors in diminishing the size of the presynaptic spike, the depolarization *per se*, and the localized depression of the spike potential by the ionic currents that give rise to the depolarization. Fig. 93 provides evidence that these ionic currents continue to flow throughout the whole duration of the PAD.

In Fig. 94 are assembled several examples of depolarizations of other types of primary afferent fibres (a I b fibre in A and cutaneous fibres in B and C) that similarly are responsible for presynaptic inhibition. In general the time courses are comparable, but the PADs of cutaneous fibres are remarkable for the large size of the response to a single cutaneous volley (Fig. 94 B; KOKETSU 1956b; ECCLES and KRNJEVIĆ 1959a; ECCLES, SCHMIDT and WILLIS

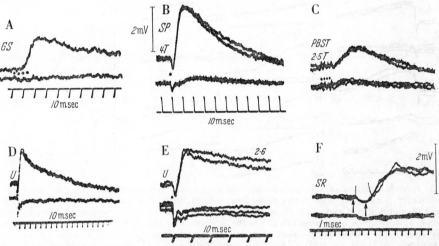

Fig. 94 A—F. Depolarizations of primary afferent fibres, the upper trace being recorded inside the fibre and the lower just outside as in Fig. 92 B. A is depolarization of a quadriceps Group Ib afferent fibre by four Group I volleys in the nerve to gastrocnemius-soleus muscle (ECCLES, MAGNI and WILLIS 1962). B and C are from the same cutaneous nerve fibre, B showing the PAD for a single cutaneous volley and C for 4 Group I PBST volleys (ECCLES, SCHMIDT and WILLIS 1963e). D, E are from the same primary afferent fibre at a depth of 1.2 mm in the cuneate nucleus, and show the PAD produced by an ulnar nerve volley at two different sweep speeds. In F are faster records from another fibre in the cuneate nucleus, the latency of the PAD set up by a volley in the superficial radial nerve being about 2 msec as measured between the 2 arrows (ANDERSEN, ECCLES, SCHMIDT and YOKOTA 1963 a)

1963 e). Usually the PADs evoked by cutaneous volleys have a central latency as brief as 2 msec, and the summit is also reached earlier than with the PADs set up by repetitive muscle volleys (A, C). Of particular interest are the PADs of presynaptic fibres in the cuneate nucleus (Fig. 94 D—F; ANDERSEN, ECCLES, SCHMIDT and YOKOTA 1963 a) because several features of these PADs suggest that the microelectrode may have impaled one of the very large synaptic knobs in the cuneate, where the profile areas are about three times larger than in the spinal cord (ROZSOS 1958). Since the extracellular potential is in the opposite direction from the intracellular, the recording must be very close to the generating site of the depolarization; and this location is also suggested by the very short latency, about 2 msec in F, and the unusually rapid rise to the summit, which is attained in 5 msec from the onset. On the other hand the duration of the PAD in D is as long as with PADs in the spinal cord. Evidently the cuneate nucleus provides very favourable opportunities for examining the influence of the PAD on the spike potential at the actual site of liberation of transmitter substance, but it has not yet been used for this purpose.

Investigations into the nature of the synaptic mechanism responsible for presynaptic inhibition have not yet allowed an evaluation of the equilibrium potential of the ionic mechanism that is presumed to produce the PAD. However, there is qualitative agreement with prediction, hyperpolarization and depolarization of the presynaptic terminals respectively increasing and

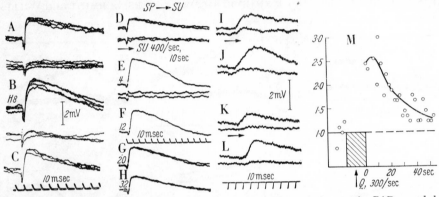

Fig. 95 A—M. Actions of hyperpolarization and post-tetanic potentiation on the PAD recorded intracellularly. Note extracellular traces under most records. In A—C a L₇ dorsal root volley set up a PAD in a fibre of S₁ dorsal root. In B the PAD was increased, relative to the controls in A and C before and after, by application of a current (8 μA) to the S₁ dorsal root that hyperpolarized its central terminals by electrotonic spread. D—M shows effect of tetanization of an afferent fibre on the PAD recorded in that fibre. In D—H, the PAD produced by a superficial peroneal volley in a sural fibre (D) is increased in E, 4 seconds after tetanization of that fibre (400/sec for 10 sec) and slowly diminishes in F—H at the indicated intervals in seconds after the end of the tetanus (ECCLES and KRNJEVIĆ 1959a). Similarly the PADs in Group Ib afferent fibres I and K are increased to J and L respectively by tetanization of the recipient fibre. The time course of the potentiation of the series of I, J is plotted in M (ECCLES, MAGNI and WILLIS 1962)

decreasing the PAD, just as has been observed with the EPSP (Figs. 17, 26, 29). In Fig. 95 B the PAD is seen to be increased, relatively to the controls in A and C, during a hyperpolarization transmitted electrotonically from a dorsal root fibre to its central terminals. Alternatively the PAD is increased during the after-hyperpolarization that follows tetanization of the fibre under observation (Fig. 95 E—H, J, L: KOKETSU 1956a; ECCLES and KRNJEVIĆ 1959a; ECCLES, SCHMIDT and WILLIS 1963c). This phenomenon accounts for the post-tetanic increase of the dorsal root potential (WOOLSEY and LARRABEE 1940; LLOYD 1952) and in Fig. 95 M it is seen to have a time course comparable with that of Fig. 39 D—F. A perplexing feature is that the large increase (often doubling) in the PADs is to a considerable extent due to their more prolonged rising phase and later summit, as may be seen by comparing J with I and L with K. However, the slope of the rise is usually increased, an average increase of about 20% being reported (ECCLES, SCHMIDT and WILLIS 1963c). The prolongation of the time course of the PAD possibly may be due to the active and passive hyperpolarizations retarding the diffusion of the transmitter out of the synaptic cleft, which could be an electrophoretic action comparable with earlier suggestions (Chapter V).

Depolarization of afferent fibres always depresses their PAD; but, even when large depolarizing currents are applied as in Fig. 29, it is not possible to reverse the PAD, which would be a convincing proof that it is due to an ionic mechanism having an equilibrium potential. Such currents merely abolish the PAD, presumably by blocking transmission of the afferent volley generating the PAD.

Pharmacological investigation of presynaptic inhibition (ECCLES, SCHMIDT and WILLIS 1963 d; SCHMIDT 1963) clearly distinguishes it from postsynaptic inhibition, and shows that it is mediated by a quite different transmitter. Even when applied in convulsive doses that heavily depress postsynaptic inhibitory action in the spinal cord (Fig. 96 A), strychnine has no appreciable action on presynaptic inhibition (Fig. 96 B). Some at least of the central inhibitory actions that have been reported as not being affected by strychnine are examples of presynaptic inhibition; for example, the inhibition of stretch reflexes in quadriceps by adequate stimulation of stretch receptors in the hamstring muscle is clearly a case of presynaptic inhibition (LIDDELL and SHERRINGTON 1925; COOPER and CREED 1927). In contrast to its ineffectiveness on postsynaptic inhibition (Chapter XII) picrotoxin depresses presynaptic inhibition, but the depression is less striking than that of strychnine on postsynaptic inhibition. A convulsive dose diminishes and shortens both the presynaptic inhibition (Fig. 96 D) and the presynaptic depolarization responsible for the inhibition (Fig. 96 C), but even the largest doses have failed to suppress presynaptic inhibitory action to a degree comparable with the effect of strychnine on postsynaptic inhibition. It has been suggested that the convulsant activity of strychnine is fully accounted for by its suppression of postsynaptic inhibition (BRADLEY, EASTON and ECCLES 1953; FATT 1954; ECCLES 1957; CURTIS 1959; LONGO 1961); however, it seems unlikely that the depressant action of picrotoxin on presynaptic inhibition is sufficient to account for all of its convulsant action.

Some anaesthetics, the barbiturates and chloralose, have a most unexpected action in increasing and prolonging both presynaptic inhibition and the associated presynaptic depolarization (Fig. 96 E, F). In very large doses (up to 80 mg/kg) they also exert a depressant action, but the presynaptic inhibition and depolarization are even further lengthened. The depression can be accounted for by the action of these anaesthetics in blocking transmission through the polysynaptic pathways responsible for the presynaptic depolarization, and the prolongation could be caused by inactivation of an enzyme responsible for destroying the transmitter. However, an alternative possibility is that the prolongation of the presynaptic depolarization is due to an increased

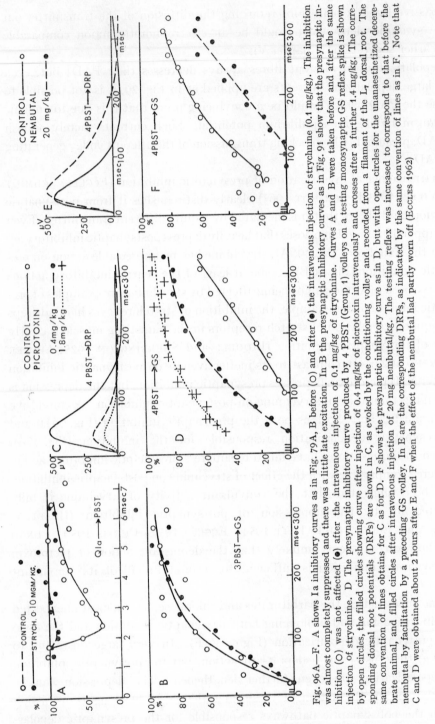

Fig. 96A–F. A shows Ia inhibitory curves as in Fig. 79A, B before (○) and after (●) the intravenous injection of strychnine (0.1 mg/kg). The inhibition was almost completely suppressed and there was a little late excitation. In B the presynaptic inhibitory curves as in Fig. 91 show that the presynaptic inhibition (○) was not affected (●) after the intravenous injection of 0.1 mg/kg of strychnine. Curves A and B were taken before and after the same injection of strychnine. D The presynaptic inhibitory curve produced by 4 PBST (Group 1) volleys on a testing monosynaptic GS reflex spike is shown by open circles, the filled circles showing curve after injection of 0.4 mg/kg of picrotoxin intravenously and crosses after a further 1.4 mg/kg. The corresponding dorsal root potentials (DRPs) are shown in C, as evoked by the conditioning volley and recorded from a filament of the L₇ dorsal root. The same convention of lines obtains for C as for D. F shows the presynaptic inhibitory curve as in D, but with open circles for the unanaesthetized decerebrate animal, and filled circles after intravenous injection of 20 mg nembutal/kg. The testing reflex was increased to correspond to that before the nembutal by facilitation by a preceding GS volley. In E are the corresponding DRPs, as indicated by the same convention of lines as in F. Note that C and D were obtained about 2 hours after E and F when the effect of the nembutal had partly worn off (ECCLES 1962)

effectiveness of the diffusional barrier which even normally so restricts diffusion that the transmitter produced by a single afferent volley acts for as long as 300 msec (cf. Figs. 92, 93, 94).

Other anaesthetics such as ether, paraldehyde, urethane and chloral-hydrate are quite different in their action, producing only a shortening and diminution of the PAD, which would be entirely explicable by the depression of transmission along the interneuronal pathway (SCHMIDT 1963). This finding that chloralose and the barbiturate group of anaesthetics are specific in prolonging the action of the presynaptic inhibitory transmitter certainly favours the postulate of enzyme inactivation rather than that of restricted diffusion, which would be expected to be non-specific in character.

With all types of excitatory synapses that have been appropriately tested there has been a close correlation between depolarization of the presynaptic fibres and inhibition of synaptic transmission. In this way presynaptic inhibition has been shown to exert a large depression on the excitatory synapses of all types of large afferent fibres entering the spinal cord: Groups I a, I b and II from muscle (Figs. 90—93; 94A; FRANK and FUORTES 1957; ECCLES, ECCLES and MAGNI 1961; ECCLES, MAGNI and WILLIS 1962; ECCLES, SCHMIDT and WILLIS 1962, 1963 a; SCHMIDT and WILLIS 1963 a, b; R. M. ECCLES and WILLIS 1963); and the alpha cutaneous fibres (Fig. 94B, C; ECCLES, KOSTYUK and SCHMIDT 1962b; ECCLES, SCHMIDT and WILLIS 1963 e). This inhibition is exerted not only on the local spinal reflexes, but also on the synaptic relays for the ascending tracts, both the cutaneous (ECCLES, KOSTYUK and SCHMIDT 1962b) and the spino-cerebellar (ECCLES, SCHMIDT and WILLIS 1963 f). Furthermore, presynaptic inhibition acts on the synaptic relays of the dorsal columns in the gracile and cuneate nuclei (Fig. 94D—F; WALL 1958; ANDERSEN, ECCLES and SCHMIDT 1962). Descending impulses from the cerebral cortex and brain stem also have a presynaptic inhibitory action on the Group I and cutaneous afferent fibres in the spinal cord and the cuneate nuclei (ANDERSEN, ECCLES and SEARS 1962; CARPENTER, LUNDBERG and NORSELL 1962; CARPENTER, ENGBERG and LUNDBERG 1962; ANDERSEN, ECCLES and SCHMIDT 1962; ANDERSEN, ECCLES, SCHMIDT and YOKOTA 1963 a, b; ANDERSEN, ECCLES, OSHIMA and SCHMIDT 1963). All the examples of presynaptic inhibition listed above are effected on the synapses of primary afferent fibres. So far there is only one example of another location—presynaptic inhibition of the secondary afferent fibres from the cuneate nucleus that relay in the thalamus (ANDERSEN, BROOKS and ECCLES 1963). Correspondingly, the characteristic type of presynaptic inhibitory synapse has been observed in a related brain nucleus, the lateral geniculate body (SZENTAGOTHAI 1963 b).

It seems likely that presynaptic inhibition is of less significance at stages of the afferent pathway after the primary afferent relay, and a thorough examination of the cerebral cortex has disclosed no sign of synaptic structures, such as in Fig. 5, that would subserve presynaptic inhibition (E. G. GRAY, personal communication). Postsynaptic inhibition is dominant at these higher levels of the nervous system (Fig. 64 H—K; Chapter X). In contrast, presynaptic inhibition is more effective than postsynaptic at most of the excitatory synapses of primary afferent fibres, which is in accord with the general concept that presynaptic inhibition functions as a negative feed-back on the inflow of sensory information into the central nervous system (ECCLES 1963). This negative feed-back has no detailed topographic pattern, but usually it tends to be concentrated within one sensory modality—Ib on Ib, and cutaneous on cutaneous. However presynaptic inhibition of Group Ia fibres is a partial exception to this generalization, because as a rule it is more effectively produced by Ib than by Ia impulses (ECCLES, ECCLES and MAGNI 1961).

B. Presynaptic inhibition on Mauthner cells

It has been shown in Chapter XIV that Mauthner cells (M-cells) of the fish brain exhibit two distinct types of inhibition: a brief electrical inhibition due to hyperpolarization of the axon-hillock region in the axon cap and a later typical IPSP due to chemical synaptic transmission. FURUKAWA, FUKAMI and ASADA (1963 a, b) have shown that in addition impulses in M-axons exert an inhibitory action on the presynaptic fibres of the 8th nerve, which themselves have a monosynaptic excitatory action on the M-cell. This presynaptic inhibitory action has about the same duration as the IPSP (about 20 msec) and is manifested in several ways: i. Diminution in the monosynaptic EPSP produced by stimulation of the 8th nerve (Fig. 97 L [open circles], H, I); ii. Diminution of the positive potential (the extracellular orthodromic response, EOR) produced in the axon cap by a volley in the contralateral or ipsilateral 8th nerve (Fig. 97 L [crosses], D, E); iii. Diminution in the presynaptic spike potentials produced by the 8th nerve volley and recorded extracellularly in the region of the lateral dendrite of the M-cell. This depression is an all-or-nothing block when single 8th nerve impulses are being recorded; iv. Increased threshold of 8th nerve fibres at the site of their stimulation, which is within 1 mm of their synaptic terminals; v. No change in antidromic response of M-cells.

The all-or-nothing character of the block and the increased presynaptic threshold sharply distinguish this type of presynaptic inhibition from the type described above (Figs. 90—92). Pharmacological tests confirm this difference, for in Fig. 97 B—K the typical blocking drug for postsynaptic inhibition, strychnine, is seen to depress the presynaptic and postsynaptic inhibitions similarly. The inhibition of the EOR (D, E) is abolished at the same time (F, G) as the inhibition of the intracellular antidromic spike (Fig. 97 B, C). Both presynaptic and postsynaptic inhibition cooperate in the depression of the EPSP (H, I); and, as would be expected, this likewise is depressed by strychnine (J, K). FURUKAWA, FUKAMI and ASADA (1963 b) explain these reactions diagrammatically (Fig. 97 A), where it is seen that the presynaptic and postsynaptic inhibitions are exerted by inhibitory cells N_3 and N_2, respectively, that have synapses blocked by strychnine.

The action of procaine distinguishes between these two types of chemical inhibition of Mauthner cells. In Fig. 97L there are plotted control inhibitory curves from observations such as those of Fig. 97B, D, E, H, I). The distinction between the IPSP action on the antidromic spike potential (filled circles) and the presynaptic inhibition of the EOR (crosses) is well shown by the longer latency of the latter, while the double composition of the EPSP depression (open

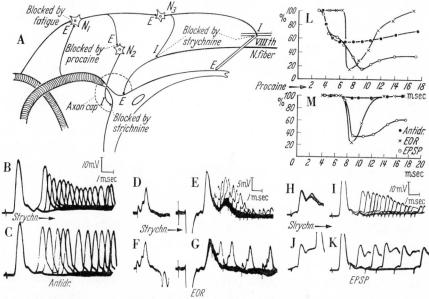

Fig. 97 A—M. A is drawing of one Mauthner cell with also the decussating axon of the other M-cell. The inhibitory pathways from collaterals of both M-axons are shown as described in the text. Also shown are a large and a small axon from the eighth nerve. The series of responses in the row B, D, E, H, I were taken before and in row C, F, G, J, K after the injection of strychnine in a dose of 0.4 mg/kg. In the upper row three different kinds of response are seen to be inhibited by antidromic impulses in the two M-axons; antidromic spike potentials in B; the EOR (see text) of D in E; the EPSP of H in I. All these inhibitions are completely eliminated by strychnine in C, G and K respectively. The plotted points of L are for inhibitory series such as in Fig. 97B, D, E, H, I as indicated by the symbols. Procaine (0.2 mg/g weight) is seen in M to abolish the component attributable to the IPSP and leave the presynaptic inhibition virturally unaffected (FURUKAWA, FUKAMI and ASADA 1963a, 1963b)

circles) is also indicated in L. Procaine causes virtually complete suppression of both IPSP actions as shown in Fig. 97M by the filled circles and the earlier part of the curve through the open circles, but leaves the presynaptic inhibition of the EOR and the EPSP virtually unaffected. In Fig. 97A it is suggested that procaine acts specifically on the synapse of N_1 cell onto N_2. It is not known if the longer latency of presynaptic inhibition is attributable to additional synapses in the pathway or to slower conduction in the fibres.

The action of strychnine (Fig. 97C, G, K) suggests that the same transmitter substance is concerned in the production of the presynaptic and postsynaptic inhibitions. In this respect this type of presynaptic inhibition resembles that of the crustacean neuromuscular junctions (Fig. 98; Dudel and Kuffler 1961c). The raised electrical threshold of the presynaptic fibres of the eighth nerve suggests that the ionic mechanism is also the same as with IPSP production, with presumably a high conductance for Cl⁻ ions. Since the stimulating site is so close to the presynaptic terminals, electrotonic spread from the sites of action of presynaptic inhibition would account for the depressed excitability; and this depression possibly can account for all the observations of presynaptic inhibitory action, without the postulate that in addition there is actually a blockage of 8th nerve impulses at the sites of presynaptic inhibitory action. Evidently further investigation is required before this type of presynaptic inhibition is established as effecting depression of naturally generated 8th nerve impulses.

C. Presynaptic inhibition in the peripheral nervous system of invertebrates

The essential observations on this phenomenon by Dudel and Kuffler (1960, 1961c) are illustrated in Fig. 98. The IPSP and EPSP of a crustacean muscle fibre are produced respectively by an inhibitory and an excitatory impulse (A and B) and are seen to sum when the inhibitory follows the excitatory by 1 msec (C), but there is a very large depression of the EPSP when the inhibitory impulse precedes the excitatory by 3 msec (D). This depression is not attributable to any interaction of the respective ionic currents across the postsynaptic membrane, because the equilibrium potential for the IPSP was at a level of 6 mV depolarization, i. e. summation of the EPSP with any residual depolarization of the IPSP would be expected to occur in D, just as observed in C. The plotted points of Fig. 98 E show that the depression of EPSP observed in D only occurs over a narrow range of stimulus intervals, I preceding E by about 1 to 6 msec, with a maximum effect at about 2.5 msec interval.

There are two possible explanations of this depression of EPSP: one is that the transmitter released by inhibitory impulses competes with the excitatory transmitter for receptor sites, as suggested by Fatt and Katz (1953b) and by Fatt (1954); the other that inhibitory impulses depress the release of excitatory transmitter in addition to the specific action of the inhibitory transmitter substance on the postsynaptic membrane (Chapters X, XI). These alternative explanations can be expressed in terms of the quantal emission of transmitter. Competitive inhibition would reduce the size of the quantal responses (cf. Fig. 11 A), but not the number of quanta released by a nerve impulse or the frequency of spontaneous emission. On the contrary, presynaptic inhibition is brought about by a reduction in the number of quanta released, the size of the quantal responses being unaltered.

Crucial experimental tests have established indubitably that the inhibition illustrated in Fig. 98 is presynaptic (Dudel and Kuffler 1961c). The much more discriminative recording by an extracellular electrode gives responses appropriate for the POISSON statistical analysis in which quantal size and number are calculated (Chapters III and VI). The results are quite decisive; the inhibition illustrated in Fig. 98 is due to a reduction in the number of quanta released by a nerve impulse, the individual quantal responses themselves being unchanged. Similarly the inhibitory impulses are found to depress the frequency, but not the size, of the spontaneous quantal release of excitatory transmitter that gives the miniature EPPs (cf. Chapter III).

Furthermore, when there is a repetitive series of inhibitory and excitatory impulses timed so that the EPP is depressed as in Fig. 98D, there is much

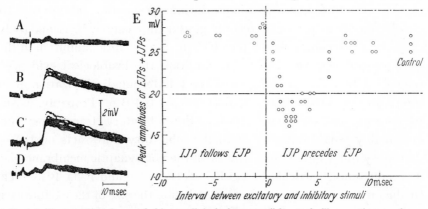

Fig. 98A—E. A to D are potentials recorded intracellularly from crayfish muscle fibre, resting membrane potential −80 mV and equilibrium potential for the IPSP at −74 mV (determined as in Fig. 66B). A and B are responses evoked by single inhibitory and excitatory impulses, IPSPs and EPSPs respectively, repeated to give superimposed traces at 5/sec. C and D are produced by combination of both impulses, the inhibitory following the excitatory by 1 msec in C and leading it by 3 msec in D. In E are the plotted points for the series partly illustrated in A—D (DUDEL and KUFFLER 1961c)

less post-tetanic potentiation of excitatory transmitter release than after an equivalent repetitive series in which the I-E timing is such that there is no EPP depression, e.g. as in Fig. 98C. This post-tetanic potentiation is exhibited both by the increased frequency of miniature potentials and by the size of a testing EPP (Fig.37; Chapter VI). Evidently these observations are in accord with the postulate that presynaptic impulses effect a mobilization of transmitter in the synaptic terminals, which contributes to the phenomena of post-tetanic potentiation. The inhibitory impulses thus act on the presynaptic terminals by depressing not only the quantal release of transmitter, but also the mobilization of transmitter during repetitive stimulation. It seems likely that this latter effect is at least to some extent a consequence of the former.

Conceivably the inhibitory impulses could act on the excitatory terminals either by some electrical transmission or by a chemical transmitter. DUDEL and KUFFLER (1961c) point out that both the timing and the duration of the presynaptic inhibition (Fig. 98E) differ from predictions derived from a direct electrical action of the inhibitory nerve impulses, which would be expected to be earlier and briefer, much as with electrical inhibitory transmission in Fig. 89. On the other hand action by an inhibitory transmitter would be expected to have these time relations, and GABA has the same presynaptic inhibitory action as inhibitory impulses (DUDEL and KUFFLER 1961 c). Since it is highly probable that GABA is the postsynaptic inhibitory transmitter at the crustacean neuro-muscular junction (Chapter XII), the same inhibitory transmitter probably mediates both the postsynaptic and the presynaptic inhibition. This identity is further indicated by the finding that both types are similarly potentiated during repetitive stimulation.

It has not been possible directly to investigate the changes that occur in the excitatory nerve terminals during presynaptic inhibition. They are too slender for intracellular recording, and they cannot be stimulated electri-cally; hence no comparison is possible with presynaptic inhibition in the verte-brate central nervous system. In addition the histological evidence merely suggests a very close association of the fine terminal arborization of the exci-tatory and inhibitory fibres (VAN HARREVELD 1939). Probably, as suggested by DUDEL and KUFFLER (1961c), the inhibitory transmitter substance, presumably GABA, released from the inhibitory fibres acts on the adjacent excitatory fibres in the same way as on the postsynaptic membrane, increasing its conductance, particularly to Cl^- ions (BOISTEL and FATT 1958). This ionic conductance would act as a shunt in reducing the size of the excitatory impulse and so its quantal emission. This type of presynaptic inhibition would in general resemble that illustrated in Figs. 90—96. However, there are several important differences which arise from the specificity of the presynaptic inhibitory mechanism in the vertebrate central nervous system. Presynaptic inhibition is effected there by special synaptic structures on the excitatory synaptic terminals (Fig. 5); and the quite different pharmacological properties of this transmission (Fig. 96) show that it is mediated by a different chemical transmitter from that responsible for postsynaptic inhibition. In addition there are quite distinctive inhibitory pathways with interneurones specialized for presynaptic and postsynaptic inhibitory action respectively (Chapter XIII; ECCLES, KOSTYUK and SCHMIDT 1962a). Finally, the durations of presynaptic inhibition in Figs. 90, 91, 96 are always very much longer than in Fig. 98.

It appears that a type of presynaptic inhibition also occurs in the giant ganglion cells of *Aplysia* and *Helix* (TAUC 1960b). In contrast to the above example, this interaction occurs between the impulses in different presynaptic fibres, whether inhibitory or excitatory, and is reciprocally exerted. Repetitive activation of one fibre causes a depression for many seconds of the EPSP or IPSP produced by another, while there is the usual post-tetanic potentiation of the response evoked by the tetanized fibre. It would seem that presynaptic inhibitory phenomena of diverse kinds are likely to be observed at many in-vertebrate synaptic junctions. But as yet their functional significance is obscure.

CHAPTER XVI

THE TROPHIC AND PLASTIC PROPERTIES OF SYNAPSES

The preceding chapters have been concerned with the mode of operation of synapses in the fully developed adult state; and even in that context they have been restricted to relatively brief events having a duration usually measured in fractions of a second, and at most a few minutes. But an immense range of problems, as yet poorly understood, is opened up by questions relating to three other aspects of synapses: the development of synapses; the so-called trophic functions of synapses; and those plastic properties of central synapses that may provide the basis of learning and forgetting. From this wide variety of problems a few examples are here selected in order to illustrate the progress that is being made in these obscure fields.

A. Vertebrate neuromuscular synapses and the peripheral nervous system

1. Development

The development of muscle fibres and the formation and maturation of neuro-muscular synapses have been studied most intensively with the rat during both foetal and postnatal life (ZELENÁ 1959, 1962; COUTEAUX 1941, 1960, 1961). Shortly before birth (the gestation period is 22 days) the primitive myotubes with central nuclei begin to change into muscle fibres by the migration of the nuclei to the periphery and by the increase in the number of myofibrils, which come to fill up the whole cross-section of the fibre. This differentiation is completed a few days after birth. The nerve fibres are already in functional contact with muscle fibres five days before birth (STRAUS and WEDDELL 1940; DIAMOND and MILEDI 1962), which is prior to the differentiation of myotubes into muscle fibres. But these innervating nerve fibres are not essentially concerned in this maturation, for it occurs with the great majority of muscle fibres even when they are denervated three days before birth (ZELENÁ 1959, 1962). By contrast this denervation procedure establishes that the differentiation of muscle spindles is entirely dependent on innervation by sensory fibres (ZELENA and HNIK 1960; ZELENÁ 1957, 1962).

The differentiation of a small area of each muscle fibre to form the characteristic structure of the motor endplate with the accumulation of nuclei (Fig. 1A) does not occur until after innervation (COUTEAUX 1941, 1961). Acetylcholinesterase (AChE) appears at an even earlier stage of the developing synapse (KUPFER and KOELLE 1951; ZELENÁ and SZENTÁGOTHAI 1957); possibly it is generated in the motoneurones and flows along the motor axons (COUTEAUX and NACHMANSOHN 1938; ZELENÁ and LUBINSKA 1962) to accumulate eventually on the post-synaptic membrane (LEWIS and HUGHES 1957). Denervation towards the end of intra-uterine life establishes that all these characteristic features of motor endplates are due to the morphogenetic influence of the motor nerve fibres; for it results in the virtual disappearance of AChE and in the survival merely of incompletely developed endplates (ZELENÁ and SZENTÁGOTHAI 1957; ZELENÁ 1959).

At a very early stage of innervation, even five days before birth, the muscle fibres of the rat diaphragm exhibit responses which presumably are of neural origin (DIAMOND and MILEDI 1962). Firstly, in most fibres there are spontaneous subthreshold depolarizations, which are the primitive homologues of the adult miniature EPPs described in Chapter III. In the foetus the frequency is very low, and the adult rate, about 100 times higher, is not attained until about 20 days after birth. Possibly this very low frequency is attributable to the small size of the synapse and the inadequacy of supply of transmitter. However, the magnitude of the min. EPPs (mean about 4 mV at birth) indicates that the ACh content of the quantum is of the same order as in the adult, but of course it is much more effective on the very small muscle fibres, which corresponds to the observations of KATZ and THESLEFF (1957a) (Chapter III). Evidently a much smaller number of quanta suffices to effect neuromuscular transmission in the foetus, and even a single min. EPP sometimes generates a muscle impulse. The slower time course of the min. EPPs of the foetus is at least in part attributable to the longer survival of the liberated ACh, which would be consequent on the low level of AChE.

It is of great significance that the entire length of the foetal muscle fibre is uniformly sensitive to ACh. Only after birth is there a retraction of this sensitive area, at first from the tendinous ends, and eventually after some weeks to the region of the nerve ending and its immediate surround (GINET-ZINSKY and SHAMARINA 1942; DIAMOND and MILEDI 1962). Presumably there is uniform sensitivity to ACh before innervation, and the development of the neuromuscular synapse is responsible for the slow retraction of this sensitive area. As reported below, reinnervation of a denervated muscle effects a similar retraction of the area sensitive to ACh, and possible explanations will be then examined.

At birth limb muscles of the rat and cat are uniformly slow in their contractions, and the adult differentiation into fast and slow muscles is not completed for several weeks. There is an initial phase of quickening during the first weeks after birth, and then a subsequent phase of lengthening, which occurs with fast as well as slow muscles, but much more prominently in the latter (BULLER, ECCLES and ECCLES 1960a; CLOSE 1963). The initial phase of accelerating contraction-times probably is largely autogenic, just as is the earlier maturation process, because it is unaffected by complete inactivation of the muscle. By contrast the later phase of lengthening is entirely dependent on neural influence; no trace survives in muscles with an intact motor innervation that are rendered quiescent by isolation of the spinal cord from all incoming impulses (BULLER, ECCLES and ECCLES 1960a). Operative cross-union of nerves to fast and slow muscles results in a transformation of fast to slow and of slow to fast, even in adults, so the neural differentiating influence must be continuously operating throughout life (BULLER, ECCLES and ECCLES 1960b; ECCLES, ECCLES and KOZAK 1962).

Already it is apparent that the inter-relationship between nerve and muscle includes much besides the phenomena of junctional transmission, nerve impulses to endplate potentials, that have been considered in earlier chapters. These additional phenomena may be broadly classified as trophic (GUTMANN and HNÍK 1962). There is of course no trophic interaction at an early stage of development of nerve and muscle, since both tissues develop independently. Even after the formation of nerve-muscle junctions it is remarkable that muscle has a considerable capacity to grow and differentiate when deprived of its nerve supply (HAMBURGER 1939; ZELENÁ 1962). This capacity declines with age, and in the adult mammal prolonged denervation usually results in progressive atrophy and the eventual destruction of the muscles. In general it can be concluded that the embryonic muscle cell has a sufficiently large autogenous supply of growth substances and that the dependence on trophic influences from nerve fibres does not become significant until some time after nerve connections have been established (HAMBURGER and LEVI-MONTALCINI 1950; SINGER 1952). A further negative statement about the trophic nerve influence on muscle is that there is no evidence of any such action by sensory or sympathetic nerve fibres (cf. GUTMANN and HNÍK 1962). On the other hand, the trophic influences of the innervating motor nerve fibres are exhibited by such phenomena as the development of the motor endplate with its associated concentration of AChE, and the retraction of the ACh sensitive area.

2. Degeneration and regeneration

The usual technique for displaying the trophic influences of nerve on muscle is to sever the nerve and study the changes thereby produced in the muscle during the nerve degeneration and their subsequent reversal with nerve regeneration. In addition several other experimental procedures have been developed in order to reveal special aspects of trophic influences. For example it is possible to modify or suppress the impulse traffic along the motor nerve fibres so that the muscle is subjected to disuse in the absence of nerve degeneration (TOWER 1937a, 1937b; TOWER, HOWE and BODIAN 1941; ECCLES 1941b, 1944b; JOHNS and THESLEFF 1961). Prolonged action of botulinum toxin also serves to eliminate the action of the neuromuscular transmitter substance and even its spontaneous quantal emission to give the miniature endplate potentials (BROOKS 1956; THESLEFF 1960a; JOSEFSSON and THESLEFF 1961).

A detailed description of the histological changes in denervated muscle has recently been given by GUTMANN and ZELENÁ (1962). The atrophy of denervated muscle is reflected first in a reduction in the diameter of the fibres, which otherwise only very slowly lose their fibrils and cross-striations and eventually disintegrate. Initially there is a hypertrophy of muscle endplate nuclei and later atrophy and disintegration. There may be a correlation between the changes in surface membrane properties described below and the changes in the muscle nuclei, which firstly swell to become more ovoid and possibly multiply, but later they disintegrate. The nuclear changes appear to be characteristic of denervated muscle, whereas the changes in muscle fibres occur also in atrophies due to disuse or tenotomy (TOWER 1937a, 1939), but further investigation is desirable. Most of the chemical and biochemical changes in denervated muscle possibly do not differ significantly from those occurring in other types of muscle atrophy induced by disuse or tenotomy (BASS 1962; ŽÁK 1962). However GUTMANN (unpublished observations) has found that after three days denervation the protein nitrogen is reduced and the glycogen greatly increased (3-fold) relative to a control muscle completely inactivated by nerve block by mesocaine.

There is a remarkable slowing of the contractile process of denervated muscles, which is revealed for example by the lengthening of the time from onset to summit of a twitch contraction (DESMEDT 1949; LEWIS 1962; ECCLES, ECCLES and KOZAK 1962). Fast muscles are relatively more affected than slow, and with both the slowing is progressive over many weeks. This slowing of contraction is not observed with a simple disuse of muscle (ECCLES 1941b; BULLER, ECCLES and ECCLES 1960a) or with tenotomized muscle (VRBOVÁ 1962), so it appears to be a specific result of denervation. The slowing is reversed by nerve regeneration (BULLER, ECCLES and ECCLES 1960b; ECCLES, ECCLES and KOZAK 1962).

In early investigations on denervated muscle it was assumed that the observed increase in sensitivity to ACh was restricted to the denervated motor endplate (BROWN 1937a; ROSENBLUETH and LUCO 1937), but evidence for an increase in sensitivity along the whole length of muscle fibres was obtained by GINET-

ZINSKY and SHAMARINA (1942) and by KUFFLER (1943). These original observations have been confirmed and extended by employing the microelectrophoretic technique to give a very localized application of ACh (Fig. 99). In this way AXELSSON and THESLEFF (1959) showed that the ACh-sensitivity of the denervated tenuissimus muscle of the cat becomes uniformly high along the whole length of the muscle fibres (Fig. 99B). With the denervated frog muscle there is likewise a spread of ACh sensitivity along the whole length of the muscle (MILEDI 1960a), but the endplate zone remains about 1000 times more sensitive

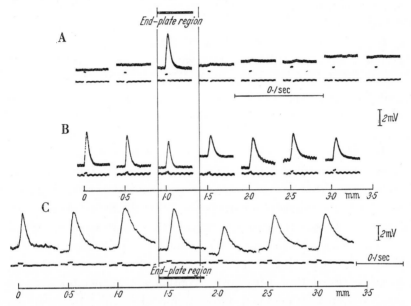

Fig. 99A—C. Depolarizing potentials (upper traces) produced by electrophoretic application of ACh as in Fig. 22 at various positions along a muscle fibre of the cat tenuissimus muscle. The ACh-containing electrode was applied close to the muscle membrane and the intracellular electrode was within 0.1 mm of the drug application. The sensitivity of the muscle fibre to ACh was tested at distances of about 0.5 mm separation along the muscle fibre. The lower traces show that the ACh was applied by the same electrophoretic current at all positions along a fibre. A. In an innervated fibre only the visible endplate region is sensitive to ACh. B. In a 14-days denervated fibre there is approximately the same sensitivity of the fibre at all positions along its length (AXELSSON and THESLEFF 1959). C. In a muscle fibre intoxicated by injection of a small quantity of botulinum toxin into its environment 3 weeks earlier, there is also approximately the same sensitivity to ACh along the whole tested length. No min. EPPs could be recorded from this fibre (THESLEFF 1960a)

than the membrane some millimetres distant therefrom. Two independent series of investigations have led to the development of two different explanations of this spreading sensitivity.

THESLEFF (1960a) found that, when chemical transmission across the neuromuscular junction is greatly depressed or suppressed by the prolonged action of botulinum toxin, the ACh sensitivity spreads along the muscle fibres from the endplates (Fig. 99C). Since no structural changes could be observed in the nerve terminals, it was concluded that suppression of the normal ACh action on the muscle endplates is a sufficient explanation of the spreading sensitivity that occurs with nerve degeneration. When complete inactivation of muscle is secured by the operative isolation of the spinal cord from all incoming impulses (JOHNS and THESLEFF 1961), there is little or no spread of the ACh sensitive area; hence it has been postulated that the spontaneous ACh release giving the miniature endplate potentials is effective in restricting the ACh sensitive area to the immediate proximity of the endplates (THESLEFF 1960b).

Evidence against this explanation is given by experiments on ACh sensitivity during regeneration. MILEDI (1960c) found that retraction of the ACh sensitive area of a denervated muscle occurs at a very early stage of nerve regeneration. At that time there has been no recovery of neuromuscular transmission; there is even no trace of an endplate potential, and the miniature endplate potentials often still have the very low frequency and the amplitudes characteristic of the denervated nerve-muscle junction (Chapter III; BIRKS, KATZ and MILEDI 1960). Furthermore MILEDI (1960a) found that bathing a denervated muscle for 24 hours in a solution of 10^{-6} ACh does not effect any appreciable retraction of the ACh sensitive area; and even after several days in this solution the increased sensitivity of the denervated muscle persists; hence it was concluded that the spontaneous liberation of ACh from the motor nerve terminals probably is not responsible for restricting the ACh sensitive zone to the immediate neighbourhood of the motor endplate (MILEDI 1960a, 1960b). It was therefore postulated that there is some other neural influence on muscle which may or may not be concurrent with the ACh transmission across the junction.

It is to be noted that with both hypotheses a further problem arises in attempting to explain the generation and spread of the ACh receptors from the denervated endplates of the muscle, and the normal restriction of these receptors to the endplate zone by a neural influence, whether this be due to the spontaneous emission of ACh or to some other influence.

However there is now evidence that muscle fibres can very effectively develop receptors independently of the endplate zone (MILEDI 1962). When the aneural pelvic quarter of the frog sartorius is severed from the innervated remainder of the muscle, it develops a high sensitivity to ACh, even more rapidly and effectively than after denervation (KATZ and MILEDI 1961). The innervated portion also exhibits an increased ACh sensitivity, hence it appears that muscle injury is itself a cause of super-sensitivity to ACh, and that muscle can respond in this way regardless of whether it is innervated or not. Muscle can respond similarly when isolated from the body, as is shown with a rat diaphragm incubated *in vitro* for several days (MILEDI and TROWELL 1962). Presumably this autogenous sensitization of muscle is comparable with that observed for foetal muscle. A further remarkable observation is that denervation of one endplate of doubly innervated muscle fibres results in an increased ACh sensitization of that endplate and its surround (MILEDI 1960a).

However, these effects are much less than in the fully denervated muscle, which suggests that the intact nerve endings exert a controlling influence along the whole length of the muscle fibres.

A few days after denervation muscles display fine fibrillary contractions that are caused by brief bursts of rhythmic impulses travelling along the muscle fibres. Reference may be made to HNÍK and ŠKORPIL (1962) for a recent comprehensive treatment and list of references. This development of fibrillary activity parallels the spreading ACh sensitization of the muscle fibres, though it cannot be a consequence of their activation by ACh because it is not depressed by curare (ROSENBLUETH and LUCO 1937; ECCLES 1941a). Fibrillation does not develop in muscles suffering from the complete functional disuse that is effected when it retains its motor innervation from a spinal cord isolated from all incoming impulses (TOWER 1937b, ECCLES 1941b). Since miniature EPPs are not appreciably changed in these disused muscles (JOHNS and THESLEFF 1961), it is an attractive postulate that the fibrillation of muscle occurs when the motor endplates are deprived of their normal background stimulation by the quantal discharge of transmitter from the nerve terminals (JOSEFSSON and THESLEFF 1961). Further support for this postulate is adduced from investigations on botulinum poisoning which parallel those on ACh sensitization. Typical fibrillations appear at 5 to 10 days after the injection of the toxin and persist for at least 60 days (JOSEFSSON and THESLEFF 1961). However, just as with the development of ACh sensitization, the development of muscle fibrillation could be due to deprivation of some neural influence other than the quantal emission of ACh.

Both the ACh sensitization and the fibrillation are primarily due to changes wrought by the denervation on the surface membrane of muscle fibres. Even more direct evidence of a change in membrane properties is provided by the lengthening of the electrical time constants, both of the strength-duration curve for stimulation and of accommodation. For example DESMEDT (1950a, 1950b, 1959) finds that shortly after denervation there is a progressive increase in chronaxie, which continues for some weeks, eventually to reach a stationary level of about 15 msec, some five times longer than for the alpha excitability of innervated muscle. Concurrently there is a slowing of accommodation, which is associated with the onset and development of fibrillation. These changes in electrical excitability do not occur when muscle atrophy is produced by other procedures such as tenotomy. Recovery from the excitability changes commences at an early stage of nerve regeneration and is nearly complete by the time that neuromuscular transmission is restored.

Regeneration in the peripheral nervous system offers good opportunities for controlled investigation into the differential sensitivity of growing nerve fibres. There is general agreement that regenerating motor fibres indiscriminately make functional contacts with any type of skeletal muscle fibre

(WEISS and HOAG 1946; BULLER, ECCLES and ECCLES 1960b; BERNSTEIN and GUTH 1961; GUTH 1962; ECCLES, ECCLES and KOZAK 1962). On the other hand preganglionic sympathetic fibres display discrimination in regenerating to make synapses on ganglion cells of appropriate modality (LANGLEY 1897; GUTH and BERNSTEIN 1961); and they even appear to displace inappropriate synapses that were formed before the "proper" presynaptic terminals had regenerated.

3. The trophic influence of nerve on muscle

In summary of the preceding section it can be stated that the evidence for a trophic influence from nerve on to muscle membrane is conclusive, but it is still uncertain whether it is entirely effected by unique trophic influences or whether in part by the spontaneous emission of quanta of ACh.

When considering the nature of the trophic influences of nerve on muscle it is important to take into account the proximo-distal flow of material in axons (YOUNG 1945, 1946; WEISS and HISCOE 1948; WEISS 1960; OCHS, DALRYMPLE and RICHARDS 1962; GUTMANN and HNÍK 1962). The flow of this material appears to be due to a kind of amoeboid propulsion, and, when a constriction is released, the rate of advance is of the order of several milli-metres a day. It is possible that the material so propelled along the motor axon is extruded from the synaptic terminals and so mediates the trophic influence on muscle. Since deprivation of this trophic influence by nerve degeneration causes changes along the whole length of each muscle fibre, a likely postulate is that the trophic material supplied by the nerve spreads intracellularly along the muscle fibre and affects the membrane from within. Alternatively it could be that the trophic material supplied by the nerve merely acts on the muscle at the motor endplate and causes it to generate the effective substance or influence that spreads along the muscle fibre.

The flow of trophic influence along the nerve was very effectively demon-strated by LUCO and EYZAGUIRRE (1955), who investigated the effect of sever-ing motor nerves at varying distances from the motor endplates. Both the ACh sensitization and the fibrillation began earlier the closer the nerve sec-tion was to the endplates. Thus it is shown that the trophic influence appa-rently travels along the motor axon with a velocity ranging from 2 mm/hour to 1 mm/hour, which is of the same order as that observed by WEISS and HISCOE (1948) for the flow of axoplasm.

B. Central nervous system

The organization of neural connections in the central nervous system bears witness to the operation during development of influences directing the growth of nerve fibres and specifying the neurones on which synapses are formed.

There have been many experimental investigations designed to demonstrate these developmental influences by observing the results of such operative procedures as limb implanation, nerve cross-union and disorientation of receptor organs such as eye or skin. Until recently these experimental investigations have been concerned with behavioural studies involving complex reactions to signals such as visuo-motor reactions (SPERRY 1951a, 1951b; SZÉKELY 1957; GAZE 1960). Under such conditions unrecognized feed-back mechanisms are likely to distort the responses and greatly to complicate their interpretation, as has been pointed out by SZENTÁGOTHAI and SZÉKELY (1956) in relation to the regeneration of retinal neurones to the amphibian optic tectum.

1. Experiments on amphibia

A remarkable example of an organized pattern of neural connections is exhibited by this retinal projection onto the primary visual area in the brain. The detailed topographic relationships have been determined for the retinal projection to the optic tectum in amphibia (GAZE 1959; MATURANA, LETTVIN, MCCULLOCH and PITTS 1959, 1960) and have formed the basis for a very rigorous re-examination of the factors controlling such a specificity of development.

In amphibians section of the optic nerve is followed by regeneration and so provides excellent opportunities for investigating whether in this regeneration there is reconstitution of the original specificity of connection between the retina and the optic tectum. In the earlier investigations a remarkable recovery of visuo-motor performance was demonstrated by behavioural tests (reviewed by SPERRY 1951a, 1951b, and by GAZE 1960). In control experiments it was shown that this behavioural recovery could not be attributed to the ability of the animal to learn the appropriate interpretation of misdirected visual information. For example after simple rotation of the eye or after rotation of the eye combined with section and regeneration of the optic nerve, the animal exhibits disorientation of visuo-motor reactions and continues to do so indefinitely. It was therefore concluded that the regenerating optic nerve fibres re-establish their "correct" terminations in the optic tectum (SPERRY 1951a, 1951b); and it was further postulated that there is some kind of retinal differentiation along at least two axes and a complementary specificity of the tectal neurones so that the regenerating fibres growing into the tectum would make the appropriate synaptic connections.

When after regeneration the retino-tectal projection is studied directly by illuminating retinal points and discovering the tectal area activated thereby, it is also found that usually there is an approximate recovery of the "correct" connections (GAZE 1959; MATURANA, LETTVIN, MCCULLOCH and PITTS 1959; GAZE and JACOBSEN 1963), so confirming the earlier behavioural experiments. However, the very detailed and rigorous studies by GAZE and JACOBSEN

(1963) disclosed many examples of incomplete and anomalous regeneration, which only in part could be attributed to experimental testing at too early a stage of regeneration. These experiments have shown how complex are the factors controlling regeneration. Simple mechanical guidance of the regenerating fibres is a quite inadequate explanation (GAZE 1960), as also is the differentiation of axons according to rate of growth. Since one retina can form organized connections to either tectum, the factors controlling development cannot discriminate between one and the other side.

GAZE and JACOBSEN (1963) and GAZE, JACOBSEN and SZÉKELEY (1963) have developed the original suggestion of SPERRY (1951b) and proposed that the organization of the retino-tectal projection is determined by a "place" specification of each element with reference to two gradients that are assumed to occur in the naso-temporal and dorso-ventral axes of the retina, and in the corresponding locations in the tectum. After transplantation of nasal or temporal halves of the retinae of larval amphibians the pattern of regeneration to the tectum was in precise agreement with predictions from the gradient hypothesis (GAZE, JACOBSEN and SZÉKELEY 1963). Besides this remarkable experimental corroboration, the gradient hypothesis is attractive because of its basic simplicity; but on the other hand it is deficient because it makes no statement with respect to the properties which define the gradients. With both the retinal and tectal neurones these properties are left entirely unspecified, though presumably some kind of chemical specificity is involved. Evidently we are still at a very primitive level in our attempts to understand the way in which the highly specific neural connections are established and maintained between retinal and tectal neurones.

There also are many examples of remarkable functional recoveries after nerve cross-union and skin transplantation in teleosts and larval amphibians (SPERRY 1950; SPERRY and DEUPREÉ 1956; ARORA and SPERRY 1957), but the observed responses were limb or jaw movements that merely signal the net result of the contractions of antagonistic muscles controlling movement at a joint. Hence it may be hazardous to use such observations in attempting to establish that there have been changes in the synaptic connections on to individual nerve cells. Nevertheless, these investigations demonstrate a remarkable functional recovery paralleling that now established for the retino-tectal connections and suggesting that many parts of the central nervous systems of teleosts and amphibians have highly specific plastic properties.

2. Investigations on mammals

In contrast to amphibians and teleosts comparable experiments on mammals give no indication of such plastic changes in the central nervous system (SPERRY 1940, 1942, 1945, 1947; MCINTYRE and ROBINSON 1958); but it has been suggested by SPERRY that embryonic mammals may have a comparable plasticity, which is already lost about the time of birth.

Recently the pattern of monosynaptic activation of motoneurones in the cat hind-limb has been defined in such detail (see assembled results in Table 1 of ECCLES, ECCLES and SHEALY 1962) that it provides quantitative demonstration of the specificity of synaptic connections; and furthermore it can form the basis for detecting even slight changes that may occur as a result of the inversion of motoneuronal function consequent on the operative cross-union of muscle nerves.

As a rule the monosynaptic activation from the Group I a fibres of any particular muscle is restricted to the motoneurones that themselves are concerned in the movements subserved by that muscle. This arrangement is singularly appropriate when the role of monosynaptic activation is considered in relation to the γ-loop control of movement (GRANIT and KAADA 1952; ELDRED, GRANIT and MERTON 1953; GRANIT 1955). The specificity of connection is very remarkable when considered in relation to the close proximity of the motoneuronal nuclei supplying muscles

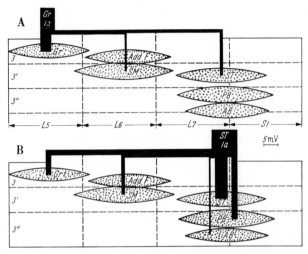

Fig. 100A and B. Diagrammatic representation of the amount of monosynaptic innervation as measured by the average size of the EPSP recorded intracellularly from motoneurones. The motoneuronal nuclei are shown as fusiform structures located at the indicated segemental level of the spinal cord (L_5 to S_1), and in the three subdivision (3,3′ and 3″) of the third longitudinal column (ROMANES 1951), Gr, gracilis; Add F, adductor femoris; SM, semimembranosus; ST, semitendinosus; PB, posterior biceps; AB, anterior biceps. In A a Group I a volley from Gr muscle enters at L_5 level and the monosynaptic innervation of Gr, SM and ST motoneurones is indicated by the widths of the black columns stemming from the Gr input. Similarly in B the ST I a input at L_7 and S_1 level is shown branching into black columns to the various motor nuclei. All connections not shown are either zero or too small to show on the scale adopted, which is indicated as the width for a 5 mV EPSP

of unrelated function, which usually have quite independent monosynaptic innervations; conversely, synergic groups of motoneurones may be relatively remote from each other, yet there are reciprocal monosynaptic connections between them. The antithesis between anatomical relationships and physiological connections is particularly well illustrated by the knee flexor and hip extensor groups of muscles, which are shown diagrammatically in Fig. 100 with the topographical arrangement reported by ROMANES (1951).

In Fig. 100 the widths of the channels are proportional to their mean potency in producing monosynaptic EPSPs (ECCLES, ECCLES and LUNDBERG

1957b; R. M. Eccles and Lundberg 1958b; Eccles, Eccles and Shealy 1962). It is seen in Fig. 100A that the Group Ia impulses from the knee flexor muscle, gracilis, enter the spinal cord at L_5 segmental level; and, in addition to monosynaptic innervation of the gracilis motoneurones at that level, they send collaterals down the spinal cord to end on the synergic motoneurones of another knee-flexor, semitendinosus, about two segments more caudally. There is much less monosynaptic innervation of hip extensor motoneurones, even though they are much closer to gracilis segmentally (semimembranosus), and in the same longitudinal cell column (adductor femoris). Reciprocally, in Fig. 100B the Group Ia fibres from the knee flexor, semitendinosus, are seen to ascend two segments to make powerful monosynaptic connections to the synergic but remote gracilis motoneurones, but have much less synaptic connection to the adjacent hip extensor motoneurones (semimembranosus, anterior biceps, and adductor femoris).

Several other examples can be given where there is a comparable concentration of monosynaptic innervation on to synergic groups of motoneurones. Thus the general statement can be made that, in the organization of monosynaptic connections of Group Ia fibres, functional relationship dominates anatomical proximity. Hence arises the question: What factors govern the development of the highly specific motoneuronal connections that are made by the afferent fibres growing in from the neuroblasts in the primitive spinal ganglion? The detailed specificity of the growth is of such an order that it is not possible to accept a mere mechanical explanation: that it is due to growth of fibres along the easiest channels between tissue planes. The variety and the degree of the developing specificity necessitate the postulate that a chemical or physicochemical property of the growing fibres provides a "selective contact guidance" (Weiss 1936, 1950a, 1950b) by means of which they reach a destination that accords with their function. A further development of this postulate is that the motoneurones innervating a synergic group of muscles and the Group Ia muscle afferent fibres making monosynaptic connections with them have a complementary specificity whereby synaptic connections are attracted and maintained. It has been proposed (Weiss 1947, 1952; Sperry 1951a, 1951b, 1958) that this complementary specificity is due to a "modulating" influence which muscle exerts on the motoneurones innervating it, so that by a process of "myotypic specification" the motoneurones innervating each muscle are adapted to attract and retain synaptic connections from the appropriate afferent fibres; for example in Fig. 100A the Group Ia fibres from gracilis muscle onto semitendinosus motoneurones, and reciprocally for Fig. 100B.

Fig. 101 illustrates cross-union experiments on young kittens which were designed to test the postulate of myotypic specification (Eccles, Eccles and Magni 1960; Eccles, Eccles, Shealy and Willis 1962). As shown in B, cross-union was effected between the nerves of two muscles, leaving one member of each synergic pair unmolested, which serve as control monosynaptic pathways (SA$_1$ and SA$_2$) and control motoneurones (SMN$_1$ and SMN$_2$). The final experiment was usually performed more than six months after cross-union and involved observing the monosynaptic innervation of each of the four types of motoneurones in Fig. 101 by each of the four types of Group Ia afferents. In parallel control experiments the same muscle nerves were severed

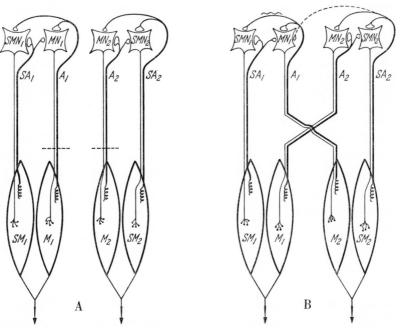

Fig. 101 A and B. A: diagrammatic representation of monosynaptic pathways for two pairs of synergic muscles: M_1 and SM_1; M_2 and SM_2. The afferent fibers, A_1, SA_1, A_2, SA_2, respectively, from the annulo-spiral endings are seen to make monosynaptic connections to motoneurones of their own muscle (homonymous endings) and of the synergic muscle (heteronymous endings). The larger synaptic knobs for the homoymous endings symbolize the more powerful excitatory action. The broken lines drawn across the nerves to M_1 and M_2 muscles indicate the site of section and self-union in the control experiments. B: diagrammatic representation of cross-union of the nerves to M_1 and M_2 muscles with regeneration. Broken line from SA_2 to MN_1 represents the new connections which appear to occur under certain conditions (see text), and which would be due to growth-specificity. The wavy line above the connection from A_1 to SMN_1 symbolizes the decreased synaptic excitatory action which appears to occur under certain conditions (see text), and which would be due to regression-specificity (ECCLES, ECCLES, SHEALY and WILLIS 1962)

but self-united, so that the condition of Fig. 101 A was restored by regeneration. In these two types of experiments the monosynaptic responses of almost two thousand motoneurones were fully examined so that reliable statistical analysis could be made.

There are two main types of prediction from the myotypic specification hypothesis: one is concerned with the growth of new monosynaptic connections which are in accord with the newly acquired function that derives from the nerve cross-union, and which may be called "growth-specificity;" the other is concerned with the regression of the monosynaptic connections that are rendered inappropriate by the nerve cross-union, and which may be called "regression-specificity." The dotted line in Fig. 101 B shows the one variety of growth-specificity which occurred with a high degree of statistical probability, namely for intact Group Ia afferents to motoneurones with cross-united axons. There was likewise one variety of regression-specificity for which statistical evidence was highly significant—namely from the cross-unioned Group Ia afferent fibres on to intact motoneurones, there being regression of synapses made by the pathway indicated by the wavy line in Fig. 101 B.

These statistically significant changes occurred with cross-unions between some muscle nerves, not with others. In explanation of this failure it may plausibly be postulated that, for the development of new connections from one species of afferent fibre onto a particular species of motoneurone, a necessary condition is that these afferent fibres must already be in the immediate neighbourhood of such motoneurones, even within a few microns. Probably it is significant that growth of new connections does not occur onto motoneurones with intact axons, SMN_1 and SMN_2 in Fig. 101 B, nor is there regression of synapses belonging to intact afferent fibres, SA_1 and SA_2 in Fig. 101 B. The plastic changes are restricted to motoneurones and afferent fibres that suffer injury from the cross-union operation. It is suggested that this chromatolytic injury causes reversion towards an embryonic type with a consequent increased tendency to plastic changes, just as occurs with injured muscle (KATZ and MILEDI 1961).

However not all the observed growth of new connections was in accord with prediction from the myotypic specification hypotheses. With one variety of the cross-union experiment the chromatolyzed motoneurones received monosynaptic connections from muscles that were functionally quite unrelated to the newly acquired function of these motoneurones.

Certainly cross-union investigations have made it highly probable that plastic changes may ensue when motoneurone and muscle afferent functions are changed by cross-union operations in young kittens. These plastic changes are relatively small, and can be demonstrated convincingly only under favourable circumstances; nevertheless they suggest the existence of properties in the mammalian central nervous system that have the greatest theoretical and practical significance. The magnitude of this effect is far less than would be expected for a process that is postulated to account for the embryological development of specific connections such as those illustrated in Fig. 100. Possibly specification is much more effective at the very early stage of development. As postulated by WEISS (1947) and SPERRY (1951a, 1951b, 1958), one can envisage the growing nerve fibre as chemically sensing the surface along which it grows, and being specifically attracted to form synapses by the chemical properties of some surfaces and not by others. It remains to be determined whether the developments of aberrant monosynaptic connections here reported are further instances of the influence of specific chemical affinities, i. e. of the postulated specification process, and, in addition, of changes which muscles can produce in motoneuronal specification, the postulated myotypic specification; but as reported above some exceptional developments were observed.

The role of modality specificity in determining the site of synaptic contacts on neurones in the central nervous system is suggested by the very restricted location of inhibitory synapses on the soma and dendritic stumps of the hippocampal pyramidal cells (Figs. 85—87; ANDERSEN, ECCLES and LØYNING 1963; BLACKSTAD and FLOOD 1963); and the inhibitory synapses on Purkinje cells in the cerebellum also seem to have a similarly restricted location (ANDERSEN, ECCLES and VOORHOEVE 1963). It is, of course, an example of good physiological design to have inhibitory synapses located on the soma, because they would there exercise the most effective control of the discharge of impulses down the axon. But in the present context it can be asked what developmental control ensures that the inhibitory synapses are concentrated on the soma and the excitatory more remotely on the dendrites, particularly on the dendritic spines (Figs. 2B, 3B)?

Evidently the simplest hypothesis is that these specific locations result from chemical sensing by the growing nerve terminals, and that the discrimination between different parts of the neuronal surface is effected because in the proximity of the nucleus the metabolism of the nerve cell (pyramidal or Purkinje) is different from that in the remote dendritic regions. In the mammalian central nervous system the excitatory and inhibitory neurones are chemically unique and have unique synaptic connections (Chapter XIII); hence it is envisaged that the inhibitory type of fibre is attracted by the special chemical character of the surface membrane in proximity to the nucleus, whereas the excitatory type of fibre would be repelled, and on the contrary is attracted by the dendritic surface remote from the nucleus and by the even more remote dendritic spines. It remains for further investigation to disclose how far the location of inhibitory synapses in the perikaryal region of nerve cells is a general feature of the central nervous system.

3. Experiments in birds

The plasticity of the nervous system at a very early stage of development has been investigated by transplanting limbs heterotopically into chick embryos at the third day of incubation and then studying the reflex responses evoked from these supernumerary limbs several weeks after hatching (SZÉKELY and SZENTÁGOTHAI 1962). Unfortunately the reflex responses were very various and complex, so that no simple interpretation is possible. It was concluded that they are not satisfactorily explained by the Weiss-Sperry concept of specific modulation with the consequent development of specific neural pathways in the central nervous system. Rather it is suggested that the specificity of the responses arises on account of the spatio-temporal pattern of the impulse discharges evoked from the supernumerary limb. This preliminary investigation on birds is important because it opens up the possibility of operative interference at a very early stage of neural development. However, it will be necessary eventually to employ microelectrode techniques in order to obtain precise information on the synaptic developments resulting from operations on embryos.

C. The trophic influence of muscle on nerve

WEISS (1960) has suggested that, in addition to the proximo-distal flow of material in nerve that was considered above, there is also a flow in the reverse direction; and flow in both directions has recently been demonstrated by ZELENÁ and LUBINSKA (1962) for the AChE in peripheral nerve. The flow from muscle up nerve fibres conceivably could form the basis of the trophic influence of muscle on nerve. It is postulated that deficiency of this trophic influence causes atrophy of nerve fibres that fail to regenerate to muscle fibres or regenerate to an insufficient number (WEISS, EDDS and CAVANAUGH 1945; SANDERS and YOUNG 1946; AITKEN, SHARMAN and YOUNG 1947; HAMBURGER and LEVI MONTALCINI 1950; EVANS and VIZOSO 1951). Probably some of the reduction in size is attributable to the deficiency of impulse traffic along these nerve fibres (EDDS 1950), and a small reduction was found in the nerves to tenotomized muscle where there was also a reduction of impulse traffic (GUTMANN and VRBOVÁ 1952; GUTMANN 1958). However, crucial experiments on disuse and nerve atrophy (TOWER 1937a, 1937b) showed that from the chronically isolated lumbo-sacral spinal cord there was almost complete absence of all discharges along motor nerve fibres; yet these nerve fibres in the ventral roots showed no reduction in size even after many months of disuse. Peripherally also these motor nerve fibres showed little sign of atrophy until it suddenly occurred when the muscle destruction was far advanced. Evidently disuse plays but a minor role in the atrophy of motor nerve fibres that fail to establish adequate muscle connections.

Apparently the atrophy of nerves with inadequate innervation results from a deficiency of trophic influence from muscle. In this trophic action there is of course no evidence of the specificity of muscle action on nerve fibres that is necessitated by the hypothesis of myotypic specification. Nevertheless, the experiments on cross-union give evidence suggesting that even in post-natal life there is a specific flow of information from muscles up to motoneurones. There will be general agreement that there are still many unsolved problems in the extensive field of the functional interrelationship of muscle and nerve.

D. Plastic changes in the potency of synaptic transmission

Two explanations, not mutually exclusive, have been proposed for the neurological basis of learning and conditioning (HEBB 1949; YOUNG 1951; ECCLES 1953; THORPE 1956).

According to one, learning is a dynamic process due to continuously circulating patterns of impulses in closed neural chains (RASHEVSKY 1938; YOUNG 1938; HILGARD and MARQUIS 1940; HOUSEHOLDER and LANDAHL 1945). As a consequence, the reaction of the nervous system to any particular sensory input is changed in a unique way so long as this circulation of impulses continues. Conceivably, this explanation could apply at brief intervals—seconds or minutes—after some initial conditioning stimulus. It certainly cannot account for memories or conditioned behaviours that survive either a virtual suppression of all activity in the cerebral cortex—e.g. deep anaesthesia, concussion, coma, extreme cold, or even deep sleep—or the converse, convulsive seizures of the whole cortex.

The alternative explanation is that activation of synapses increases their efficacy by some enduring change in their fine structure (TANZI 1893; RAMON y CAJAL 1911; KONORSKI 1948, 1950; HEBB 1949; TÖNNIES 1949; YOUNG 1951; ECCLES 1953; JUNG 1953; McINTYRE 1953; THORPE 1956). We may assume that a given sensory input results in a uniquely patterned activation of central neurones; and, according to this explanation, a subsequent re-presentation of this input would tend to be channelled along the same pathways because of the increased efficacy of the synaptic actions exerted by all those neurones activated initially. There would thus be a further reinforcement of the synapses responsible for the unique pattern of activation and response, with consequently a more effective channelling; and so on, cumulatively, for each successive application of that sensory input. Necessarily, the postulated changes in synaptic efficacy must be of very long duration—days or weeks. There is no way in which relatively brief durations of synaptic change for each synapse of a serial arrangement can sum to give a more prolonged change.

In designing experiments to test for this postulated effect of use in causing a prolonged increase in synaptic efficacy, it was initially much simpler to test for the opposite effect—namely regression of synaptic function with disuse. Furthermore, the postulated effects of use in increasing synaptic efficacy and of disuse in depressing it can be investigated most rigorously with monosynaptic pathways.

The only reliable way to produce prolonged total disuse of the monosynaptic pathway is to sever the afferent nerve fibers. When this is done just peripheral to the dorsal root ganglion in order to preserve the central pathways of these fibers, there is found to be, some weeks later, a depression of monosynaptic reflexes relative to the control side (ECCLES and McINTYRE 1953). These relatively depressed reflexes are more potentiated by prolonged high-frequency activation (post-tetanic potentiation) than are the corresponding reflexes on the control side; and they exhibit, in addition, prolonged residual potentiation for several hours.

Comparable results have been obtained using intracellular recording of the excitatory postsynaptic potentials induced monosynaptically in moto-neurones (ECCLES, KRNJEVIĆ and MILEDI 1958). Disuse is effected by severing the nerve to one muscle of a synergic group, the other one or more nerves serving to give control synaptic activation. It is found that, relative to the control afferent path, the monosynaptic excitatory action of the disused path on the same motoneurone is reduced to about half after 2—4 weeks of complete inactivity. Furthermore, it is increased relatively much more by post-tetanic potentiation, so that the normal size is almost regained during the maximum potentiation a few seconds after an intense conditioning activation. Thereafter, the synaptic potential progressively declines; but often a small residual potentiation occurs for as long as 20 minutes, while, after application of a similar conditioning stimulation to a control nerve, the post-tetanic potentiation usually passes over into a prolonged phase of depression, as in Fig. 39 E.

All these operative procedures for inducing disuse by sectioning the afferent fibers have the disadvantage that a small shrinkage of the dorsal root fibers occurs (ECCLES and MCINTYRE 1953; SZENTÁGOTHAI and RAJKOVITS 1955). Conceivably, this shrinkage may extend right to the synaptic terminals and account for at least part of the depressed synaptic efficacy. However the prolonged potentiations following conditioning tetani show that disuse had caused changes in synapses that were not simply attributable to depressed function, but which indicated that the disused synapses had acquired special properties.

It was suggested (ECCLES 1958b) that tenotomy was a convenient way of reducing the discharge of impulses from the annulospiral endings of muscle spindles belonging to the muscle under test. However, it was surprising to find that, some weeks after the operation, volleys in the nerves of the teno-tomized muscles had a more powerful monosynaptic action than the control nerves on the other side (BERANEK and HNÍK 1959; BERANEK, HNÍK, VYK-LICKÝ and ZELENÁ 1961; KOZAK and WESTERMAN 1961): the increase in monosynaptic reflexes and the shortening of the synaptic delays were both highly significant statistically. These changes were localized in the spinal cord, for they were not changed by spinalization of the animal at the final experimental test; nor was there any significant change in the afferent fibres of the tenotomized muscle either in diameter or conduction velocity.

When attempting to interpret these results it is important to realize that the annulospiral endings are not silenced in resting muscle (ELDRED, GRANIT and MERTON 1953), and recording from the muscle nerves of tenotomized muscles reveals that the barrage of afferent impulses is actually increased relative to the control. If this increased discharge of tenotomized muscles were in the Group Ia afferent fibres, the increased synaptic potency would be readily explained as a result of increased use. However HNIK, BERANEK, VYKLICKÝ and ZELENÁ (1963) find that there is little if any increase in the frequencies of discharges of the muscle spindles of tenotomized muscles, so apparently most of the increased barrage was not in Group Ia fibres. On the other hand KOZAK and WESTERMAN (1961) report that in chronic spinal animals there is no increase in the monosynaptic reflexes from tenotomized muscles, and suggest that in tenotomized muscles there may be an increased supraspinal activation of gamma motoneurones with a consequent increase in the Group Ia discharge. It can be concluded that these tenotomy experiments are important in displaying plastic properties of monosynaptic reflexes, but that they cannot yet be regarded as establishing that increased use raises the potency of synapses.

The enigmas attending experiments designed to produce long-term changes in synaptic activity are well illustrated by the attempt to increase synaptic use by denervating all the muscles but one of a synergic group (R. M. ECCLES, KOZAK and WESTERMAN 1962). Synergic groups of ankle and toe extensor muscles were chosen because as anti-gravity muscles they must be subjected to considerable stretch by posture and movement. It was postulated that, under these conditions, the remaining innervated muscle is under greater mechanical stress than its control fellow on the other side, which could lead to an increased discharge up Group Ia fibres and so to an increased activation of their synapses. In one experimental series the animals were given forced walking exercise for half to one hour every day; and relative to the control side there was the expected large increase in monosynaptic reflexes from each residual muscle nerve of the synergic group, whereas there was approximate symmetry of performance for the synergic groups that were not subjected to operative depletion. However, exactly the same asymmetry of monosynaptic reflexes from each residual muscle nerve was observed in chronic spinal animals in which the residual muscles were carefully protected fom all mechanical stress. As with the tenotomy experiments it can be concluded that these experiments do demonstrate a plastic increase in synaptic potency, but do not show that it is a consequence of excess use. However, both types of experiment can form the basis of further investigations into this very fundamental problem of plastic changes in synapses.

It will be appreciated that these proposals for further experimental investigation are restricted to the monosynaptic pathway. If it can be established that, in this simplest synaptic system, excess activation gives a prolonged increase in synaptic efficacy, experimental investigation could be extended to the more complex polysynaptic reflex pathways, and, finally to pathways in the higher levels of the nervous system. Since investigations of learning and of conditioned reflexes have been carried out almost exclusively with these higher levels of the central nervous system, it has generally been thought that synapses at these levels had properties of "plasticity" that were not shared by synapses in the spinal cord. Experimental evidence is now against any such qualitative distinction between the synapses of higher and lower levels of the central nervous system. However, there may be quantitative differences, the synapses at higher levels having some properties much more highly developed than with synapses at lower levels.

Firstly there is the phenomenon of frequency-potentiation that is usually poorly developed with synapses in the cord, but is very powerful at synapses made by cortical pyramidal cells (Chapter VI). This large increase in synaptic potency (up to six-fold) during high frequency tetanization certainly indicates that some cortical cells have a degree of lability of synaptic function far transcending that of lower centres. Frequency-potentiation during brief tetani has been attributed to the effectiveness of mobilization of transmitter within the presynaptic terminals, and it is conceivable that the continuous exercise of this transmitter-mobilization may leave an enduring trace of increased synaptic efficacy.

Secondly, postsynaptic inhibitory action is far more powerful and prolonged in higher centres than in the spinal cord. It has been recognized that learning involves selectivity of response, and presumably inhibition would be significantly concerned in the repression of irrelevant responses. Possibly the highly developed recurrent inhibitory mechanisms in the neocortex and hippocampus are important in this respect (Chapters X and XIII).

Thirdly, it is now recognized that in both the neocortex and hippocampus the excitatory synapses on pyramidal cells are concentrated on the dendrites and particularly on the dendritic spines. Possibly dendritic spines are specially concerned in learning phenomena, for example hypertrophing as a consequence of intense activation. It is of interest that the dendritic spines of both neocortex and hippocampus contain a unique structure, the spine apparatus (HAMLYN 1962). It is further possible that the profuse and extensive dendritic development of cortical pyramidal cells may greatly enhance the enduring changes produced in these cells by intensive stimulation. For example excitatory synaptic action on the remote regions of dendrites can be effective in evoking the discharge of impulses down the axon if it sets up in the dendrites some propagating depolarization of self-regenerative character, either local responses or fully developed impulses. Intensive activation may enhance the ability of dendrites to respond in this manner.

There are great technical difficulties in the design of precise controlled experiments on the effect of excess use on cortical synapses, but there is progress. For example the powerful commissural pathway through the corpus callosum give a means of subjecting a cortical area to excess synaptic bombardment. Prolonged paroxysmal activity of a cortical area induces in the mirror-image area a state of hyperexcitability which continues indefinitely after its isolation from the original focus (MORRELL 1961).

Besides these investigations into the physiological effects of excess use, it is important to see whether electron microscopy reveals any structural changes in the presynaptic terminals. Already it has been reported that, after several days of disuse brought about by complete darkness, there is dimi-nution in the size of the synaptic vesicles at the synapses made by both rods and cones with the bipolar cells in the rabbit retina (DE ROBERTIS and FRANCHI 1956). A further observation was that, after one day of darkness, the synaptic vesicles tended to accumulate close to the presynaptic membrane.

One explanation of the synaptic basis of learning needs to be reconsidered in the light of the recent findings of electronmicroscopy. SHIMBEL (1950) suggested that excess use could give increased synaptic efficacy by a general lowering of the postsynaptic threshold. However, this postulated effect would increase the responsiveness of a nerve cell to all synaptic influences incident on it and so would not have the selectivity of performance required for discriminative learning (ECCLES 1953, p. 219). But it can now be recognized that the postsynaptic component of a synapse can uniquely contribute to its potency. The active zones have postsynaptic as well as presynaptic components (Chapter II; GRAY 1959; COUTEAUX 1961), and an increase in the proportion of a synapse occupied by active zones presumably would increase its potency. In this context it will be recalled that HAMLYN (1962) suggested that the spine apparatus in the dendritic spines of cortical pyramidal cells may be specially related to the presumed high performance of cortical synapses in learning. Conceivably they could exercise this effect by increasing the efficiency of the postsynaptic component of the active zones on that spine.

The ultimate aim of the investigations on plasticity is to correlate the observed structural and functional changes and to understand the way these changes are brought about by excess use and by disuse. Inevitably, such a programme involves questions relating to the control of the manufacture of transmitter substance and to its availability for release by the activated synapses. Possibly use gives increased function by enhancing the manufacture and availability of transmitter substance, but enlargement of synaptic knobs and even the sprouting of new knobs would seem to be more probable devices for securing an increased synaptic action that may persist throughout a life time (KONORSKI 1948, 1950; HEBB 1949; YOUNG 1951; ECCLES 1953). Evident-ly, further investigation by electron microscopy is of the greatest significance in providing evidence discriminating between these alternatives.

This postulate that increased activity leads to synaptic growth is sup-ported by the refined experiments of HYDÉN (1959) in which it was shown that RNA and protein are produced in nerve cells at a rate which is high even at resting conditions, but is considerably increased in activity. Conceivably this increase of RNA and the protein synthesis deriving therefrom could lead to a growth of existing synapses or even to the sprouting of presynaptic terminals to give additional synaptic knobs. HYDÉN (1959) has proposed a biochemical hypothesis of learning in which the uniqueness of each remembered event is carried by a specific encoding of RNA molecules in the nerve cells. Unfortunately, this hypothesis ignores the immense organizational specificity of the nervous system and instead assumes that the specificity attaches to the frequency pattern of the nerve impulses, and not to the lines of communication of the nerve fibres. This hypothesis is therefore unacceptable on neurological grounds; nevertheless HYDÉN's experiments are of great value in relation to the orthodox growth theory of learning.

Perhaps the most unsatisfactory feature of the attempt to explain the phenomena of learning and conditioning by the demonstrated changes in synaptic efficacy is that long periods of excess use or disuse are required in order to produce a detectable synaptic change. In contrast, conditioned reflexes are established by relatively few presentations, and unique events may be remembered for a life time. A probable explanation is that prolonged reverberatory activity occurs in the neuronal network, so that a single event may activate each synaptic link in a spatio-temporal pattern thousands of times within a few seconds. HEBB (1949) makes a related postulate when he supposes that "a reverberatory trace might co-operate with the structural change, and carry the memory until the growth change is made." A similar suggestion has been made by GERARD (1949) and KONORSKI (1961). Furthermore we may suppose that the plastic changes in synapses are susceptible to reinforcement by the replaying of the specific spatio-temporal patterns each time that the memory is recalled.

EPILOGUE

This book has been entirely devoted to the modes of communication between nerve cell and nerve cell and between nerve cell and effector organs. As such it has born witness to the enduring contributions made by neurohistologists, notably RAMON Y CAJAL, in establishing the concept of the neurone as the structural unit, and by physiologists, notably SHERRINGTON, in developing the concept of the synapse. It will be recognized that I have exercised much discrimination in respect both of the experimental data that I have reported and of the hypotheses that I have considered. For example my account is based exclusively on the ionic theory of the membrane potential and of the nerve impulse as developed particularly by HODGKIN and his collaborators; but only by so doing am I able to give a coherent account of synaptic action. This book has the personal outlook of a monograph; it is not a hand-book or a text book. I will further admit that I have concentrated on topics that seemed to me to be of fundamental significance or that appeared to have important implications for future developments. Much fine experimental work has therefore been neglected or quite inadequately treated. But I hope that my personal selection has at least the merit of resulting in relatively clear pictures and hypotheses of the various modes of synaptic action.

After the controversies of recent decades with respect to the rival chemical and electrical hypotheses of synaptic transmission one can feel elated that there is now a truce based on a clearly defined territorial agreement. There has apparently been no difficulty in distinguishing between the electrical and chemical transmitting synapses; and confidence in this classification is even increased by the discovery of synapses that transmit both electrically and chemically (Chapters IX and XIV). In this final summing up it is opportune to list the properties of synapses under the three headings given below (A, B, C), which relate to the nature of the transmission. It will emerge in C that some properties which had hitherto been regarded as of significance for the purpose of distinguishing between the chemical and electrical transmitting synapses are common to both types of synapse (cf. FURSHPAN and POTTER 1959a).

A. Properties exclusively relating to chemical transmitting synapses, whether excitatory or inhibitory.

1. Liberation of a specific transmitter from activated presynaptic terminals. However, with the exception of acetylcholine, noradrenaline, gamma-aminobutyric acid and possibly 5-hydroxy-tryptamine, the transmitters have not yet been identified.

2. Pharmacological properties attributable to specific chemical actions: (a) Postsynaptic depolarization or hyperpolarization by the transmitter and its homologues (Chapters V, XII). (b) Actions of specific blocking agents that are attributable to occupation of receptor sites, cholinoceptive, adrenoceptive (Chapter V), and also the receptor sites for the postsynaptic and the presynaptic inhibitory transmitters in the vertebrate central nervous system (Chapters XII, XV). (c) Prolongation of synaptic excitatory action by suppression of the enzyme destroying the transmitter: anti-AChEs in Chapter V, and possibly barbiturates in Chapter XV.

3. Miniature postsynaptic potentials (Chapter III) and the quantal composition of the postsynaptic potential (Chapter VI). This quantal character has as yet been demonstrable only with relatively few types of synapse, but these include adrenergic as well as cholinergic synapses and also synapses in the central nervous system, so it is probably a general property of chemically transmitting synapses.

4. Long duration of active phase of transmitter action (Chapters IV, X, XV). This is demonstrable only with some chemically transmitting synapses. Synapses with brief transmitter actions may be either chemical, e.g. the squid giant synapse, or electrical.

5. Reversal of the EPSP by intense depolarization of the postsynaptic membrane (Chapter IV), and of the IPSP by hyperpolarization (Chapter X). Eventually these reversals should be demonstrable with all chemical synapses that can be studied by a microelectrode in the postsynaptic element. When, as with the chick ciliary ganglion, there is both electrical and chemical transmission for the same synapse, the two components can be separated by this criterion (Chapter IX).

6. Presence of synaptic vesicles in the presynaptic element (Chapter II). It is essential that the vesicles be demonstrated as forming aggregates in close relationship to the membrane fronting the synaptic cleft. This criterion has been found to characterize the synapses for both types of chemical inhibition (postsynaptic and presynaptic), as well as for excitation.

B. Properties revealing a clear distinction between chemical and electrical synapses.

1. Synaptic delay is negligible for electrical synapses, the postsynaptic potential rising concurrently with the presynaptic spike potential

(Chapters IX and XIV). With chemical synapses the synaptic delay has always been so long that the onset of the postsynaptic response does not begin until the declining phase of the presynaptic spike or even later (Chapters IV, X, XIII).

2. Electric coupling with the excitatory electrical synapses is necessarily large for presynaptic depolarization to postsynaptic depolarization (Chapter IX). With chemical transmitting synapses this coupling has usually been negligible (Chapter III), but there is significant coupling with some chemical synapses in which consequently there may be superposition of chemical and electrical transmission (Chapter IX).

3. Preliminary study by electron-microscopy has shown that the synaptic cleft is more constricted with the electrical transmitting synapse (Chapter IX). It is important for the efficient operation of chemical synapses that there be a low resistance from the cleft into the interstitial space (Chapters IV, X), whereas the converse holds for the electrical synapses (Chapter IX). No doubt, after a thorough investigation by electron-microscopy, the structural correlates of these two diverse requirements will be important distinguishing features between the two types of synapse.

C. Properties that may be shared by both chemical and electrical synapses (cf. FURSHPAN and POTTER 1959a).

1. One-way transmission. With chemical synapses there is usually no transmission from the postsynaptic element to the presynaptic, but the exceptions with chemical synapses are described in Chapter VIII. Electrical synapses may have one-way transmission, but often transmission is reversible (Chapter IX).

2. Similar time courses of postsynaptic potentials. In both types the postsynaptic depolarization is produced by a depolarizing current that has an initial intense phase; hence the postsynaptic potential rises steeply and has a slower decay that often is governed largely by the electric time constant of the postsynaptic membrane. However, in most types of chemical synapse there is a prolonged active phase due to residual transmitter action (Chapters IV, X, XV).

3. During the flow of the postsynaptic depolarizing current the postsynaptic element will exhibit a lower membrane resistance. If this increased conductance occurs in the electrical synapse, it is due to rectification; with the chemical synapses the transmitter causes an increased ionic permeability, which is for particular species of ions as described in Chapters IV, X and XI.

4. With both chemical and electrical excitatory synapses hyperpolarization of the postsynaptic membrane may increase the postsynaptic potential, while depolarization decreases it. With the electrical synapse this occurs

on account of the characteristics of the rectification of the synaptic membrane (FURSHPAN and POTTER 1959a). The equilibrium potential for the ionic mechanism provides the explanation with the chemical synapses (Chapters IV).

5. Electrical inexcitability of the synaptic membrane. Electrical inexcitability may seem an anomalous property for an electrical synapse. However, as shown in Fig. 56F, and as pointed out by KUFFLER (personal communication), the synaptic membrane has merely to be an efficient channel for the current that depolarizes and thus electrically excites the postsynaptic membrane adjacent to the synapse. Very careful study of the effects of current flow on this synaptic membrane (FURSHPAN and POTTER 1959a) failed to disclose any evidence that an outward current across it would result in the inward sodium current characteristic of electrical excitability. The electrical inexcitability of the subsynaptic membrane of chemical synapses has already been discussed in Chapters VII and IX.

It will be understood that the lists of distinguishing criteria in Sections A and B can hardly ever be employed *in toto*. There is no doubt that the vertebrate neuromuscular junction provides the site *par excellence* at which chemical transmission has been most rigorously established, but even here some of the criteria are incomplete. For example, the electrical uncoupling between presynaptic and postsynaptic elements has not been as well established in the backward direction as would be desirable, and reversal of the EPP with depolarization has been demonstrated only with the tonic muscles of amphibia. But once the general pattern of properties of chemically transmitting synapses has been defined, relatively few criteria suffice for discrimination. For example, the simplest criterion to apply is the synaptic delay, measured as in Fig. 46. With intracellular recording from the postsynaptic cell it should also be possible to see if there is a large degree of electric uncoupling, as shown by the spike potential of the presynaptic impulse appearing to a negligible extent across the postsynaptic membrane. A further criterion that should be more generally applied is the reversal of the EPSP or EPP when the potential across the postsynaptic membrane is sufficiently reduced or reversed. In the future electron-microscopy also will provide distinguishing criteria if it is generally established that synaptic *vesicles* occur only in the presynaptic terminals of chemically transmitting synapses.

Where the presynaptic element is very small relative to the postsynaptic, as in all neuromuscular junctions, chemical transmission is obligatory. No matter how ingenious the electrical arrangements, there is no way of introducing amplification into the electrical coupling between the presynaptic and postsynaptic membranes. With amphibian neuromuscular junctions the maximum current that could be provided by the presynaptic element would fail by a factor of hundreds to produce the transfer of charge of $2-4 \times 10^{-9}$ coulombs that FATT and KATZ (1951) calculate to occur across the uncurarized endplate membrane.

It seems probable that many examples of electrical transmitting synapse may be discovered when invertebrate nervous system are intensively investigated. With the vertebrate central nervous system the invariable presence of a considerable synaptic delay would exclude electrical transmission as significantly contributing to any of the synaptic transmissions that so far have been investigated by intracellular recording. There is a possible exception with frog, where motoneuronal depolarization is produced by the antidromic invasion of adjacent motoneurones (KUBOTA and BROOKHART 1962; KATZ and MILEDI 1963; Chapter IX). It is possible also that electrical transmission may be significantly concerned in effecting synchronization of rhythmically responding neurones, as for example in the rhythmic burst responses of the thalamus (Fig. 88 E, F).

It must be realized that we are as yet at a very early stage of investigation of synaptic transmission. In the central nervous system of vertebrates there are only a few types of synapse that have been intensively studied, and with invertebrates the achievements of recent years in *mollusca* and *crustacea* open up the most attractive vistas for future exploration in the immense field of the comparative physiology of synapses. The account given in this book shows that in the last few years the application of the microtechniques has resulted in an encouraging progress; and the pace quickens.

REFERENCES

[Numbers in square brackets at end of each entry indicate the pages on which it is cited.]

ADRIAN, E. D.: Some recent work on inhibition. Brain 47, 399—416 (1924). [5, 8]
— Afferent discharges to the cerebral cortex from peripheral sense organs. J. Physiol. (Lond.) 100, 159—191 (1941). [215]
—, and D. W. BRONK: The discharge of impulses in motor nerve fibres. Part II. The frequency of discharge in reflex and voluntary contractions. J. Physiol. (Lond.) 67, 119—151 (1929). [82, 116]
ADRIAN, R. H.: Potassium chloride movement and the membrane potential of frog muscle. J. Physiol. (Lond.) 151, 154—185 (1960). [177]
— Internal chloride concentration and chloride efflux of frog muscle. J. Physiol. (Lond.) 156, 623—632 (1961). [177]
—, and W. H. FREYGANG: The potassium and chloride conductance of frog muscle membrane. J. Physiol. (Lond.) 163, 61—103 (1962). [177]
AITKEN, J. T., and J. E. BRIDGER: Neuron size and neuron population density in the lumbosacral region of the cat's spinal cord. J. Anat. (Lond.) 95, 38—53 (1961). [44]
— M. SHARMAN and J. Z. YOUNG: Maturation of regenerating nerve fibres with various peripheral connexions. J. Anat. (Lond.) 81, 1—22 (1947). [254]
ALBE-FESSARD, D. : Modifications de l'activité des organes électriques par des courants d'origine extérieure. Arch. Sci. physiol. 5, 45—73 (1951). [29, 108]
— Sur l'origine des ondes lentes observées en dérivation intracellulaire dans divers structures cérébrales. C.R. Soc. Biol. (Paris) 154, 11—16 (1960). [160]
—, et P. BUSER: Réception intracellular de l'activité d'un neurone des lobes électriques de Torpedo marmorata. C.R. Acad. Sci. (Paris) 235, 1688 (1952). [37]
— — Explorations de certaines activités du cortex moteur du chat par microélectrodes: dérivations endo-somatiques. J. Physiol. (Paris) 45, 14—16 (1953). [160]
— — Analyse microphysiologique de la transmission reflexes au niveau du lobe électrique de la torpille (Torpedo marmorata). J. Physiol. (Paris) 46, 923—946 (1954). [37]
— — Activités intracellulaires recueillies dans le cortex sigmoide du Chat: participation des neurones pyramidaux au «potential evoqué» somesthétique. J. Physiol. (Paris) 47, 67—69 (1955). [160]
ALEXANDROWICZ, J. S.: Muscle receptor organs in the abdomen of Homarus vulgaris and Palinurus vulgaris.. Quart. J. micr. Sci. 92, 163—199 (1951). [201]
ALTAMARINO, M., C. W. COATES and H. GRUNDFEST: Mechanisms of direct and neural excitability in electroplaques of electric eel. J. gen. Physiol. 38, 319—360 (1955). [108]
ALVORD, E. C., and M. G. F. FUORTES: Reflex activity of extensor motor units following muscular afferent excitation. J. Physiol. (Lond.) 122, 302—321 (1953). [117]
AMASSIAN, V. E., et J. L. DE VITO: La transmission dans le noyau de Burdach. In: Microphysiologie comparée des elements excitables. Coll. int. centre nat. recherche sci. (Paris) 67, 353—393 (1957). [46]
AMBACHE, N., W. L. M. PERRY and P. A. ROBERTSON: The effect of muscarine on perfused superior cervical ganglia of cats. Brit. J. Pharmacol. 11, 442—448 (1956). [136]

ANDERSEN, P.: Interhippocampal impulses. II. Apical dendritic activation of CA 1 neurons. Acta physiol. scand. **48**, 178—208 (1960a). [18, 110, 111, 112]
— Interhippocampal impulses. III. Basal dendritic activation of CA 3 neurons. Acta physiol. scand. **48**, 209—230 (1960b). [211]
— C. McC. BROOKS and J. C. ECCLES: Electrical responses of the ventro-basal nucleus of the thalamus. In: Progress in brain research, Ed. J. P. SCHADÉ. Amsterdam: Elsevier Publ. Co. 1963. [46, 161, 174, 214, 215, 233]
—, and J. C. ECCLES: Inhibitory phasing of nuronal discharge. Nature (Lond.) **196**, 645—647 (1962). [161, 214, 215]
— — and Y. LØYNING: Recurrent inhibition in the hippocampus with identification of the inhibitory cell and its synapses. Nature (Lond.) **198**, 541—542 (1963). [17, 161, 174, 189, 210, 212, 253]
— — T. OSHIMA and R. F. SCHMIDT: Mechanisms of synaptic transmission in the cuneate nucleus. (In course of publication.) (1963). [161, 174, 233]
— — and R. F. SCHMIDT: Presynaptic inhibition in the cuneate nucleus. Nature (Lond.) **194**, 741—743 (1962). [233]
— — — and T. YOKOTA: Depolarization of presynaptic fibres in the cuneate nucleus Submitted to J. Neurophysiol. (1963 a). [229, 233]
— — — — Identification of relay cells and interneurones in the cuneate nucleus. (In preparation) (1963 b). [46]
— — and T. A. SEARS: Presynaptic inhibitory action of cerebral cortex on the spinal cord. Nature (Lond.) **194**, 740—741 (1962). [233]
— — and P. E. VOORHOEVE: Inhibitory synapses on somas of Purkinje cells in the cerebellum. Nature (Lond.) **199**, 655—656 (1963). [18, 162, 214, 253]
ANDERSON-CEDERGREN, E: Ultrastructure of motor end plate and sarcoplasmic components of mouse skeletal muscle fiber. J. Ultrastruct. Res., Suppl. **1** (1959). [12, 26]
ARAKI, T.: Effects of electrotonus on the electrical activities of spinal motoneurons of the toad. Jap. J. Physiol. **10**, 518—532 (1960). [50, 104]
— J. C. ECCLES and M. ITO: Correlation of the inhibitory postsynaptic potential of motoneurones with the latency and time course of inhibition of monosynaptic reflexes. J. Physiol. (Lond.) **154**, 354—377 (1960). [157, 158, 159, 168, 169, 170, 205, 206]
— M. ITO, P. G. KOSTYUK, O. OSCARSSON and T. OSHIMA: Injection of alkaline cations into cat spinal motoneurones. Nature (Lond.) **196**, 1319—1320 (1962). [53, 178]
— — and O. OSCARSSON: Anion permeability of the synaptic and non-synaptic motoneurone membrane. J. Physiol. (Lond.) **159**, 410—435 (1961). [53, 174, 175, 177]
— — and T. OSHIMA: Potential changes produced by application of current steps to motoneurones. Nature (Lond.) **191**, 1104—1105 (1961). [113, 114]
—, and T. OTANI: Response of single motoneurones to direct stimulation in toad's spinal cord. J. Neurophysiol. **18**, 472—485 (1955). [37, 103, 104]
— — Accommodation and local response in motoneurones of toad's spinal cord. Jap. J. Physiol. **9**, 69—83 (1959). [116, 118, 119]
— — and T. FURUKAWA: The electrical activities of single motoneurones in toad's spinal cord, recorded with intracellular electrodes. Jap. J. Physiol. **3**, 254—267 (1953). [35, 37, 103, 160]
—, and C. A. TERZUOLO: Membrane currents in spinal motoneurones associated with the action potential and synaptic activity. J. Neurophysiol. **25**, 772—789 (1962). [44, 48, 103, 104, 106, 109, 110, 154, 155, 156, 170]
ARORA, H. L., and R. W. SPERRY: Myotypic respecification of regenerated nerve fibres in Cichlid fishes . J. Embryol. exp. Morph. **5**, 256—263 (1957). [248]
ARVANITAKI, A.: Effects evoked in an axon by the electric activity of a contiguous one. J. Neurophysiol. **5**, 89—108 (1942). [IV, 8]
—, et N. CHALANOZITIS: Prototypes d'interactions neuroniques et transmission synaptiques. Données bioélectriques de préparations cellulaires. Arch. Sci. physiol. **3**, 547—565 (1949). [9]

References

ARVANITAKI, A., et N. CHALANOZITIS: Activations du soma géant d'*Aplysia* par voie orthodrome et par voie antidrome (derivation endocytaire). Arch. Sci. physiol. **10**, 95—128 (1956). [106]

— — Interactions électriques entre le soma géant A et les somata immédiatement contigus (Ganglion pleurobranchial d'Aplysia). Bull. Inst. oceanog. No 1143, 1—30 (1959). [145]

ASADA, Y.: Effects of intracellularly injected anions on the Mauthner cells of gold fish. Jap. J. Physiol. (In press) (1963). [177, 218]

AUERBACH, L.: Nervenendigung in den Centralorganen. Neurol. Zbl. **17**, 445—454 (1898). [2]

AXELROD, J.: The metabolism of catecholamines *in vivo* and *in vitrio*. Pharmacol. Rev. **11**, 402—408 (1959). [61]

AXELSSON, J., and S. THESLEFF: The desensitizing effect of acetylcholine on the mammalian motor end-plate. Acta physiol. scand. **43**, 15—26 (1958). [64, 99]

— — A study of supersensitivity in denervated mammalian skeletal muscle. J. Physiol. (Lond.) **147**, 178—193 (1959). [52, 108, 243]

BACQ, Z. M.: La transmission chimique des influx dans le système nerveux autonome Ergebn. Physiol. **37**, 82—185 (1935). [8, 61]

— L'acetylcholine et l'adrenaline. Leur role dans la transmission de l'influx nerveux. Liège: Georges Thone. Bibl. Sci. Belge 1937. [8]

— Action de l'ésérine chez les *Holothuries* et chez les *Ascidies*. Présence de nerfs cholinergiques chez les *Holothuries*. Arch. int. Physiol. **49**, 25—32 (1939). [74]

— L'acétylcholine et l'adrénaline chez les invertébrés. Biol. Rev. **22**, 73—91 (1947). [199]

—, et G. COPPÉE: Reaction des *Vers* et des *Mollusques* a l'ésérine. Existence de nerfs cholinergiques chez les *Vers*. Arch. int. Physiol. **45**, 310—324 (1937). [74]

BANNISTER, J., and M. SCRASE: Acetylcholine synthesis in normal and denervated sympathetic ganglia of the cat. J. Physiol. (Lond.) **111**, 437—444 (1950). [57, 58]

BARR, M. L.: Some observations on the morphology of the synapse in the cat's spinal cord. J. Anat. (Lond.) **74**, 1—11 (1939). [2, 111]

— Axon reaction in motoneurones and its effect upon the end-bulbs of Held-Auerbach. Anat. Rec. **77**, 367—374 (1940). [3]

BARRON, D. H., and B. H. C. MATTHEWS: Electrotonus in ventral roots of the spinal cord. J. Physiol. (Lond.) **87**, 26P—27P (1936). [6, 37]

— — The interpretation of potential changes in the spinal cord. J. Physiol. (Lond.) **92**, 276—321 (1938). [6, 68, 117, 220]

BARTELMEZ, G. W.: Mauthner's cell and nucleus motorius tegmenti. J. comp. Neurol. **25**, 87—128 (1915). [216]

—, and N. L. HOERR: The vestibular club endings in Aneiurus. Further evidence on the morphology of the synapse. J. comp. Neurol. **57**, 401—428 (1933). [2]

BASS, A.: Energy metabolism in denervated muscle. In: The denervated muscle, ed. by E. GUTMANN, chapt. VIII, pp. 203—272. Prague: Czechoslovak Academy of Sciences. 1962. [242]

BAZEMORE, A. W., K. A. C. ELLIOTT and E. FLOREY: Isolation of Factor I. J. Neurochem. **1**, 334—339 (1957). [192, 195]

BENNETT, M. V. L.: Electrical connections between supramedullary neurons. Fed. Proc. **19**, 282 (1960). [144]

— Modes of operation of electric organs. Ann. N.Y. Acad. Sci. **94**, 458—509 (1961). [29, 100, 108, 113]

— E. ALJURE, Y. NAKAJIMA and G. D. PAPPAS: Electrotonic junctions between teleost spinal neurones: electrophysiology and ultrastructure. Science **141**, 262—264 (1963). [144]

—, S. M. CRAIN, and H. GRUNDFEST: Electrophysiology of supramedullary neurons in *Spheroides maculatus*. I. Orthodromic and antidromic responses. J. gen. Physiol. **43**, 159—188 (1959a). [144]

— — — Electrophysiology of supramedullary neurons in *Spheroides maculatus*. III. Organization of the supramedullary neurons. J. gen. Physiol. **43**, 221—250 (1959b). [142, 144]

BENNETT, M. V. L., and H. GRUNDFEST: Studies on the morphology and electrophysiology of electric organs. III. Electrophysiology of electric organs in mormyrids. From "Bioelectrogenesis". Edit. C. CHAGAS and A. PAES DE CARVALHO, pp. 113—135. Amsterdam: Elsevier Publ. Co. 1961. [29]

BERÁNEK, R., and P. HNÍK: Long-term effects of tenotomy on spinal monosynaptic response in the cat. Science 130, 981—982 (1959). [256]

— — L. VYLICKÝ and J. ZELENÁ: Facilitation of the monosynaptic reflex due to long-term tenotomy. Physiol. bohemoslov. 10, 543—552 (1961). [256, 257]

BERNHARD, C. G.: Slow cord potentials of opposite sign correlated to reciprocal functions. Acta physiol. scand. Suppl. 47, 1—25 (1947). [6]

— The cord dorsum potentials in relation to peripheral source of afferent stimulation. Cold Spr. Harb. Symp. quant. Biol. 17, 221—232 (1952). [220]

— The spinal cord potentials in leads from the cord dorsum in relation to peripheral source of afferent stimulation. Acta physiol. scand. 29, Suppl. 106, 1—29 (1953). [220]

BERNSTEIN, J. J., and L. GUTH: Nonselectivity in establishment of neuromuscular connections following nerve regeneration in the rat. Exp. Neurol. 4, 262—275 (1961). [246]

BIELSCHOWSKY, M.: C. Zentrale Nervenfasern. D. Übersicht über den gegenwärtigen Stand der Neuronenlehre und die gegen sie erhobenen Einwände. In: Handbuch der mikroskopischen Anatomie des Menschen, Bd. IV, S. 97—142. Berlin: Springer 1928. [2]

BIRKS, R., H. E. HUXLEY and B. KATZ: The fine structure of the neuromuscular junction of the frog. J. Physiol. (Lond.) 150, 134—144 (1960). [12, 26, 30, 92, 93, 244]

— B. KATZ and R. MILEDI: Physiological and structural changes at the amphibian myoneural junction, in the course of nerve degeneration. J. Physiol. (Lond.) 150, 145—168 (1960). [26, 32]

—, and F. C. MacINTOSH: Acetylcholine metabolism at nerve-endings. Brit. med. Bull. 13 157—161 (1957). [55, 92]

— — Acetylcholine metabolism of a sympathetic ganglion. Canad. J. Biochem. 39, 787—827 (1961). [55, 56, 57, 58, 60, 85, 92, 136]

BISHOP, G. H.: The dendrite: receptive pole of the neurone. Electroenceph. clin. Neurophysiol., Suppl. 10, 12—21 (1958). [112]

—, and J. L. O'LEARY: Factors determining the form of the potential record in the vicinity of the synapses of the dorsal nucleus of the lateral geniculate body. J. cell. comp. Physiol. 19, 315—331 (1942). [123]

BISHOP, P. O.: Synaptic transmission. An analysis of the electrical activity of the lateral geniculate nucleus in the cat after optic nerve stimulation. Proc. roy. Soc. B 141, 362—392 (1953). [37]

— W. BURKE and W. R. HAYHOW: Repetitive stimulation of optic nerve and lateral geniculate synapses. Exp. Neurol. 1, 534—555 (1959). [99, 100]

BLACKMAN, J. G., B. L. GINSBORG and C. RAY: The release of acetylcholine at a ganglionic synapse. J. Physiol. (Lond.)162, 58P (1962). [36, 75]

BLACKSTAD, T. W.: Commissural connections of the hippocampal region in the rat, with special reference to their mode of termination. J. comp. Neurol. 105, 417—536 (1956). [210]

— On the termination of some afferents to the hippocampus and fascia dentata. Acta anat. (Basel) 35, 202—214 (1958). [210]

— Ultrastructural studies on the hippocampal region. In: Progress in Brain research, ed. J. P. SCHADÉ. Amsterdam: Elsevier Publ. Co. 1963. [17, 18, 189]

—, and H. A. DAHL: Quantitative evaluation of structures in contact with neuronal somata. Acta morph. neerl. scand. 4, 329—343 (1962). [23]

—, and P. R. FLOOD: Ultrastructure of hippocampal axo-somatic synapses. Nature (Lond.) 198, 542—543 (1963). [17, 253]

BODIAN, D.: The structure of the vertebrate synapse. A study of the axon endings on Mauthner's cell and neighboring centers in the goldfish. J. comp. Neurol. 68, 117—159 (1937). [2, 216, 218, 219]

References

Bodian, D.: Further notes on the vertebrate synapse. J. comp. Neurol. **73**, 323—343 (1940). [2]
— Cytological aspects of synaptic function. Physiol. Rev. **22**, 146—169 (1942). [2, 216]
— Introductory survey of neurons. Cold Spr. Harb. Symp. quant. Biol. **17**, 1—13 (1952). [2, 3, 15, 111, 216]
Boeke, J.: Beiträge zur Kenntnis der motorischen Nervenendigungen. I. Die Form und Struktur der motorischen Endplatte der quergestreiften Muskelfasern bei den höheren Vertebraten. II. Die akzessorischen Fasern und Endplättchen. Internat. Mschr. Anat. Physiol. **28**, 377—436 (1911). [2]
— Nerve endings, motor and sensory. In: Cytology and cellular pathology of the nervous system, ed. W. Penfield, vol. 1, p. 243—315. 1932. [2]
— Problems of nervous anatomy. London: Oxford University Press 1940. [2]
Boistel, J., and P. Fatt: Membrane permeability change during transmitter action in crustacean muscle. J. Physiol. (Lond.) **144**, 176—191 (1958). [164, 177, 187, 196, 201, 238]
Bonnet, V., et F. Bremer: La transmission synaptique dans la substance grise spinale. J. Physiol. Path. gén. **40**, 117-A—119-A (1948). [6, 9]
Boyd, I. A., and A. R. Martin: Spontaneous subthreshold activity at mammalian neuromuscular junctions. J. Physiol. (Lond.) **132**, 61—73 (1956a). [33, 75]
— — The end-plate potential in mammalian muscle. J. Physiol. (Lond.) **132**, 74—91 (1956b). [46, 47, 76, 87, 106]
Bradley, K., D. M. Easton and J. C. Eccles: An investigation of primary or direct inhibition. J. Physiol. (Lond.) **122**, 474—488 (1953). [6, 168, 190, 191, 231]
—, and G. G. Somjen: Accommodation in motoneurones of the rat and the cat. J. Physiol. (Lond.) **156**, 75—92 (1961). [114, 115, 116]
Bradley, P. B., and J. H. Wolstencroft: Excitation and inhibition of brain-stem neurones by noradrenaline and acetylcholine. Nature (Lond.) **196**, 840—873 (1962). [69]
Branch, C. L., and A. R. Martin: Inhibition of Betz cell activity by thalamic and cortical stimulation. J. Neurophysiol. **21**, 380—390 (1958). [161]
Bremer, F.: Aspects electrophysiologiques de la transmission synaptique. Arch. int. Physiol. **59**, 588—602 (1951). [9]
—, et V. Bonnet: Contributions à l'étude de la physiologie générale des centres nerveux. II. L'inhibition réflexe. Arch. int. Physiol. **52**, 153—194 (1942). [220]
— — et J. Moldaver: Contribution à l'étude de la physiologie générale des centres nerveux. I. La sommation centrale. Arch. int. Physiol. **52**, 1—56 (1942). [6]
Brock, L. G., J. S. Coombs and J. C. Eccles: Action potentials of motoneurones with intracellular electrode. Proc. Univ. Otago med. Sch. **29**, 14—15 (1951). [37]
— — — The recording of potentials from motoneurones with an intracellular electrode. J. Physiol. (Lond.) **117**, 431—460 (1952). [7, 28, 35, 37, 40, 117, 151, 203]
—, and R. M. Eccles: The membrane potentials during rest and activity of the ray electroplate. J. Physiol. (Lond.) **142**, 251—274 (1958). [29, 108]
— — and R. D. Keynes: The discharge of individual electroplates in *Raia clavata*. J. Physiol. (Lond.) **122**, 4—6P (1953). [29, 108]
—, and A. K. McIntyre: Responses of motoneurones to stimulation by internal microelectrodes. Proc. Univ. Otago med. Sch. **31**, 19—20 (1953). [114]
Bronk, D. W.: Synaptic mechanisms in sympathetic ganglia. J. Neurophysiol. **2**, 380—401 (1939). [9, 133, 135]
Brookhart, J. M., and E. Fadiga: Potential fields initiated during monosynaptic activation of frog motoneurones. J. Physiol. (Lond.) **150**, 633—655 (1960). [111]
Brooks, C. McC., C. B. B. Downman and J. C. Eccles: After-potentials and excitability of spinal motoneurones following orthodromic activation. J. Neurophysiol. **13**, 157—176 (1950). [6]
—, and J. C. Eccles: An electrical hypothesis of central inhibition. Nature (Lond.) **159**, 760—764 (1947a). [9]

BROOKS, C. McC., and J. C. ECCLES: Electrical investigation of the monosynaptic pathway through the spinal cord. J. Neurophysiol. 10, 251—274 (1947 b). [6, 37, 38, 123]

— — and J. L. MALCOLM: Synaptic potentials of inhibited motoneurones. J. Neurophysiol. 11, 417—430 (1948). [220]

BROOKS, V. B.: An intracellular study of the action of repetitive nerve volleys and of botulinum toxin on miniature end-plate potentials. J. Physiol. (Lond.) 134, 264—277 (1956). [30, 95, 99, 191, 242]

— D. R. CURTIS and J. C. ECCLES: The action of tetanus toxin on the inhibition of moto-neurones. J. Physiol. (Lond.) 135, 655—672 (1957). [168, 190, 191]

BROWN, G. L.: The actions of acetylcholine on denervated mammalian and frog's muscle. J. Physiol. (Lond.) 89, 438—461 (1937a). [127, 242]

— Transmission at nerve endings by acetylcholine. Physiol. Rev. 17, 485—513 (1937 b). [8]

— H. H. DALE and W. FELDBERG: Reactions of the normal mammalian muscle to acetylcholine and to eserine. J. Physiol. (Lond.) 87, 394—424 (1936). [8, 127]

— B. N. DAVIES and C. B. FERRY: Effect of neuronal rest on output of sympathetic transmitter from the spleen. J. Physiol. (Lond.) 159, 365—380 (1961). [56, 61]

—, and J. C. ECCLES: The action of a single vagal volley on the rhythm of the heart beat. J. Physiol. (Lond.) 82, 211—241 (1934). [8, 166]

—, and W. FELDBERG: The acetylcholine metabolism of a sympathetic ganglion. J. Physiol. (Lond.) 88, 265—283 (1936). [55, 57]

—, and J. S. GILLESPIE: The output of sympathetic transmitter from the spleen of the cat. J. Physiol. (Lond.) 138, 81—102 (1957). [47, 56, 61]

BROWN, K. T., and T. N. WIESEL: Intraretinal recording with micropipette electrodes in the intact cat eye. J. Physiol. (Lond.) 149, 537—562 (1960). [118]

BROWN, M. C., and P. B. C. MATTHEWS: The effect on a muscle twitch of the back-re-sponse of its motor nerve fibres. J. Physiol. (Lond.) 150, 332—346 (1960). [IV, 128]

BÜLBRING, E.: The action of adrenaline on transmission in the superior cervical ganglion. J. Physiol. (Lond.) 103, 55—67 (1944). [133]

BULLER, A. J., J. C. ECCLES and R. M. ECCLES: Differentiation of fast and slow muscles in the cat hind limb. J. Physiol. (Lond.) 150, 399—416 (1960a). [241, 242]

— — — Interactions between motoneurones and muscles in respect of the characteristic speeds of their responses. J. Physiol. (Lond.) 150, 417—439 (1960 b). [241, 242, 246]

BULLOCK, T. H.: Functional organization of the giant fiber system of Lumbricus. J. Neurophysiol. 8, 55—71 (1945). [138, 140, 141]

— Properties of a single synapse in the stellate ganglion of squid. J. Neurophysiol. 11, 343—364 (1948). [37]

—, and S. HAGIWARA: Further study of the giant synapse in the stellate ganglion of squid. Biol. Bull. 109, 341—342 (1955). [37]

— — Intracellular recording from the giant synapse of the squid. J. gen. Physiol. 40, 565—577 (1957). [27, 28, 36, 39, 143]

BURGEN, A. S. V., and L. M. CHIPMAN: The location of cholinesterase in the central nervous system. Quart. J. exp. Physiol. 37, 61—74 (1952). [70]

— F. DICKENS and L. J. ZATMAN: The action of botulinum toxin on the neuromuscular junction. J. Physiol. (Lond.) 109, 10—24 (1948). [132]

—, and S. W. KUFFLER: Two inhibitory fibres forming synapses with a single nerve cell in the lobster. Nature (Lond.) 180, 1490—1491 (1957). [201]

—, and K. G. TERROUX: On the negative inotropic effect in the cat's auricle. J. Physiol. (Lond.) 120, 449—464 (1953). [166, 187]

BURKE, W.: Spontaneous potentials in slow muscle fibres of the frog. J. Physiol. (Lond.) 135, 511—521 (1957). [29, 33, 76]

—, and B. L. GINSBORG: The electrical properties of the slow muscle fibre membrane. J. Physiol. (Lond.) 132, 586—598 (1956a). [29, 101, 108, 109]

— — The action of the neuromuscular transmitter on the slow fibre membrane. J. Physiol. (Lond.) 132, 599—610 (1956b). [29, 47, 50, 101]

BURN, J. H., and M. J. RAND: The cause of the supersensitivity of smooth muscle to noradrenaline after sympathetic degeneration. J. Physiol. (Lond.) 147, 135—143 (1959). [35, 62]

BURNS, B. D., and W. D. M. PATON: Depolarization of the motor end-plate by decamethonium and acetylcholine. J. Physiol. (Lond.) 115, 41—73 (1951). [65]

BURNSTOCK, G., G. CAMPBELL, M. BENNETT and M. E. HOLMAN: The transmission of inhibition from autonomic nerves to the smooth muscle of the Guinea Pig Taenia Coli. Nature (Lond.) 200, 581—582 (1963). [167, 171]

—, and M. E. HOLMAN: The transmission of excitation from autonomic nerve to smooth muscle. J. Physiol. (Lond.) 155, 115—133 (1961). [35, 40, 47, 61, 90]

— — Spontaneous potentials at sympathetic nerve endings in smooth muscle. J. Physiol. (Lond.) 160, 446—460 (1962a). [35, 61, 90, 167]

— — Effect of denervation and of reserpine treatment on transmission at sympathetic nerve endings. J. Physiol. (Lond.) 160, 461—469 (1962b). [35, 62, 90]

CAESAR, R., A. EDWARDS and H. RUSKA: Architecture and nerve supply of mammalian smooth muscle tissue. J. biophys. biochem. Cytol. 3, 867—878 (1957). [61]

CANNON, W. B., and Z. M. BACQ: Studies on the conditions of activity in endocrine organs, XXVI. A hormone produced by sympathetic action on smooth muscle. Amer. J. Physiol. 96, 392—412 (1931). [8]

—, and A. ROSENBLUETH: Studies on conditions of activity in endocrine organs. XXIX. Sympathin E and Sympathin I. Amer. J. Physiol. 104, 557—574 (1933). [8]

— — The supersensitivity of denervated structures, pp. 245. New York: Macmillan & Co. 1949. [137]

CARLSSON, A., B. FALCK, K. FUXE and N.-Å. HILLARP: Cellular localization of monamines in the spinal cord. Acta physiol. scand. (In press) (1963). [61]

CARPENTER, D., I. ENGBERG and A. LUNDBERG: Presynaptic inhibition in the lumbar cord evoked from the brain stem. Experientia (Basel) 18, 450—451 (1962). [233]

— A. LUNDBERG and U. NORRSELL: Effects from the pyramidal tract on primary afferents and on spinal reflex actions to primary afferents. Experientia (Basel) 18, 337—338 (1962). [233]

CASTRO, F. DE: Evolución de los ganglios simpáticos vertebrales y prevertebrales. Conexiones y citoarquitectonia de algunos grupos de ganglios en el nino y hombre adulto. Trab. Lab. Invest. Biol. Univ. Madr. 20, 113—208 (1922). [2]

— Sympathetic ganglia, normal and pathological. In: Cytology and cellular pathology of the nervous system, vol. 1, p. 317—379, ed. W. PENFIELD. New York: Hoeber 1932. [2]

CHAGAS, C.: Studies on the mechanism of curare fixation by cells. In: Curare and curarelike agents, p. 327, ed. D. BOVET, F. BOVET-NITTI and G. B. MARINI-BETTÒLO. Amsterdam: Elsevier Publ. Co. 1959. [66]

CLARE, M. H., and G. H. BISHOP: Properties of dendrites; apical dendrites of the cat cortex. Electroenceph. clin. Neurophysiol. 7, 85—98 (1955). [112]

CLARK, W. E. LE GROS, and T. P. S. POWELL: On the thalamo-cortical connexions of the general sensory cortex of Macaca. Proc. roy. Soc. B 141, 467—487 (1953). [215]

CLOSE, R.: Force: velocity properties of rat skeletal muscles during development. J. Physiol. (Lond.) (In press) (1963). [241]

COHEN, J. A., and C. H. POSTHUMUS: The mechanism of action of anti-cholinesterases. Acta physiol. pharmacol. neerl. 4, 17—36 (1955). [137]

COLE, K. S., and H. J. CURTIS: Electric impedance of the squid giant axon during activity. J. gen. Physiol. 22, 649—670 (1939). [109]

COLE, W. V.: Structural variations of nerve endings in the striated muscles of the rat. J. comp. Neurol. 108, 445—464 (1957). [64]

COOMBS, J. S., D. R. CURTIS and J. C. ECCLES: The interpretation of spike potentials of motoneurones. J. Physiol. (Lond.) 139, 198—231 (1957a). [103, 107, 109]

— — — The generation of impulses in motoneurones. J. Physiol. (Lond.) 139, 232—249 (1957b). [7, 102, 103, 104, 105, 106, 109, 206]

COOMBS, J. S., D. R. CURTIS and J. C. ECCLES: The electrical constants of the moto-neurone membrane. J. Physiol. (Lond.) **145**, 505—528 (1959).[114, 170]
— J. C. ECCLES and P. FATT: The action of the inhibitory synaptic transmitter. Aust. J. Sci. **16**, 1—5 (1953). [174]
— — — The electrical properties of the motoneurone membrane. J. Physiol. (Lond.) **130**, 291—325 (1955a). [110, 111, 178, 179]
— — — The specific ionic conductances and the ionic movements across the moto-neuronal membrane that produce the inhibitory post-synaptic potential. J. Physiol. (Lond.) **130**, 326—373 (1955b). [155, 156, 165, 174, 177, 178, 179, 180, 183]
— — — Excitatory synaptic action in motoneurones. J. Physiol. (Lond.) **130**, 374—395 (1955c). [49, 50, 53, 73, 103]
— — — The inhibitory suppression of reflex discharges from motoneurones. J. Physiol. (Lond.) **130**, 396—413 (1955d). [171]
COOPER, S., and R. S. CREED: More reflex effects of active muscular contraction. J. Physiol. (Lond.) **64**, 199—214 (1927). [231]
COUTEAUX, R.: Recherches sur l'histogénèse du muscle strié des mammifères et la for-mation des plaques motrices. Bull. biol. France et Belg. **75**, 101—239 (1941). [239, 240]
— Morphological and cytochemical observations on the post-synaptic membrane at motor end-plates and ganglionic synapses. Exp. Cell. Res., Suppl. **5**, 294—322 (1958). [11, 12, 65, 122]
— Motor end-plate structure. In: The structure and function of muscle, vol. 1, Ed. G. H. BOURNE. New York: Academic Press 1960. [239]
— Principaux critères morphologiques et cytochimiques utilisables aujourd'hui pour dé-finir les divers types de synapses. Actualités neurophysiol. **3**, 145—173 (1961). [11, 17, 23, 25, 26, 239, 240, 259]
—, and D. NACHMANSOHN: Cholinesterase at the endplate of voluntary muscles after nerve degeneration. Nature (Lond.) **142**, 1481 (1938). [240]
—, et J. TAXI: Recherches histochimiques sur la distribution des activités cholin-estérasiques au niveau de la synapse myoneurale. Arch. Anat. micr. Morph. exp. **41**, 352—392 (1952). [12]
CRAGG, B. G., and L. H. HAMLYN: Action potentials of the pyramidal neurones in the hippocampus of the rabbit. J. Physiol. (Lond.) **129**, 608—627 (1955). [110, 112]
CURTIS, D. R.: Pharmacological investigations upon inhibition of spinal neurones. J. Physiol. (Lond.) **145**, 175—192 (1959). [190, 191, 197, 231]
— The effects of drugs and amino acids upon neurons. In: The regional chemistry, physiology and pharmacology of the nervous system, p. 403—422, Ed. S. KETY. Oxford: Pergamon Press 1961a. [71]
— The identification of mammalian inhibitory transmitters. In: Nervous inhibition, pp. 342—349, Ed. E. FLOREY. Oxford: Pergamon Press 1961b. [54, 71, 192, 195]
— Direct extracellular application of drugs. Biochem. Pharmacol. **9**, 205—212 (1962a). [72]
— The depression of spinal inhibition by electrophoretically administered strychnine. Int. J. Neuropharmacol. **1**, 239—250 (1962b). [190, 191]
— Acetylcholine as a central transmitter. Canad. J. Biochem. (In press) (1963a). [67, 68, 69]
— The pharmacology of central and peripheral inhibition. Pharmacol. Rev. **15**, 333—363 (1963b). [191, 192, 194, 195, 197]
—, and P. ANDERSEN: Acetylcholine: a central transmitter? Nature (Lond.) **195**, 1105—1106 (1962). [69]
—, and R. DAVIS: Pharmacological studies upon neurones of the lateral geniculate nucleus of the cat. Brit. J. Pharmacol. **18**, 217—246 (1962). [69, 71]
— — The excitation of lateral geniculate neurones by quaternary ammonium deriva-tives. J. Physiol. (Lond.) **165**, 62—82 (1963). [69]
—, and J. C. ECCLES: The time courses of excitatory and inhibitory synaptic actions. J. Physiol. (Lond.) **145**, 529—546 (1959). [43, 44, 117, 153, 154, 157, 170, 226]

References

CURTIS, D. R., and J. C. ECCLES: Synaptic action during and after repetitive stimulation. J. Physiol. (Lond.) **150**, 374—398 (1960). [83, 84, 85, 96, 97]
— — and R. M. ECCLES: Pharmacological studies on spinal reflexes. J. Physiol. (Lond.) **136**, 420—434 (1957). [67]
— — and A. LUNDBERG: Intracellular recording from cells in Clarke's column. Acta physiol. scand. **43**, 303—314 (1958). [105, 160, 174, 208]
—, and R. M. ECCLES: The excitation of Renshaw cells by pharmacological agents applied electrophoretically. J. Physiol. (Lond.) **141**, 435—445 (1958a). [67]
— — The effect of diffusional barriers upon the pharmacology of cells within the central nervous system. J. Physiol. (Lond.) **141**, 446—463 (1958b). [67, 68, 136]
—, and K. KOIZUMI: Chemical transmitter substances in brain stem of cat. J. Neurophysiol. **24**, 80—90 (1961). [71]
—, and J. W. PHILLIS: The action of procaine and atropine on spinal neurones. J. Physiol. (Lond.) **153**, 17—34 (1960). [136]
— — and J. C. WATKINS: The depression of spinal neurones by γ-amino-*n*-butyric acid and β-alanine. J. Physiol. (Lond.) **146**, 185—203 (1959). [193, 194]
— — — The chemical excitation of spinal neurones by certain acidic amino acids. J. Physiol. (Lond.) **150**, 656—682 (1960). [71, 72, 74, 194]
— — — Actions of amino-acids on the isolated hemisected spinal cord of the toad. Brit. J. Pharmacol. **16**, 262—283 (1961a). [71, 73, 74]
— — — Cholinergic and non-cholinergic transmission in the spinal cord. J. Physiol. (Lond.) **158**, 296—323 (1961b). [67, 68, 72]
— and R. W. RYALL: On the nicotinic receptors of Renshaw cells. (In course of publication) (1963). [67]
—, and J. C. WATKINS: The excitation and depression of spinal neurones by structurally related amino acids. J. Neurochem. **6**, 117—141 (1960b). [71, 74, 193, 195]
— — Analogues of glutamic and γ-amino-*n*-butyric acids having potent actions on mammalian neurones. Nature (Lond.) **191**, 1010—1011 (1961). [71, 73, 74]
— — Acidic amino acids with strong excitatory actions on mammalian neurones. J. Physiol. (Lond.) **166**, 1—14 (1963). [71, 74]
DAHLBACK, O., D. ELMQVIST, T. R. JOHNS, S. RADNER and S. THESLEFF: An electrophysiologic study of the neuromuscular junction in myasthenia gravis. J. Physiol. (Lond.) **156**, 336—343 (1962). [60]
DALE, H. H.: The action of certain esters and ethers of choline, and their relation to muscarine. J. Pharmacol. exp. Ther. **6**, 147—190 (1914). [7]
— Pharmacology and nerve endings. Proc. roy. Soc. Med. **28**, 319—332 (1935). [8, 9]
— Transmission of nervous effects by acetylcholine. Harvey Lect. **32**, 229—245 (1937). [8]
— Acetylcholine as a chemical transmitter substance of the effects of nerve impulses. The William Henry WelchLectures 1937. J. Mt Sinai Hosp. **4**, 401—429 (1938). [7, 8]
— Transmission of effects from nerve endings. London: Oxford University Press 1952. [54]
—, and W. FELDBERG: Chemical transmission at motor nerve endings in voluntary muscle? J. Physiol. (Lond.) **81**, 39P (1934). [59]
— — and M. VOGT: Release of acetylcholine at voluntary motor nerve endings. J. Physiol. (Lond.) **86**, 353—380 (1936). [8, 59]
DAVIS, H.: Some principles of sensory receptor action. Physiol. Rev. **41**, 391—416 (1961). [IV]
DEL CASTILLO, J., and L. ENGBAEK: The nature of the neuromuscular block produced by magnesium. J. Physiol. (Lond.) **124**, 370—384 (1954). [33, 77]
—, and B. KATZ: The effect of magnesium on the activity of motor nerve endings. J. Physiol. (Lond.) **124**, 553—559 (1954a). [29]
— — Quantal components of the end-plate potential. J. Physiol. (Lond.) **124**, 560—573 (1954b). [29, 33, 75, 76]
— — Statistical factors involved in neuromuscular facilitation and depression. J. Physiol. (Lond.) **124**, 574—585 (1954c). [87, 94]

DEL CASTILLO, J., and B. KATZ: Changes in end-plate activity produced by pre-synaptic polarization. J. Physiol. (Lond.) **124**, 586—604 (1954d). [30, 77, 99]

— — The membrane change produced by the neuromuscular transmitter. J. Physiol. (Lond.) **125**, 546—565 (1954e). [50, 53, 88, 106, 107, 108]

— — On the localization of acetylcholine receptors. J. Physiol. (Lond.) **128**, 157—181 (1955a). [62, 63, 64]

— — Local activity at a depolarized nerve-muscle junction. J. Physiol. (Lond.) **128**, 396—411 (1955b). [30]

— — Production of membrane potential changes in the frog's heart by inhibitory nerve impulses. Nature (Lond.) **175**, 1035 (1955c). [166]

— — Localization of active spots within the neuromuscular junction of the frog. J. Physiol. (Lond.) **132**, 630—649 (1956a). [29, 30, 33, 75]

— — Biophysical aspects of neuro-muscular transmission. Prog. Biophys. **6**, 121—170 (1956b). [29, 30, 32, 62, 75, 77]

— — A study of curare action with an electrical micro-method. Proc. roy. Soc. B **146**, 339—356 (1957a). [48, 62, 64, 65, 136, 191]

— — A comparison of acetylcholine and stable depolarizing agents. Proc. roy. Soc. B **146**, 362—368 (1957b). [62, 64, 65]

— — Interaction at end-plate receptors between different choline derivatives. Proc. roy. Soc. B **146**, 369—381 (1957c). [62, 65, 66]

— — Modifications de la membrane produites par des influx nerveux dans la région du pace-maker du coeur. In: Microphysiologie comparée des elements excitables. Coll. int. centre national recherche sci. (Paris) **67**, 271—279 (1957d). [166, 167]

—, and L. STARK: Local responses in single medullated nerve fibres. J. Physiol. (Lond.) **118**, 207—215 (1952). [33, 77, 87]

DE LORENZO, A. J.: The fine structure of synapses. Biol. Bull. **117**, 390 (1959). [149]

— The fine structure of synapses in the ciliary ganglion of the chick. J. biophys. biochem. Cytol. **7**, 31—36 (1960). [23, 25, 147]

— Electron microscopy of the cerebral cortex. I. The ultrastructure and histochemistry of synaptic junctions. Bull. Johns Hopk. **108**, 258—279 (1961). [16, 17, 70]

DEMPSHER, J., M. G. LARRABEE, F. B. BANG and D. BODIAN: Physiological changes in sympathetic ganglia infected with pseudorabies virus. Amer. J. Physiol. **182**, 203—216 (1955). [136]

—, and W. K. RIKER: The role of acetylcholine in virus-infected sympathetic ganglia. J. Physiol. (Lond.) **139**, 145—156 (1957). [136, 137]

—, and J. ZABARA: A study of presynaptic slow potentials in virus-infected sympathetic ganglia of the rat. J. Physiol. (Lond.) **151**, 217—224 (1960). [136]

DENNY-BROWN, D.: On the nature of postural reflexes. Proc. roy. Soc. B **104**, 253—301 (1929). [116]

DENZ, F. A.: On the histochemistry of the myoneural junction. Brit. J. exp. Path. **34**, 329—339 (1953). [12]

DE ROBERTIS, E. D. P.: Submicroscopic changes in the synapse after nerve section in the acoustic ganglion of guinea pig. An electron microscope study. J. biophys. biochem. Cytol. **2**, 503—512 (1956). [3, 16, 26, 93]

— Submicroscopic morphology and function of the synapse. Exp. Cell Res., Suppl. **5**, 347—369 (1958). [15, 16, 25, 26, 93]

— Submicroscopic morphology of the synapse. Int. Rev. Cytol. **8**, 61—96 (1959a). [15, 16, 26]

— Histophysiology of the synapse. Internat. Congr. Physiol. Sci. **21**, 213—216 (1959b). [26]

—, and H. S. BENNETT: Submicroscopic vesicular component in the synapse. Fed. Proc. **13**, 35 (1954). [15, 23, 25]

— — Some features of the submicroscopic morphology of synapses in frog and earthworm. J. biophys. biochem. Cytol. **1**, 47—58 (1955). [15, 16, 23]

References

DE ROBERTIS, E. D. P., and C. M. FRANCHI: Electron microscope observations on synaptic vesicles in synapses of the retinal rods and cones. J. biophys. biochem. Cytol. 2, 307—318 (1956). [3, 26, 259]

—, and H .M. GERSCHENFELD: Submicroscopic morphology and function of glial cells. Int. Rev. Neurobiol. 3, 1—65 (1961). [22, 23, 109]

— A. PELLEGRINO DE IRALDI, G. RODRIGUEZ DE LORES ARNAIZ and L. SALGANICOF: Cholinergic and non-cholinergic nerve endings in rat brain. I. Isolation and subcellular distribution of acetylcholine and acetylcholinesterase. J. Neurochem. 9, 23—35 (1962). [70]

DESMEDT, J. E.: Les propriétés electrophysiologiques du muscle squelettique au cours de la dégénérescence wallérienne, et dans le cas d'une atrophie non wallérienne (résection tendineuse). Arch. int. Physiol. 57, 98—101 (1949). [242]

— Étude expérimentale de la dégénérescence wallérienne et de la réinnervation du muscle squelettique. I. Évolution de la constante de temps d'excitation. Arch. int. Physiol. 58, 23—68 (1950a). [245]

— Étude expérimentale de la dégénérescence wallérienne et de la réinnervation du muscle squelettique. II. Évolution de la constante de temps d'accommodation. Arch. int. Physiol. 58, 125—156 (1950b). [245]

— Myasthenic-like features of neuromuscular transmission in myasthenic patients: 'post-tetanic exhaustion'. Nature (Lond.) 179, 156—157 (1958). [60]

— The physio-pathology of neuromuscular transmission and the trophic influence of motor innervation. Amer. J. phys. Med. 38, 248—261 (1959). [245]

— Neuromuscular defect in myasthenia gravis: electrophysiological and histopathological evidence, pp. 150—178. In: Myasthenia gravis, Ed. HENRY R. VIETS. Springfield (Ill.): Ch. C. Thomas 1961. [60]

— Auditory-evoked potentials from cochlea to cortex as influenced by activation of the efferent olivo-cochlear bundle. J. acoust. Soc. Amer. 34, 1478—1496 (1962). [191]

—, et P. MONACO: Suppression par la strychnine de l'éffet inhibiteur centrifuge exercé par le faisceau olivo-cochléaire. Arch. int. Pharmacodyn. 129, 244—248 (1960). [191, 207]

— — The pharmacology of a centrifugal inhibitory pathway in the cat's acoustic system. In: Proceedings of the First Internat. Pharmacological Meeting, Ed. B. UVNÄS, vol. 8, p. 183—188. New York, Pergamon Press 1962. [191, 207]

DIAMOND, J.: Variation in the sensitivity to gamma-amino-butyric acid of different regions of the Mauthner neurone. Nature (Lond.) 199, 773—775 (1963). [194]

—, J. A. B. GRAY and D. R. INMAN: The relation between receptor potentials and the concentration of sodium ions. J. Physiol. (Lond.) 142, 382—394 (1958). [106]

— — and M. SATO: The site of initiation of impulses in Pacinian corpuscles. J. Physiol. (Lond.) 133, 54—67 (1956). [106]

—, and R. MILEDI: A study of foetal and new-born rat muscle fibres. J. Physiol. (Lond.) 162, 393—408 (1962). [239, 240]

DIXON, W. E.: Vagus inhibition. Brit. med. J. 2, 1807 (1906). [7]

DOUGLAS, W. W., D. W. LYWOOD and R. W. STRAUB: On the excitant effect of acetylcholine on structures in the preganglionic trunk of the cervical sympathetic: with a note on the anatomical complexities of the region. J. Physiol. (Lond.) 153, 250—264 (1960). [133]

— — — The stimulant effect of barium on the release of acetylcholine from the superior cervical ganglion. J. Physiol. (Lond.) 156, 515—522 (1961). [58]

DU BOIS-REYMOND, E.: Gesammelte Abhandl. d. allgem. Muskel- und Nervenphysik 2, 700 (1877). [7]

DUDEL, J.: Effect of inhibition on the presynaptic nerve terminal in the neuromuscular junction of the crayfish. Nature (Lond.) 193, 587—588 (1962a). [126, 127]

— The mechanism of facilitation and the effect of 5-hydroxy-tryptamine on the crayfish neuromuscular junction. XXII. Proc. Int. Union Physiol. Sci. vol. 2. Communication No. 857 (1962b). [126, 127]

DUDEL, J., R. GRYDER, A. KAJI, S. W. KUFFLER and D. D. POTTER: Gamma-aminobutyric acid and other blocking compounds in Crustacea. I. Central nervous system. J. Neurophysiol. **26**, 721—728 (1963). [197]

—, and S. W. KUFFLER: Excitation at the crayfish neuromuscular junction with decreased membrane conductance. Nature (Lond.) **187**, 246—247 (1960). [166, 234]

— — The quantal nature of transmission and spontaneous miniature potentials at the crayfish neuromuscular junction. J. Physiol. (Lond.) **155**, 514—529 (1961a). [34, 47, 90]

— — Mechanism of facilitation at the crayfish neuromuscular junction. J. Physiol. (Lond.) **155**, 530—542 (1961b). [75, 90, 94, 95, 99]

— — Presynaptic inhibition at the crayfish neuromuscular junction. J. Physiol. (Lond.) **155**, 543—562 (1961c). [126, 127, 166, 196, 201, 236, 237, 238]

—, and R. K. ORKAND: Spontaneous potential changes at crayfish neuromuscular junctions. Nature (Lond.) **186**, 476—477 (1960). [34]

ECCLES, J. C.: Slow potential waves in the superior cervical ganglion. J. Physiol. (Lond.) **85**, 464—501 (1935). [37]

— Synaptic and neuromuscular transmission. Ergebn. Physiol. **38**, 339—444 (1936). [6, 8]

— Synaptic and neuro-muscular transmission. Physiol. Rev. **17**, 538—555 (1937). [8]

— Changes in muscle produced by nerve degeneration. Med. J. Aust. **1**, 573—575 (1941a). [245]

— Disuse atrophy of skeletal muscle. Med. J. Aust. **2**, 160—164 (1941b). [242, 245]

— Synaptic potentials and transmission in sympathetic ganglion. J. Physiol. (Lond.) **101**, 465—483 (1943). [37, 83]

— The nature of synaptic transmission in a sympathetic ganglion. J. Physiol. (Lond.) **103**, 27—54 (1944a). [8, 133, 135]

— Investigations on muscle atrophies arising from disuse and tenotomy. J. Physiol. (Lond.) **103**, 253—266 (1944b). [242]

— Synaptic potentials of motoneurones. J. Neurophysiol. **9**, 87—120 (1946a). [6, 37, 38, 102]

— An electrical hypothesis of synaptic and neuro-muscular transmission. Ann. N.Y. Acad. Sci. **47**, 429—455 (1946b). [9]

— A review and restatement of the electrical hypotheses of synaptic excitatory and inhibitory action. Arch. Sci. physiol. **3**, 567—584 (1949). [9]

— The neurophysiological basis of mind. The principles of neurophysiology, 314 pp. Oxford: Clarendon Press 1953. [102, 103, 117, 159, 255, 259]

— The physiology of nerve cells, 270 pp. Baltimore: Johns Hopkins Press 1957. [7, 40, 73, 103, 110, 133, 177, 191, 197, 209, 231]

— The behaviour of nerve cells. Ciba Symp. Neurological basis of behaviour, pp. 28—47. London: J. & A. Churchill Ltd. 1958(a). [7, 153, 168]

— Problems of plasticity and organization at simplest levels of mammalian central nervous system. Perspect. Biol. Med. **1**, 379—396 (1958b). [256]

— The nature of central inhibition. Proc. roy Soc. B **153**, 445—476 (1961a). [168, 175, 177, 209]

— Membrane time constants of cat motoneurones and time courses of synaptic action. Exp. Neurol. **4**, 1—22 (1961b). [43, 44, 226]

— The mechanism of synaptic transmission. Ergebn. Physiol. **51**, 299—430 (1961c). [21]

— Inhibitory pathways to motoneurones. In: Nervous inhibition, Ed. E. FLOREY pp. 47—60. New York: Pergamon Press 1961 (d). [21]

— The synaptic mechanism of postsynaptic inhibition. In: Nervous inhibition, Ed. E. FLOREY, pp. 71—86. New York: Pergamon Press 1961 (e). [177, 188]

— Spinal neurones: Synaptic connexions in relation to chemical transmitters and pharmacological responses. In: Proceedings first inter. Pharmacol. meeting, vol. 8, p. 157—182, Ed. B. UVNÄS. Oxford: Pergamon Press 1962. [191, 197, 232]

— Presynaptic and postsynaptic inhibitory actions in the spinal cord. In: Brain mechanisms, Ed. G. MORUZZI. Amsterdam: Elsevier Publ. Co. 1963. [224, 234]

References

Eccles, J. C., R. M. Eccles and P. Fatt: Pharmacological investigations on a central synapse operated by acetylcholine. J. Physiol. (Lond.) **131**, 154—169 (1956). [45, 67, 68, 121]

— — A. Iggo and M. Ito: Distribution of recurrent inhibition among motoneurones. J. Physiol. (Lond.) **159**, 479—499 (1961). [160]

— — — and A. Lundberg: Electrophysiological investigations of Renshaw cells. J. Physiol. (Lond.) **159**, 461—478 (1961). [35, 43, 45, 120, 121]

— — and M. Ito: Effects of intracellular potassium and sodium injections on the inhibitory postsynaptic potential. Proc. roy. Soc. B 1964a (In press). [174, 178, 179, 180]

— — — Effects produced on inhibitory postsynaptic potentials by the coupled injections of cations and anions into motoneurones. Proc. roy. Soc. B (1964b) (In press). [174, 178, 181, 182, 183]

— — and W. Kozak: Further investigations on the influence of motoneurones on the speed of muscle contraction. J. Physiol. (Lond.) **163**, 324—339 (1962). [241, 242, 246]

— — and A. Lundberg: Synaptic actions on motoneurones in relation to the two components of the group I muscle afferent volley. J. Physiol. (Lond.) **136**, 527—546 (1957a). [41]

— — — The convergence of monosynaptic excitatory afferents on to many different species of alpha motoneurones. J. Physiol. (Lond.) **137**, 22—50 (1957b). [103, 250]

— — — Synaptic actions on motoneurones caused by impulses in Golgi tendon organ afferents. J. Physiol. (Lond.) **138**, 227—252 (1957c). [159, 208]

— — — The action potentials of the alpha motoneurones supplying fast and slow muscles. J. Physiol. (Lond.) **142**, 275—291 (1958). [117]

— — — Types of neurone in and around the intermediate nucleus of the lumbo-sacral cord. J. Physiol. (Lond.) **154**, 89—114 (1960). [46, 105, 119, 120, 203, 208]

— — and F. Magni: Monosynaptic excitatory action on motoneurones regenerated to antagonistic muscles. J. Physiol. (Lond.) **154**, 68—88 (1960). [250]

— — — Central inhibitory action attributable to presynaptic depolarization produced by muscle afferent volleys. J. Physiol. (Lond.) **159**, 147—166 (1961). [221, 222, 223, 224, 227, 233, 234]

— —, and C. N. Shealy: An investigation into the effect of degenerating primary afferent fibers on the monosynaptic innervation of motoneurons. J. Neurophysiol. **25**, 544—558 (1962). [249, 250]

— — — and W. D. Willis: Experiments utilizing monosynaptic excitatory action on motoneurons for testing hypotheses relating to specificity of neuronal connection. J. Neurophysiol. **25**, 559—579 (1962). [250, 251]

— P. Fatt and K. Koketsu: Cholinergic and inhibitory synapses in a pathway from motor-axon collaterals to motoneurones. J. Physiol. (Lond.) **216**, 524—562 (1954). [45, 67, 68, 121, 159, 160, 191, 208]

— — and S. Landgren: The "direct" inhibitory pathway in the spinal cord. Aust. J. Sci. **16**, 130—134 (1954). [203, 207, 209]

— — The central pathway for the direct inhibitory action of impulses in the largest afferent nerve fibres to muscle. J. Neurophysiol. **19**, 75—98 (1956). [45, 203, 207]

— R. Granit and J. Z. Young: Impulses in the giant nerve fibres of earthworms. J. Physiol. (Lond.) **77**, 23P—24P (1932). [138]

—, and H. E. Hoff: The rhythmic discharge of motoneurones. Proc. roy. Soc. B **110**, 483—514 (1932). [117]

— J. I. Hubbard and O. Oscarsson: Intracellular recording from cells of the ventral spino-cerebellar tract. J. Physiol. (Lond.) **158**, 486—516 (1961). [86, 105, 160, 161, 171, 207, 208]

—, and J. C. Jaeger: The relationship between the mode of operation and the dimensions of the junctional regions at synapses and motor end-organs. Proc. roy. Soc. B **148**, 38—56 (1958). [28, 82, 126]

Eccles, J. C., B. Katz and S. W. Kuffler: Nature of the 'endplate potential' in curarized muscle. J. Neurophysiol. **4**, 362—387 (1941). [37, 38, 48, 83]

— — — Effect of eserine on neuromuscular transmission. J. Neurophysiol. **5**, 211—230 (1942). [48, 127, 128, 129]

— P. G. Kostyuk and R. F. Schmidt: Central pathways responsible for depolarization of primary afferent fibres. J. Physiol. (Lond.) **161**, 237—257 (1962a). [46, 220, 226, 238]

— — — Presynaptic inhibition of the central actions of flexor reflex afferents. J. Physiol. (Lond.) **161**, 258—281 (1962b). [233]

— — — The effect of electric polarization of the spinal cord on central afferent fibres and on their excitatory synaptic action. J. Physiol. (Lond.) **162**, 138—150 (1962c). [80, 81, 99, 228]

—, and K. Krnjević: Potential changes recorded inside primary afferent fibres within the spinal cord. J. Physiol. (Lond.) **149**, 250—273 (1959a). [99, 130, 229, 230]

— — Presynaptic changes associated with post-tetanic potentiation in the spinal cord. J. Physiol. (Lond.) **149**, 274—287 (1959b). [99]

— — and R. Miledi: Delayed effects of peripheral severance of afferent nerve fibres on the efficacy of their central synapses. J. Physiol. (Lond.) **145**, 204—220 (1959). [99, 103, 256]

—, and S. W. Kuffler: Initiation of muscle impulses at neuromuscular junction. J. Neurophysiol. **4**, 402—417 (1941). [37]

— B. Libet and R. R. Young: The behaviour of chromatolysed motoneurones studied by intracellular recording. J. Physiol. (Lond.) **143**, 11—40 (1958). [107, 111]

—, and A. W. Liley: Factors controlling the liberation of acetylcholine at the neuromuscular junction. Amer. J. phys. Med. **38**, 96—103 (1959). [77, 82]

—, and W. V. Macfarlane: Actions of anticholinesterases on endplate potential of frog muscle. J. Neurophysiol. **12**, 59—80 (1949). [87]

—, and J. W. Magladery: The excitation and response of smooth muscle. J. Physiol. (Lond.) **90**, 31—67 (1937). [8, 40]

— F. Magni and W. D. Willis: Depolarization of central terminals of Group I afferent fibres from muscle. J. Physiol. (Lond.) **160**, 62—93 (1962). [220, 221, 225, 227, 229, 230, 233]

—, and J. L. Malcolm: Dorsal root potentials of the spinal cord. J. Neurophysiol. **9**, 139—160 (1946). [68, 226]

—, and A. K. McIntyre: The effects of disuse and of activity on mammalian spinal reflexes. J. Physiol. (Lond.) **121**, 492—516 (1953). [255, 256]

—, and W. J. O'Connor: Action potentials evoked by indirect stimulation of curarized muscle. J. Physiol. (Lond.) **94**, 9P—11P (1938). [37]

— — Responses which nerve impulses evoke in mammalian striated muscles. J. Physiol. (Lond.) **97**, 44—102 (1939). [37]

— O. Oscarsson and W. D. Willis: Synaptic action of Group I and II afferent fibres of muscle on the cells of the dorsal spino-cerebellar tract. J. Physiol. (Lond.) **158**, 517—543 (1961). [45, 86, 160, 161, 171, 208]

—, and J. J. Pritchard: The action potential of motoneurones. J. Physiol. (Lond.) **89**, 43P—45P (1937). [4, 6, 37]

—, and W. Rall: Effects induced in a monosynaptic reflex path by its activation. J. Neurophysiol. **14**, 353—376 (1951). [98, 99]

— R. F. Schmidt and W. D. Willis: Presynaptic inhibition of the spinal monosynaptic reflex ׀pathway. J. Physiol. (Lond.) **161**, 282—297 (1962). [221, 223, 224, 227, 233]

— — — Depolarization of central terminals of Group Ib afferent fibers of muscle. J. Neurophysiol. **26**, 1—27 (1963a). [220, 227]

— — — The location and the mode of action of the presynaptic inhibitory pathways on the Group I afferent fibers from muscle. J. Neurophysiol. **26**, 506—522 (1963b). [220, 222, 225]

References

Eccles, J. C., R. F. Schmidt and W. D. Willis: The mode of operation of the synaptic mechanism producing presynaptic inhibition. J. Neurophysiol. **26**, 523—536 (1963c). [227, 228, 230]
— — — Pharmacological studies on presynaptic inhibition. J. Physiol. (Lond.) (In press) (1963d). [224, 231]
— — — Depolarization of the central terminals of cutaneous afferent fibres. J. Neurophysiol. **26**, 646—661 (1963e). [229, 233]
— — — Inhibition of discharges into the dorsal and ventral spinocerebellar tracts. J. Neurophysiol. **26**, 635—645 (1963f). [233]
Eccles, R. M.: Responses of isolated curarized sympathetic ganglia. J. Physiol. (Lond.) **117**, 196—217 (1952). [131, 132, 134, 137]
— Intracellular potentials recorded from a mammalian sympathetic ganglion. J. Physiol. (Lond.) **130**, 572—584 (1955). [37, 85, 102, 103, 105]
— Orthodromic activation of single ganglion cells. J. Physiol. (Lond.) **165**, 387—391 (1963). [102, 105]
— W. Kozak and R. A. Westerman: Enhancement of spinal monosynaptic reflex responses after denervation of synergic hind-limb muscles. Exp. Neurol. **6**, 451—464 (1962). [257]
—, and B. Libet: Origin and blockade of the synaptic responses of curarized sympathetic. ganglia. J. Physiol. (Lond.)**157**, 484—503 (1961). [69, 131, 132, 134, 137, 194]
—, and A. Lundberg: The synaptic linkage of 'direct' inhibition. Acta physiol. scand. **43**, 204—215 (1958a). [203]
— — Integrative patterns of Ia synaptic actions on motoneurones of hip and knee muscles. J. Physiol. (Lond.) **144**, 271—298 (1958b). [250]
— — Synaptic actions in motoneurones by afferents which may evoke the flexion reflex. Arch. ital. Biol. **97**, 199—221 (1959). [159, 208]
—, and W. D. Willis: Presynaptic inhibition of the monosynaptic reflex pathway in kittens. J. Physiol. (Lond.) **165**, 403—420 (1962). [224, 233]
Eckert, R.: Electrical interaction of paired ganglion cells in the leech. J. gen. Physiol. **46**, 573—587 (1963). [143]
Edds, MacV.: Collateral regeneration of residual motor axons in partially denervated muscles. J. exp. Zool. **113**, 517—551 (1950). [254]
Edwards, C.: Physiology and pharmacology of the crayfish stretch receptor. In: Inhibition in the nervous system and γ-aminobutyric acid, pp. 386—408, Ed. E. Roberts. New York: Pergamon Press 1960. [195]
—, and S. Hagiwara: Potassium ions and the inhibitory process in the crayfish stretch receptor. J. gen. Physiol. **43**, 315—321 (1959). [183]
—, and S. W. Kuffler: The blocking effect of γ-aminobutyric acid (GABA) and the action of related compounds on single nerve cells. J. Neurochem. **4**, 19—30 (1959). [183, 195]
—, and D. Ottoson: The site of impulse initiation in a nerve cell of a crustacean stretch receptor. J. Physiol. (Lond.) **143**, 138—148 (1958). [106, 111]
Ehrenpreis, S.: Isolation and identification of the acetylcholine receptor protein of electric tissue. Biochem. biophys. Acta (Amst.) **44**, 561—577 (1960). [66]
— The isolation and identification of the acetylcholine receptor protein from electric tissue of *electrophorus electricus* (L.). In: Bioelectrogenesis, pp. 379—396, Ed. C. Chagas and A. Paes de Carvalho. Amsterdam: Elsevier Publ. Co. 1961. [66]
— Immunohistochemical localization of drug-binding protein in tissues of the electric eel. Nature (Lond.) **194**, 586—587 (1962). [66]
Eide, E., A. Lundberg and P. Voorhoeve: Monosynaptically evoked inhibitory postsynaptic potentials in motoneurones. Acta physiol. scand. **53**, 185—195 (1961). [206, 207]
Eldred, E., R. Granit and P. A. Merton: Supraspinal control of the muscle spindles and its significance. J. Physiol. (Lond.) **122**, 498—523 (1953). [249, 256]
Elliott, K. A. C., and E. Florey: Factor I — Inhibitory factor from Brain. Assay. Conditions in Brain. Simulating and antagonising substances. J. Neurochem. **1**, 181—191 (1956). [195]

ELLIOTT, K. A. C., and H. H. JASPER: Gamma-aminobutyric acid. Physiol. Rev. **39**, 383—406 (1959). [195]

ELLIOTT, T. R.: On the action of adrenalin. J. Physiol. (Lond.) **31**, 20P (1904). [7]

ELMQVIST, D., T. R. JOHNS and S. THESLEFF: A study of some electrophysiological properties of human intercostal muscle. J. Physiol. (Lond.) **154**, 602—607 (1960). [29]

— D. J. M. QUASTEL and S. THESLEFF: Prejunctional action of HC-3 on neuromuscular transmission. J. Physiol. (Lond.) **167**, 47 P—48 P (1963). [32, 60, 62]

EMMELIN, N. G., and F. C. MacINTOSH: Some conditions affecting the release of acetylcholine in sympathetic ganglia and skeletal muscles. Acta physiol. scand., Suppl. **53**, 17—18 (1948). [55, 59, 134, 135]

— — The release of acetylcholine from perfused sympathetic ganglia and skeletal muscles. J. Physiol. **131**, 477—496 (1956). [55, 63]

ENGSTRÖM, H.: Electron micrographic studies of the receptor cells of the organ of Corti. From: Neural mechanisms of the auditory and vestibular systems, Ed. G. L. RASMUSSEN and W. WINDLE. Springfield (Ill).: Ch. C. Thomas 1961. [191]

ERLANGER, J.: The initiation of impulses in axons. J. Neurophysiol. **2**, 370—379 (1939). [9]

ESTABLE, C.: Notes sur la structure comparative de l'écorce cérébelleuse, et derivées physiologiques possibles. Trab. Lab. Invest. Biol. Univ. Madrid **21**, 169—256 (1923). [17]

EULER, U. S. v.: A specific sympathomimetric ergone in adrenergic nerve fibres (Sympathin) and its relations to adrenaline and nor-adrenaline. Acta physiol. scand. **12**, 73—97 (1946). [61]

— Autonomic neuroeffector transmission. In: Handbook of physiology, Section 1, Neurophysiology, vol. 1, chapt. VII, p. 215—237, Ed. J. FIELD. Washington: Amer. Physiol. Soc. 1959. [61, 194]

—, and N.-Å. HILLARP: Evidence for the presence of noradrenaline in submicroscopic structures of adrenergic axons. Nature (Lond.) **177**, 44—45 (1956). [61]

EVANS, D. H. L., and A. D. VIZOSO: Observations on the mode of growth of motor nerve fibers in rabbits during post-natal development. J. comp. Neurol. **95**, 429—461 (1951). [254]

EVARTS, E. V., and J. R. HUGHES: Relation of posttetanic potentiation to subnormality of lateral geniculate potentials. Amer. J. Physiol. **188**, 238—244 (1957). [100]

EYZAGUIRRE, C., and S. W. KUFFLER: Processes of excitation in the dendrites and in the soma of single isolated sensory nerve cells of the lobster and crayfish. J. gen. Physiol. **39**, 87—119 (1955a). [118, 172]

— — Further study of soma, dendrite and axon excitation in single neurons. J. gen. Physiol. **39**, 121—153 (1955b). [111, 172]

FADIGA, E., and J. M. BROOKHART: Monosynaptic activation of different portions of the motor neuron membrane. Amer. J. Physiol. **198**, 693—703 (1960). [41, 45, 76, 103, 111, 119]

— — Interactions of excitatory postsynaptic potentials generated at different sites on the frog motoneuron. J. Neurophysiol. **25**, 790—804 (1962). [40, 87]

FATT, P.: Biophysics of junctional transmission. Physiol. Rev. **34**, 674—710 (1954). [63, 64, 197, 231, 236]

— Electric potentials occuring around a neurone during its antidromic activation. J. Neurophysiol. **20**, 27—60 (1957a). [110]

— Sequence of events in synaptic activation of a motoneurone. J. Neurophysiol. **20**, 61—80 (1957b). [103]

— Skeletal neuromuscular transmission. In: Handbook of physiology, Section 1, Neurophysiology, vol. 1, chapt. VI, Ed. J. FIELD, pp. 199—213. Washington: Amer. Physiol. Soc. 1959. [63]

— Alterations produced in the post-junctional cell by the inhibitory transmitter. In: Inhibition in the nervous system and gamma-aminobutyric acid. pp. 104—114, Ed. E. ROBERTS. New York: Pergamon Press 1960. [177]

References

FATT, P.: The change in membrane permeability during the inhibitory process. In: Nervous inhibition, Ed. E. FLOREY, pp. 87—91, Oxford: Pergamon Press 1961. [188]
—, and B. KATZ: Membrane potentials changes at the motor end-plate. J. Physiol. (Lond.) 111, 46 P—47 P (1950). [37]
— — An analysis of the end-plate potential recorded with an intra-cellular electrode. J. Physiol. (Lond.) 115, 320—369 (1951). [28, 37, 46, 47, 48, 51, 53, 106, 108, 109, 265]
— — The electric activity of the motor end-plate. Proc. roy. Soc. B 140, 183—186 (1952a). [37]
— — Spontaneous subthreshold activity at motor nerve endings. J. Physiol. (Lond.) 117, 109—128 (1952b). [29, 30, 130]
— — Distributed 'end-plate potentials' of crustacean muscle fibres. J. exp. Biol. 30, 433—439 (1953a). [37, 47, 108]
— — The effect of inhibitory nerve impulses on a crustacean muscle fibre. J. Physiol. (Lond.) 121, 374—389 (1953b). [164, 165, 166, 201, 236]
FELDBERG, W.: Present views on the mode of action of acetylcholine in the central nervous system. Physiol. Rev. 25, 596—642 (1945). [9, 68, 70]
— Sme aspects in pharmacology of central synaptic transmission. Arch. int. Physiol. 59, 0544—560 (1951). [9]
— Central and sensory transmission. Pharmacol. Rev. 6, 85—93 (1954). [70]
— Acetylcholine. From: Metabolism of the nervous system, p. 493—509, Ed. D. RIGHTER, London: Pergamon Press 1957. [68, 70]
—, and J. H. GADDUM: The chemical transmitter at synapses in a sympathetic ganglion. J. Physiol. (Lond.) 81, 305—319 (1934). [8]
— J. A. B. GRAY and W. L. M. PERRY: Effects of close arterial injections of acetylcholine on the activity of the cervical spinal cord of the cat. J. Physiol. (Lond.) 119, 428—438 (1953). [68]
—, and A. VARTIAINEN: Further observations on the physiology and pharmacology of a sympathetic ganglion. J. Physiol. (Lond.) 83, 103—128 (1934). [8, 55]
—, and M. VOGT: Acetylcholine synthesis in different regions of the central nervous system. J. Physiol. (Lond.) 107, 372—381 (1948). [9, 61, 68, 70]
FENG, T. P.: Studies on the neuro-muscular junction. XVIII. The local potentials around N-M junctions induced by single and multiple volleys. Chin. J. Physiol. 15, 367—404 (1940). [37, 87]
—, and T. H. LI: Studies on the neuromuscular junction. XXIII. A new aspect of the phenomena of eserine potentiation and post-tetanic facilitation in mammalian muscles. Chin. J. Physiol. 16, 37—50 (1941). [127, 129, 130]
FERNANDEZ DE MOLINA, A., J. A. B. GRAY and J. F. PALMER: Effects of acetylcholine on the activity of the lumbosacral cord of the cat. J. Physiol. (Lond.) 141, 169—176 (1958). [68]
FESSARD, A.: Reflexions dans le prolongement d'une discussion sur les mécanismes synaptiques. Arch. int. Physiol. 59, 605—618 (1951). [9]
—, et J. POSTERNAK: Les mécanismes élémentaires de la transmission synaptique. J. Physiol. Path. gén. 42, 319—445 (1950). [10, 29, 108]
—, et L. TAUC: Comparaison entre la dissipation des potentiels postsynaptiques et électrotoniques dans le soma neuronique de l'Aplysie. J. Physiol. (Paris) 49, 162—164 (1957). [42]
FEX, J.: Auditory activity in centrifugal and centripetal cochlear fibres in cat. Acta physiol. scand., Suppl. 189, 55, 1—68 (1962). [191]
FLOREY, E.: An inhibitory and an excitatory factor of mammalian central nervous system, and their action on a single sensory neuron. Arch. int. Physiol. 62, 33—53 (1954). [192]
— Physiological evidence for naturally occurring inhibitory substances. From: Inhibition in the nervous system and γ-aminobutyric acid, Ed. E. ROBERTS, pp. 72—84. Oxford: Pergamon Press 1960. [195]

FLOREY, E.: Comparative physiology: transmitter substances. Ann. Rev. Physiol. **23**, 501—528 (1961). [68, 74, 195]
— Comparative neurochemistry: Inorganic ions, amino acids and possible transmitter substances of invertebrates. In: Neurochemistry, 2nd ed. Springfield (Ill.): Ch. C. Thomas 1962. [195]
— Amino-acids as transmitter substances. In: Some major problems of neuro-endocrinology. (1963) (In press). [195, 196, 197]
—, and M. A. BIEDERMAN: Studies on the distribution of Factor I and acetylcholine in crustacean peripheral nerve. J. gen. Physiol. **43**, 509—522 (1960). [197]
—, and D. D. CHAPMAN: The non-identity of the transmitter substance of crustacean inhibitory neurons and gamma-aminobutyric acid. Comp. Biochem. Physiol. **3**, 92—98 (1961). [197]
—, and E. FLOREY: Microanatomy of the abdominal stretch receptors of the crayfish (Astacus fluviatilis l.) J. gen. Physiol. **39**, 69—85 (1955). [201]
—, and G. HOYLE: Neuromuscular synaptic activity in the crab (Cancer Magister). In: Nervous inhibition, pp. 105—110, Ed. E. FLOREY. New York: Pergamon Press 1961. [195, 196]
—, and H. McLENNAN: Effects of an inhibitory factor (Factor I) from brain on central synaptic transmission. J. Physiol. (Lond.) **130**, 446—455 (1955). [194]
— — The effects of Factor I and of gamma-amino-butyric acid on smooth muscle preparations. J. Physiol. (Lond.) **145**, 66—76 (1959). [192]
—, and H. J. MERWIN: Inhibition in molluscan hearts and the role of acetylcholine. In: Nervous Inhibition, pp. 136—143, Ed. E. FLOREY. New York: Pergamon Press 1961. [200]
FOERSTER, O., O. GAGEL u. D. SHEEHAN: Veränderungen an den Endösen im Rückenmark des Affen nach Hinterwurzeldurchschneidung. Z. Anat. Entwickl.-Gesch. **101**, 553—565 (1933). [2]
FORBES, A.: The interpretation of spinal reflexes in terms of present knowledge of nerve conduction. Physiol. Rev. **2**, 361—414 (1922). [5]
— Problems of synaptic function. J. Neurophysiol. **2**, 465—472 (1939). [9]
FOREL, A.: Einige hirnanatomische Betrachtungen und Ergebnisse. Arch. Psychiat. Nervenkr. **18**, 162—198 (1887). [1]
FRANK, K.: Basic mechanisms of synaptic transmission in the central nervous system. I.R.E. Trans. Med. Electron ME-6, 85—88 (1959). [168, 220, 221, 223]
—, and M. G. F. FUORTES: Potentials recorded from the spinal cord with microelectrodes. J. Physiol. (Lond.) **130**, 625—654 (1955). [37]
— — Unitary activity of spinal interneurones of cats. J. Physiol. (Lond.) **131**, 425—435 (1956a). [119, 121]
— — Stimulation of spinal motoneurones with intracellular electrodes. J. Physiol. (Lond.) **134**, 451—470 (1956b). [7, 103, 114, 170]
— — Presynaptic and postsynaptic inhibition of monosynaptic reflexes. Fed. Proc. **16**, 39—40 (1957). [220, 221, 223, 233]
— — Accommodation of spinal motoneurones of cats. Arch. ital. Biol. **98**, 165—170 (1960). [115, 116]
— — Excitation and conduction. Ann. Rev. Physiol. **23**, 357—386 (1961). [7, 103]
FRANKENHAEUSER, B.: Delayed currents in myelinated nerve fibres of Xenopus laevis investigated with voltage clamp technique. J. Physiol. (Lond.) **160**, 40—45 (1962a). [124]
— Instantaneous potassium currents in myelinated nerve fibres of Xenopus laevis. J. Physiol. (Lond.) **160**, 46—53 (1962b). [124]
— Potassium permeability in myelinated nerve fibres of Xenopus laevis. J. Physiol. (Lond.) **160**, 54—61 (1962c). [124]
FREYGANG, W. H.: An analysis of extracellular potentials from single neurons in the lateral geniculate nucleus of the cat. J. gen. Physiol. **41**, 543—564 (1958). [109]
—, and K. FRANK: Extracellular potentials from single spinal motoneurons. J. gen. Physiol. **42**, 749—760 (1959). [109]

References

Fukami, Y.: Postsynaptic potentials (PSP) in toad's spinal motoneurons due to muscle afferent volleys. Jap. J. Physiol. **11**, 596—604 (1961). [41, 160, 174, 209]

Fuortes, M. G. F.: Direct current stimulation of motoneurones. J. Physiol. (Lond.) **126**, 494—506 (1954). [117]

— K. Frank and M. C. Becker: Steps in the production of motoneuron spikes. J. gen. Physiol. **40**, 735—752 (1957). [103, 104, 109]

—, and F. Mantegazzini: Interpretation of the repetitive firing of nerve cells. J. gen. Physiol. **45**, 1163—1179 (1962). [115, 116]

Furshpan, E. J., and T. Furukawa: Intracellular and extracellular responses of the several regions of the Mauthner cell of the goldfish. J. Neurophysiol. **25**, 732—771 (1962). [103, 106]

—, and D. D. Potter: Mechanism of nerve-impulse transmission at a crayfish synapse. Nature (Lond.) **180**, 342—343 (1957). [10]

— — Transmission at the giant synapses of the crayfish. J. Physiol. (Lond.) **145**, 289—325 (1959a). [10, 139, 140, 147, 148, 149, 150, 261, 263, 264]

— — Slow post-synaptic potentials recorded from the giant motor fibre of the crayfish. J. Physiol. (Lond.) **145**, 326—335 (1959b). [163, 164, 196, 197]

Furukawa, T., Y. Fukami and Y. Asada: A third type of inhibition in the Mauthner cell of goldfish. J. Neurophysiol. **26** 759—774 (1963a). [219, 234, 235]

— — — Effects of strychnine and procaine on collateral inhibition of the Mauthner cell. (1963b). (In course of publication). [234, 235]

—, and E. J. Furshpan: Two inhibitory mechanisms in the Mauthner neurons of goldfish. J. Neurophysiol. **26**, 140—176 (1963). [216, 217, 218, 219]

—, and A. Furukawa: Effects of methyl- and ethyl-derivatives of NH_4^+ on the neuromuscular junction. Jap. J. Physiol. **9**, 130—142 (1959). [52]

— — and T. Takagi: Fibrillation of muscle fibers produced by ammonium ions and its relation to the spontaneous activity at the neuromuscular junction. Jap. J. Physiol. **7**, 252—263 (1957). [30, 31]

— T. Takagi and T. Sugihara: Depolarization of end-plates by acetylcholine externally applied. Jap. J. Physiol. **6**, 98—107 (1956). [52]

Galambos, R.: Suppression of auditory nerve activity by stimulation of efferent fibers to cochlea. J. Neurophysiol. **19**, 424—437 (1956). [191]

Gaskell, W. H.: On the action of muscarine upon the heart, and on the electrical changes in non-beating cardiac muscle brought about by stimulation of the inhibitory and augmentory nerves. J. Physiol. (Lond.) **8**, 404—414 (1887). [166]

Gasser, H. S.: The control of excitation in the nervous system. Harvey Lect. **32**, 169—193 (1937). [6, 220]

— Axons as samples of nervous tissue. J. Neurophysiol. **2**, 361—369 (1939). [9]

—, and H. T. Graham: Potentials produced in the spinal cord by stimulation of the dorsal roots. Amer. J. Physiol. **103**, 303—320 (1933). [220, 222]

Gaze, R. M.: Regeneration of the optic nerve in *Xenopus laevis*. Quart. J. exp. Physiol. **44**, 290—308 (1959). [247]

— Regeneration of the optic nerve in amphibia. Int. Rev. Neurobiol. **2**, 1—40 (1960). [247, 248]

—, and M. Jacobson: A study of the retinotectal projection during regeneration of the optic nerve in the frog. Proc. roy. Soc. B **157**, 420—448 (1963). [247, 248]

— — and G. Székely: The retino-tectal projection in *Xenopus* with compound eyes. J. Physiol. (Lond.) **165**, 484—499 (1963). [248]

Gehuchten, A. van: La structure des centres nerveux la moelle épinière et le cervelet. Cellule **7**, 79—122 (1891). [1]

— La structure des lobes optiques chez l'embryon de poulet. Cellule **8**, 1—43 (1892).

Gerard, R. W.: Physiology and Psychiatry. Amer. J. Psychiat. **106**, 161—173 (1949). [260]

GEREBTZOFF, M. A.: Cholinesterases. A histochemical contribution to the solution of some functional problems, 195 pp. New York: Pergamon Press 1959. [70]

GERLACH, J.: Von dem Rückenmarke. In: Handbuch der Lehre von den Geweben, Bd. 2, Ed. STRICKER. 1871. [1]

GERSCHENFELD, H. M.: Submicroscopic bases of synaptic organization in gasteropod nervous system. Fifth Int. Congr. for electron microscopy 1962. [25]

—, and L. TAUC: Pharmacological specificities of neurones in an elementary central nervous system. Nature (Lond.) 189, 924—925 (1961). [74]

GINETZINSKY, A. G., and N. M. SHARMARINA: The tonomotor phenomenon in denervated muscle. Usp. sovrem. Biol. 15, 283—294 (1942). [240, 243]

GINSBORG, B. L.: Spontaneous activity in muscle fibres of the chick. J. Physiol. (Lond.) 150, 707—717 (1960) [34]

GÖPFERT, H., u. H. SCHAEFER: Über den direkt und indirekt erregten Aktionsstrom und die Funktion der motorischen Endplatte. Pflügers Arch. ges. Physiol. 239, 597—619 (1938). [37]

GOLGI, C.: Sulla minuta anatomia degli organi centrali del sistema nervoso. Milano 1885. [1]

— Über den feineren Bau des Rückenmarkes. Anat. Anz. 5, 372—396 (1890). [2]

— Le réseau nerveux diffus des centres du système nerveux. Ses attributs physiologiques. Méthode suivie dans les recherches histologiques. Arch. ital. Biol. 15, 434—463 (1891). [2]

GRANIT, R.: Receptors and sensory perception, 366 pp. New Haven: Yale University Press 1955. [82, 117, 249]

— J. HAASE and L. T. RUTLEDGE: Recurrent inhibition in relation to frequency of firing and limitation of discharge rate of extensor motoneurones. J. Physiol. (Lond.) 154, 308—328 (1960). [115]

— H. D. HENATSCH and G. STEG: Tonic and phasic ventral horn cells differentiated by post-tetanic potentiation in cat extensors. Acta physiol. scand. 37, 114—126 (1956). [119]

—, and B. R. KAADA: Influence of stimulation of central nervous structures on muscle spindles in cat. Acta physiol. scand. 27, 130—160 (1952). [249]

— D. KERNELL and G. K. SHORTESS: Quantitative aspects of repetitive firing of mammalian motoneurones, as caused by injected currents. J. Physiol. (Lond.) (In press) (1963). [114, 115, 116, 117]

—, and C. G. PHILLIPS: Excitatory and inhibitory processes acting upon individual Purkinje cells of the cerebellum in cats. J, Physiol. (Lond.) 133, 520—547 (1956). [35, 162]

— — S. SKOGLUND and G. STEG: Differentiation of tonic from phasic alpha ventral horn cells by stretch, pinna and crossed extensor reflexes. J. Neurophysiol. 20, 470—481 (1957). [119]

—, and B. RENKIN: Net depolarization and discharge rate of motoneurones, as measured by recurrent inhibition. J. Physiol. (Lond.) 158, 461—475 (1961). [115]

—, and C. R. SKOGLUND: Facilitation, inhibition and depression at the 'Artificial Synapse' formed by the cut end of a mammalian nerve. J. Physiol. (Lond.) 103, 435—448 (1945a). [8]

— — The effect of temperature on the artificial synapse formed by the cut end of the mammalian nerve. J. Neurophysiol. 7, 211—217 (1945b). [8]

GRAY, E. G.: Axo-somatic and axo-dendritic synapses of the cerebral cortex: an electron microscope study. J. Anat. (Lond.) 93, 420—433 (1959). [IV, 15, 16, 17, 19, 58, 189, 259]

— Ultra-structure of synapses of the cerebral cortex and of certain specialisations of neuroglial membranes. In: Electron microscopy in Anatomy, pp. 54—73, Ed. BOYD et al. London: Edward Arnold (1961a). [16, 17, 19, 22, 23, 189]

— The granule cells, mossy synapses and Purkinje spine synapses of the cerebellum: Light and electron microscope observations. J. Anat. (Lond.) 95, 345—356 (1961b). [19, 21, 26]

References

GRAY, E. G.: A morphological basis for pre-synaptic inhibition? Nature (Lond.) **193**, 82—83 (1962). [20]
— Electron microscopy of presynaptic organelles of the spinal cord. J. Anat. (Lond.) **97**, 101—106 (1963). [14, 15, 16, 17, 19, 20, 59]
—, and V. P. WHITTAKER: The isolation of synaptic vesicles from the central nervous system. J. Physiol. (Lond.) **153**, 35P—37P (1960). [70]
GRAY, J. A. B.: Initiation of impulses at receptors. In: Handbook of Physiology, Section 1, Neurophysiology, vol. 1, chapt. IV, Ed. J. FIELD, pp. 123—145. Washington: Amer. Physiol. Soc. 1959. [106]
GRUNDFEST, H.: Some properties of excitable tissue. In: Fifth conf. on Nerve impulse, p. 187. New York: Josiah Macy jr. Foundation. 1955. [108]
— Excitation triggers in post-junctional cells. In: Physiological triggers and discontinuous rate processes, Ed. T. H. BULLOCK. Washington: Amer. Physiol. Soc. 1957(a). [29, 101, 107, 108]
— Electrical inexcitability of synapses and some consequences in the central nervous system. Physiol. Rev. **37**, 337—361 (1957b). [29, 107, 108]
— Electrophysiology and pharmacology of dendrites. Electroenceph. clin. Neurophysiol., Suppl. **10**, 22—41 (1958). [110]
— Synaptic and ephaptic transmission. In: Handbook of Physiology, Section 1, Neurophysiology, vol. 1, chapt. V, pp. 147—197, Ed. J. FIELD. Washington: Amer. Physiol. Soc. 1959. [IV, 29, 107, 108]
— Central inhibition and its mechanisms. In: Inhibition in the nervous system and γ-aminobutyric acid, pp. 47—65, Ed. E. ROBERTS. New York: Pergamon Press 1960(a). [107, 108]
— Functional specifications for membranes in excitable cells. From: Fourth int. neurochem. symposium, pp. 378—402. Oxford: Pergamon Press 1960(b). [107, 108]
— Ionic mechanisms in electrogenesis. Ann. N.Y. Acad. Sci. **94**, 405—457 (1961a). [107, 108]
— General physiology and pharmacology of junctional transmission. In: Biophysics of physiological and pharmacological actions, pp. 329—389 1961(b). [107, 108]
— In discussion on H. GRUNDFEST and M. V. L. BENNETT, Electrophysiology of marine electric fishes, pp. 57—101. In: Bioelectrogenesis, Ed. C. CHAGAS and ANTONIO PAES DE CARVALHO. Amsterdam: Elsevier Press 1961(c). [108, 113]
—, and M. V. L. BENNETT: Studies on the morphology and electrophysiology of electric organs. 1. Electrophysiology of marine electric fishes. From: Bioelectrogenesis, pp. 57—101, Ed. C. CHAGAS and A. PAES DE CARVALHO. Amsterdam: Elsevier Publ. Co. 1961. [50]
—, and J. P. REUBEN: Neuromuscular synaptic activity in lobster. In: Nervous inhibition, pp. 92—104, Ed. E. FLOREY. Oxford: Pergamon Press 1961. [34]
— — and W. H. RICKLES: The electrophysiology and pharmacology of lobster neuromuscular synapses. J. gen. Physiol. **42**, 1301—1323 (1959). [196]
GUTH, L.: Neuromuscular function after regeneration of interrupted nerve fibers into partially denervated muscle. Exp. Neurol. **6**, 129—141 (1962). [246]
—, and J. J. BERNSTEIN: Selectivity in the re-establishment of synapses in the superior cervical sympathetic ganglion of the cat. Exp. Neurol. **4**, 59—69 (1961). [246]
GUTMAN, E.: Die funktionelle Regeneration der peripheren Nerven, 262 pp. Berlin: Akademie-Verlag 1958. [254]
GUTMANN, E., and P. HNÍK: Denervation studies in research of neurotrophic relationships. In: The denervated muscle, Ed. E. GUTMANN, chapt. I, pp. 13—56. Prague: Czechoslovak Academy of Sciences 1962. [241, 246]
—, u. G. VRBOVÁ: Die Physiologie des tenotomierten Muskels. (In Russian, German Summary.) Physiol. bohemoslov. **1**, 205 (1952). [254]
—, and J. ZELENA: Morphological changes in the denervated musclé. In: The Denervated Muscle. Ed. by E. GUTMANN, chapt. 2, pp. 57—102. Prague: Czechoslovak Academy of Sciences. 1962. [242]

HAAPANEN, L., G. M. KOLMODIN and C. R. SKOGLUND: Membrane and action potentials of spinal interneurones in the cat. Acta physiol. scand. **43**, 315—348 (1958). [45]

HAGGAR, R. A., and M. L. BARR: Quantitative data on the size of synaptic end-bulbs in the cat's spinal cord. J. comp. Neurol. **93**, 17—35 (1950). [92]

HAGIWARA, S.: Synaptic potential in the motor giant axon of the crayfish. J. gen. Physiol. **41**, 1119—1128 (1958). [164]

— Nervous activities of the heart in crustacea. Ergebn. Biol. **24**, 287—311 (1961). [106, 108, 142, 143, 151]

—, and T. H. BULLOCK: Intracellular potentials in pacemaker and integrative neurons of the lobster cardiac ganglion. J. cell. comp. Physiol. **50**, 25—47 (1957). [83, 106, 142]

—, and K. KUSANO: Synaptic inhibition in giant nerve cell of *Onchidium verruculatum*. J. Neurophysiol. **24**, 167—175 (1961). [162, 163, 200]

— — and S. SAITO: Membrane changes in crayfish stretch receptor neuron during synaptic inhibition and under action of gamma-aminobutyric acid. J. Neurophysiol. **23**, 505—515 (1960). [163, 184, 195, 201, 202]

—, and H. MORITA: Electrotonic transmission between two nerve cells in leech ganglion. J. Neurophysiol. **25**, 721—731 (1962). [143, 144]

—, and N. SAITO: Mechanism of action potential production in the nerve cell of a Puffer. Proc. Jap. Acad. **33**, 682—685 (1957). [42]

— — Membrane potential change and membrane current in supramedullary nerve cell of Puffer. J. Neurophysiol. **22**, 204—221 (1959). [42]

—, and I. TASAKI: A study of the mechanism of impulse transmission across the giant synapse of the squid. J. Physiol. (Lond.) **143**, 114—137 (1958). [27, 28, 38, 39, 44, 49, 50, 78, 79, 99]

— A. WATANABE and N. SAITO: Potential changes in syncytial neurons of lobster cardiac ganglion. J. Neurophysiol. **22**, 554—572 (1959). [43, 44, 49, 50, 103, 106, 108, 142, 143]

HAMA, K.: Some observations on the fine structure of the giant nerve fibers of the earthworm, *Eisenia foetida*. J. biophys. biochem. Cytol. **6**, 61—66 (1959). [140]

HAMBURGER, V.: Motor and sensory hyperplasia following limb-bud transplantation. Physiol. Zool. **13**, 268—284 (1939). [241]

—, and R. LEVI-MONTALCINI: Some aspects of neuroembryology. In: Genetic neurology pp. 128—160, Ed. P. WEISS. Chicago: Chicago University Press 1950. [241, 254]

HAMLYN, L. H.: The fine structure of the mossy fibre endings in the hippocampus of the rabbit. J. Anat. (Lond.) **96**, 112—120 (1962). [16, 17, 19, 258, 259]

HARREVELD, A. VAN: The nerve supply of double and triply innervated crayfish muscles related to their function. J. comp. Neurol. **70**, 267—284 (1939). [238]

—, and C. A. G. WIERSMA: The triple innervation of crayfish muscle and its function in contraction and inhibition. J. exp. Biol. **14**, 448—461 (1937). [201]

HARRIS, E. J., and O. F. HUTTER: The action of acetylcholine on the movements of potassium ions in the sinus venosus of the heart. J. Physiol. (Lond.) **133**, 58P—59P (1956). [187]

HARVEY, A. M., and F. C. MACINTOSH: Calcium and synaptic transmission in a sympathetic ganglion. J. Physiol. (Lond.) **97**, 408—416 (1940). [58]

HASSÓN, A.: Interaction of quaternary ammonium bases with a purified acid polysaccharide and other macromolecules from the electric organ of electric eel. Biochim. biophys. Acta (Amst.) **56**, 275—292 (1962). [66]

—, and C. CHAGAS: Purification of macromolecular components of the aqueous extract of the electric organ [*E. Electricus (L.)*] with binding capacity in vitro, for quaternary ammonium bases. In: Bioelectrogenesis, pp. 362—378, Ed. C. CHAGAS and A. PAES DE CARVALHO. Amsterdam: Elsevier Publ. Co. 1961. [66]

HAYASHI, T., and K. NAGAI: Action of ω-amino acids on the motor cortex of higher animals, especially γ-amino-β-oxybutyric acid as the real inhibitory principle in brain. Abstr. Comm. XX Internat. Physiol. Congress p. 410, 1956. [192]

References

HEBB, C. O.: Biochemical evidence for the neural function of acetylcholine. Physiol. Rev. **37**, 196—220 (1957). [68, 70]
— Chemical agents of the nervous system. Int. Rev. Neurobiol. **1**, 165—193 (1959). [68, 70]
— Cholinergic neurons in vertebrates. Nature (Lond.) **192**, 527—529 (1961). [68]
— Acetylcholine content of the rabbit plantaris muscle after denervation. J. Physiol. (Lond.) **163**, 294—306 (1962). [59]
—, and A. SILVER: Choline acetylase in the central nervous system of man and some other mammals. J. Physiol. (Lond.) **134**, 718—728 (1956). [70]
—, and B. N. SMALLMAN: Intracellular distribution of choline acetylase. J. Physiol. (Lond.) **134**, 385—392 (1956). [70]
—, and G. M. H. WAITES: Choline acetylase in antero- and retrograde degeneration of a cholinergic nerve. J. Physiol. (Lond.) **132**, 667—671 (1956). [57]
—, and V. P. WHITTAKER: Intracellular distributions of acetylcholine and choline acetylase. J. Physiol. (Lond.) **142**, 187—196 (1958). [70]
HEBB, D. O.: The organization of behaviour. New York: John Wiley and Sons, 1949. [255, 260]
HELD, H.: Die zentralen Bahnen des Nervus acusticus bei der Katze. Arch. Anat. Pyhsiol., Lpz., 270—291 (1891). [1]
— Beiträge zur Struktur der Nervenzellen und ihrer Fortsätze. Zweite Abhandlung. Arch. Anat. Physiol. (Lpz.) **21**, 204—294 (1897). [2]
— Zur Kenntniss einer neurofibrillaren. Continuität im Centralnervensystem der Wirbelthiere. Arch. Anat. Physiol. (Lpz.) **55**—78 (1905). [2]
— Die Entwicklung des Nervengewebes, S. 378. Leipzig 1909. [2]
— Die Lehre von den Neuronen und vom Neurencytium und ihr heutiger Stand. Fortschr. naturwiss. Forsch., N.F., H. 8 (1929). [2]
HERN, J. E. C., S. LANDGREN, C. G. PHILLIPS and R. PORTER: Selective excitation of corticofugal neurones by surface-anodal stimulation of the baboon's motor cortex. J. Physiol. (Lond.) **161**, 73—90 (1962). [159, 160, 208]
HILD, W., and I. TASAKI: Morphological and physiological properties of neurons and glial cells in tissue culture. J. Neurophysiol. **25**, 277—304 (1962). [22, 110]
HILGARD, E. R., and D. G. MARQUIS: Conditioning and learning. New York: D. Appleton Century Company 1940. [255]
HINSEY, J. C.: The innervation of skeletal muscle. Physiol. Rev. **14**, 514—585 (1934). [2]
HIS, W.: Zur Geschichte des menschlichen Rückenmarks und der Nervenwurzeln. Leipzig 1886. [1]
— Die Neuroblasten und deren Entstehung im embryonalen Marke. Abh. math.-physik. Kl. sächs. Akad. Wiss. **15**, 311—372 (1889)· [1]
HNÍK, P., R. BERÁNEK, L. VYKLICKÝ and J. ZELENÁ: Sensory outflow from chronically tenotomized muscles. Physiol. bohemoslov. **12**, 23—29 (1963). [251]
—, and V. ŠKORPIL: Fibrillation activity in denervated muscle. In: The denervated muscle, Ed. by E. GUTMANN, chapt. V, pp. 135—150. Prague: Czechoslovak Academy of Sciences 1962. [245]
✓ HODGKIN, A. L.: The local electric changes associated with repetitive action in a non-medullated axon. J. Physiol. (Lond.) **107**, 165—181 (1948). [117]
— The ionic basis of electrical activity in nerve and muscle. Biol. Rev. **26**, 339—409 (1951). [109]
— Ionic movements and electrical activity in giant nerve fibres. Proc. roy. Soc. B **148**, 1—37 (1958). [124, 177]
—, and P. HOROWICZ: The influence of potassium and chloride ions on the membrane potential of single muscle fibres. J. Physiol. (Lond.) **148**, 127—160 (1959). [177]
—, and A. F. HUXLEY: A quantitative description of membrane current and its application to conduction and excitation in nerve. J. Physiol. (Lond.) **117**, 500—544 (1952). [109]

Hoff, E. C.: Central nerve terminals in the mammalian spinal cord and their examination by experimental degeneration. Proc. roy. Soc. B **111**, 175—188 (1932). [2]

Hoffmann, P.: Über die doppelte Innervation der Krebsmuskeln. Zugleich ein Beitrag zur Kenntnis nervöser Hemmungen. Z. Biol. **63**, 411 (1914). [201]

— Untersuchungen über die Eigenreflexe (Sehnenreflexe) menschlicher Muskeln, 106 pp. Berlin: Springer 1922. [3]

Holmqvist, B., A. Lundberg and O. Oscarsson: Functional organization of the dorsal spino-cerebellar tract in the cat. V. Further experiments on convergence of excitatory and inhibitory actions. Acta physiol. scand. **38**, 76—90 (1956). [119]

Honour, A. J., and H. McLennan: The effects of γ-aminobutyric acid and other compounds on structures of the mammalian nervous system which are inhibited by Factor I. J. Physiol. (Lond.) **150**, 306—318 (1960). [194]

Horstmann, E., u. H. Meves: Die Feinstruktur des molekularen Rindengraues und ihre physiologische Bedeutung. Z. Zellforsch. **49**, 569—604 (1959). [16, 22, 109]

Householder, A. S., and H. D. Landahl: Mathematical biophysics of the central nervous system. Bloomington (Indiana): Principia Press 1945. [255]

Howland, B., J. Y. Lettvin, W. S. McCulloch, W. Pitts and P. D. Wall: Reflex inhibition by dorsal root interaction. J. Neurophysiol. **18**, 1—17 (1955). [220]

Hoyle, G., and C. A. G. Wiersma: Excitation at neuromuscular junctions in crustacea. J. Physiol. (Lond.) **143**, 403—425 (1958 a). [47, 90, 108]

— — Inhibition at neuromuscular junctions in crustacea. J. Physiol. (Lond.) **143**, 426—440 (1958b). [164, 166, 196, 201]

Hubbard, J. I.: Post-activation changes at the mammalian neuromuscular junction. Nature (Lond.) **184**, 1945 (1959). [83, 87, 95, 99, 100]

— The effect of calcium and magnesium on the spontaneous release of transmitter from mammalian motor nerve endings. J. Physiol. (Lond.) **159**, 507—517 (1961). [31, 33, 34, 77, 92]

— Prolonged effects of stimulation at the mammalian neuromuscular junction. J. Physiol. (Lond.) (In press) (1963). [83, 87, 96]

—, and R. F. Schmidt: Stimulation of motor nerve terminals. Nature (Lond.) **191**, 1103—1104 (1961). [125, 128, 129]

— — Repetitive activation of motor nerve endings. Nature (Lond.) **196**, 378—379 (1962). [89]

— — An electrophysiological investigation of mammalian motor nerve terminals. J. Physiol. (Lond.) **166**, 145—167 (1963). [29, 39, 82, 83, 90, 94, 95, 99, 100, 124, 125, 129, 130]

—, and W. D. Willis: Mobilization of transmitter by hyperpolarization. Nature (Lond.) **193**, 174—175 (1962a). [79]

— — Hyperpolarization of mammalian motor nerve terminals. J. Physiol. (Lond.) **163**, 115—137 (1962b). [79, 92]

— — Reduction of transmitter output by depolarization. Nature (Lond.) **193**, 1294—1925 (1962c). [80, 81]

— — The effect of use on the transmitter release mechanism at the mammalian neuromuscular junction. In: The effect of use and disuse on neuromuscular functions. Prague: Czechoslovak Academy of Sciences 1963. [80, 90, 91]

Hughes, B.: The isolated heart of *Mya arenaria* as a sensitive preparation for the assay of acetylcholine. Brit. J. Pharmacol. **10**, 36—38 (1955). [200]

Hughes, J., and H. S. Gasser: Some properties of the cord potentials evoked by a single afferent volley. Amer. J. Physiol. **108**, 295—306 (1934a). [220]

— — The response of the spinal cord to two afferent volleys. Amer. J. Physiol. **108**, 307—321 (1934b) [220]

Hughes, J. R.: Post-tetanic potentiation. Physiol. Rev. **38**, 91—113 (1958). [100]

Hunt, C. C.: Monosynaptic reflex response of spinal motoneurons to graded afferent stimulation. J. gen. Physiol. **38**, 813—852 (1955). [6, 103]

HUNT, C. C., and S. W. KUFFLER: Pharmacology of the neuromuscular junction. Pharmacol. Rev. **2**, 96—120 (1950). [8]

—, and KUNO, M.: Properties of spinal interneurones. J. Physiol. (Lond.) **147**, 346—363 (1959). [45, 105, 119, 120, 121]

—, and E. R. PERL: Spinal reflex mechanisms concerned with skeletal muscle. Physiol. Rev. **40**, 538—579 (1960). [103]

HUTTER, O. F.: Post-tetanic restoration of neuromuscular transmission blocked by d-Tubocurarine. J. Physiol. (Lond.) **118**, 216—227 (1952). [83]

— Mode of action of autonomic transmitters on the heart. Brit. med. Bull. **13**, 176—180 (1957). [166]

—, and K. KOSTIAL: Effect of magnesium and calcium ions on the release of acetylcholine. J. Physiol. (Lond.) **124**, 234—241 (1954). [58]

—, and W. TRAUTWEIN: Vagal effects on the sinus venosus of the frog's heart. J. Physiol. (Lond.) **129**, 48P (1955). [166]

— — Vagal and sympathetic effects on the pacemaker fibers in the sinus venosus of the heart. J. gen. Physiol. **39**, 715—733 (1956). [166, 167, 171]

HYDÉN, H.: Biochemical changes in glial cells and nerve cells at varying activity. Proc. Fourth Inter. Congr. Biochemistry, vol. 3, p. 64—89, Ed. O. HOFFMANN-OSTENHOF. London: Pergamon Press 1959. [259, 260]

ITO, M.: The electrical activity of spinal ganglion cells investigated with intracellular microelectrodes. Jap. J. Physiol. **7**, 297—323 (1957). [110]

— P. G. KOSTYUK and T. OSHIMA: Further study on anion permeability in cat spinal motoneurones. J. Physiol. (Lond.) **164**, 150—156 (1962). [174, 175, 177]

—, and T. OSHIMA: Temporal summation of after-hyperpolarization following a motoneurone spike. Nature (Lond.) **195**, 910—911 (1962). [183]

— — The extrusion of sodium from the spinal motoneurones of the cat. (In course of publication) (1963). [174, 178, 179, 183]

JACK, J., A. K. McINTYRE and G. SOMJEN: Excitability of motoneurones during reflex facilitation and inhibition. Internat. Congr. Physiol. Sci. 1959, vol. 21, Comm., p. 136. [157, 169, 170]

JENKINSON, D. H.: The nature of the antagonism between calcium and magnesium ions at the neuromuscular junction. J. Physiol. (Lond.) **138**, 434—444 (1957). [33, 77]

— The antagonism between tubocurarine and substances which depolarize the motor end-plate. J. Physiol. (Lond.) **152**, 309—324 (1960). [65]

JOB, C., and A. LUNDBERG: On the significance of post- and presynaptic events for facilitation and inhibition in the sympathetic ganglion of the cat. Acta physiol. scand. **28**, 14—28 (1953). [83]

JOHNS, T. R., and S. THESLEFF: Effects of motor inactivation on the chemical sensitivity of skeletal muscle. Acta physiol. scand. **51**, 136—141 (1961). [242, 243, 245]

JOLLY, W. A.: The time relations of the knee-jerk and simple reflexes. Quart. J. exp. Physiol. **4**, 67—87 (1911). [3]

JOSEFSSON, J. O., and S. THESLEFF: Electromyographic findings in experimental botulinum intoxication. Acta physiol. scand. **51**, 163—168 (1961). [244, 245]

JUNG, R.: Allgemeine Neurophysiologie. In: Handbuch der Inneren Medizin, pp. 1—181 Berlin: Springer 1953. [255]

— Neuropharmakologie: Zentrale Wirkungsmechanismen chemischer Substanzen und ihre neurophysiologischen Grundlagen. Klin. Wschr. **24**, 1153—1167 (1958). [69]

KAHLSON, G., and F. C. MacINTOSH: Acetylcholine synthesis in a sympathetic ganglion. J. Physiol. (Lond.) **96**, 277—292 (1939). [57]

KANDEL, E. R., and W. A. SPENCER: Electrophysiology of hippocampal neurons. II. After-potentials and repetitive firing. J. Neurophysiol. **24**, 243—259 (1961). [161, 211]

— — and F. J. BRINLEY: Electrophysiology of hippocampal neurons. 1. Sequential invasion and synaptic organization. J. Neurophysiol. **24**, 225—242 (1961). [105, 161, 174, 211]

KAO, C. Y.: Postsynaptic electrogenesis in septate giant axons. II. Comparison of medial and lateral giant axons of crayfish. J. Neurophysiol. **23**, 618—635 (1960). [138, 139, 140, 141]

—, and H. GRUNDFEST: Postsynaptic electrogenesis in septate giant axons. 1. Earthworm medium giant axon. J. Neurophysiol. **20**, 553—573 (1957). [138, 139]

KATZ, B.: Electric excitation of nerve, 151 pp. London: Oxford University Press 1939. [123]

— Action potentials from a sensory nerve ending. J. Physiol. (Lond.) **111**, 248—260 (1950). [112]

— Microphysiology of the neuro-muscular junction. A physiological 'quantum of action' at the myoneural junction. Bull. Johns Hopk. Hosp. **102**, 275—295 (1958a). [30, 32, 33, 76, 77, 130]

— Microphysiology of the neuro-muscular junction. The chemoreceptor function of the motor end-plate. Bull. Johns Hopk. Hosp. **102**, 296—321 (1958b). [53]

— The transmission of impulses from nerve to muscle, and the subcellular unit of synaptic action. Proc. roy. Soc. B **155**, 455—479 (1962). [30, 31, 33, 51, 77, 130, 228]

—, and R. MILEDI: The development of acetylcholine sensitivity in nerve-free muscle segments. J. Physiol. (Lond.) **156**, 24P—25P (1961). [244, 252]

— — A study of spontaneous miniature potentials in spinal motoneurones. J. Physiol. (Lond.) **168**, 389—422 (1963). [34, 35, 40, 75, 144, 160, 265]

—, and O. H. SCHMITT: Electric interaction between two adjacent nerve fibres. J. Physiol. (Lond.) **97**, 471—488 (1939). [8]

—, and S. THESLEFF: On the factors which determine the amplitude of the 'miniature end-plate potential'. J. Physiol. (Lond.) **137**, 267—278 (1957a). [32, 35, 240]

— — A study of the "desensitization" produced by acetylcholine at the motor end-plate J. Physiol. (Lond.) **138**, 63—80 (1957b). [62, 63, 64, 65, 99]

— — The interaction between Edrophonium (Tensilon) and acetylcholine at the motor end-plate. Brit. J. Pharmacol. **12**, 260—264 (1957c). [65]

KERKUT, G. A., and G. A. COTTRELL: Acetylcholine and 5-hydroxytryptamine in the snail brain. Comp. Biochem. Physiol. **8**, 53—63 (1963). [74, 200]

—, and R. C. THOMAS: Acetylcholine and the spontaneous inhibitory postsynaptic potentials in the snail neurone. Comp. Biochem. Physiol. **8**, 39—45 (1963a). [162, 185, 200]

— — Anion permeability of the inhibitory post-synaptic membrane of *Helix* neurones. J. Physiol. (Lond.) **168**, 23P—24P (1963b). [186]

—, and R. J. WALKER: The specific chemical sensitivity of *Helix* nerve cells. Comp. Biochem. Physiol. **7**, 277—288 (1962). [74, 162, 202]

KEYNES, R. D.: Active transport of chloride in the squid giant axon. J. Physiol. (Lond.) **163**, 19P (1962a). [178]

— The chloride in squid axoplasm. XXII. Int. Congr. Physiol. Science vol. 1, p. 563—564. 1962(b), [178]

KIDD, M.: Electron microscopy of the inner plexiform layer of the retina in the cat and pigeon. J. Anat. (Lond.) **96**, 179—187 (1962). [21]

KIRALY, J. K., and J. W. PHILLIS: Action of some drugs on the dorsal root potentials of the isolated toad spinal cord. Brit. J. Pharmacol. **17**, 224—231 (1961). [68, 145]

KLEE, M. R., u. H. D. LUX: Intracelluläre Untersuchungen über den Einfluß hemmender Potentiale im motorischen Cortex. II. Die Wirkungen elektrischer Reizung des Nucleus caudatus. Arch. Psychiat. Nervenkr. Neurologie **203**, 667—689 (1962). [162, 214]

KLOOT, W. G. VAN DER: Picrotoxin and the inhibitory system of crayfish muscle. In: Inhibition in the nervous system and γ-aminobutyric acid, pp. 409—412, Ed. E. ROBERTS, New York: Pergamon Press 1960. [195, 196, 197]

KOELLE, G. B.: The histochemical localization of cholinesterases in the central nervous system of the rat. J. comp. Neurol. **100**, 211—235 (1954). [70]

— A proposed dual neurohumoral role of acetylcholine: its functions at the pre- and post-synaptic sites. Nature (Lond.) **190**, 208—211 (1961). [122, 136, 137]

References

KOELLE, G. B.: A new general concept of the neurohumoral functionsof acetylcholine and acetylcholinesterase. J. Pharm. Pharmacol. **14**, 65—90 (1962). [122, 136, 137]
—, and J. S. FRIEDENWALD: A histochemical method for localizing cholinesterase activity. Proc. Soc. exp. Biol. (N. Y.) **70**, 617—622 (1949). [12]
—, and A. GILMAN: Anticholinesterase drugs. J. Pharmacol. exp. Ther. **95**, 166—216 (1949). [8]
KOELLE, W. A., and G. B. KOELLE: The localization of external or functional acetylcholinesterase at the synapses of autonomic ganglia. J. Pharmacol. exp. Ther. **126,**1—8 (1959). [55, 57, 122, 133, 137]
KÖLLIKER, A.: Zur feineren Anatomie des centralen Nervensystems. 1. Das Kleinhirn. Z. wiss. Zool. **49**, 663—689 (1890). [1]
KOIZUMI, K., J. USHIYAMA and C. McC. BROOKS: Effect of hypothermia on excitability of spinal neurons. J. Neurophysiol. **23**, 421—431 (1960). [115]
KOKETSU, K.: Intracellular slow potential of dorsal root fibers. Amer. J. Physiol. **184**, 338—344 (1956a). [68, 220, 230]
— Intracellular potential changes of primary afferent nerve fibres in spinal cords of cats. J. Neurophysiol. **19**, 375—392 (1956b). [220, 229]
—, and S. NISHI: Restoration of neuromuscular transmission in sodium-free hydrazinium solution. J. Physiol. (Lond.) **147**, 239—252 (1959). [52]
KOLMODIN, G. M., and C. R. SKOGLUND: Slow membrane potential changes accompanying excitation and inhibition in spinal moto- and interneurons in the cat during natural activation. Acta physiol. scand. **44**, 11—54 (1958). [35, 103, 117, 118, 119]
KONORSKI, J.: Conditioned reflexes and neuron organization, pp. 267. Cambridge: Cambridge University Press 1948. [255, 259]
— Mechanisms of learning. Symp. Soc. exp. Biol. **4**, 409—431 (1950). [255, 259]
— The physiological approach to the problem of recent memory. In: Brain mechanisms and learning, pp. 115—132, Ed. J. F. DELAFRESNAYE. Oxford: Blackwell Scientific Publ. 1961. [260]
KOSTYUK, P. G.: Electrophysiological characteristics of individual spinal cord neurons. Sechenov physiol. J. U.S.S.R **46**, 10—22 (1960). [105]
KOZAK, W., and R. A. WESTERMAN: Plastic changes of spinal monosynaptic responses from tenotomized muscles in cats. Nature (Lond.) **189**, 753—755 (1961). [256, 257]
KRAVITZ, E. A., S. W. KUFFLER and D. D. POTTER: Gamma-aminobutyric acid and other blocking compounds in Crustacea. III. Their relative concentrations in separated motor and inhibitory axons. J. Neurophysiol. **26**, 739—751 (1963). [197, 202]
— — — and N. M. VAN GELDER: Gamma-aminobutyric acid. and other blocking compounds in Crustacea. II. Peripheral nervous system. J. Neurophysiol. **26**, 729—738 (1963). [197]
KRNJEVIĆ, K., and R. MILEDI: Acetylcholine in mammalian neuromuscular transmission. Nature (Lond.) **182**, 805—806 (1958). [62, 63]
—, and J. F. MITCHELL: The release of acetylcholine in the isolated rat diaphragm. J. Physiol. (Lond.) **155**, 246—262 (1961). [33, 59, 63]
—, and J. W. PHILLIS: Sensitivity of cortical neurones to acetylcholine. Experientia (Basel) **17**, 469 (1961). [69, 71]
— — Excitation of Betz cells by acetylcholine. Experientia (Basel) **18**, 170—171 (1962). [69]
— — Iontophoretic studies of neurones in the mammalian cerebral cortex. J. Physiol. (Lond.) **165**, 274—304 (1963a). [69, 71]
— — Acetylcholine-sensitive cells in the cerebral cortex. J. Physiol. (Lond.) **166**, 296—327 (1963b). [69]
KUBOTA, K., and J. M. BROOKHART: Recurrent facilitation of frog motor neurons. Physiologist **5**, 170 (1962). [144, 265]
KÜHNE, W.: On the origin and causation of vital movement. Proc. roy. Soc. **44**, 427—448 (1888). [7]

KUFFLER, S. W.: Electric potential changes at an isolated nerve-muscle junction. J. Neurophysiol. **5**, 18—26 (1942a). [37, 106, 108]
— Further study on transmission in an isolated nerve-muscle fibre preparation. J. Neurophysiol. **5**, 309—322 (1942b). [37, 48, 106]
— Specific excitability of the endplate region in normal and denervated muscle. J. Neurophysiol. **6**, 99—110 (1943). [243]
— Physiology of neuro-muscular junctions: electrical aspects. Fed. Proc. **7**, 437—446 (1948). [38]
— Transmitter mechanism at the nerve-muscle junction. Arch. Sci. physiol. **3**, 585—601 (1949). [8, 9, 38]
— Transmission processes at nerve muscle junctions. In: Modern trends in physiology and biochemistry, pp. 277—290. New York: Academic Press 1952. [8]
— Synaptic inhibitory mechanisms, properties of dendrites and problems of excitation in isolated sensory nerve cells. Exp. Cell. Res., Suppl. **5**, 493—519 (1958). [201]
— Excitation and inhibition in single nerve cells. Harvey Lect., pp. 176—218. New York: Academic Press Inc. 1960. [117, 164, 165, 166, 195, 196, 201]
—, and C. EDWARDS: Mechanism of gamma-aminobutyric acid (GABA) action and its relation to synaptic inhibition. J. Neurophysiol. **21**, 589—610 (1958). [183, 184, 195]
—, and C. EYZAGUIRRE: Synaptic inhibition in an isolated nerve cell. J. gen. Physiol. **39**, 155—184 (1955). [162, 163, 164, 167, 172, 201]
—, and D. POTTER: Glia in the leech central nervous system. Physiological properties and neuron glia relationship. J. Neurophysiol. (In press) (1963). [22]
—, and E. M. V. WILLIAMS: Properties of the 'slow' skeletal muscle fibres of the frog. J. Physiol. (Lond.) **121**, 318—340 (1953). [29, 101, 108]
KUNO, M.: Effects of strychnine on the intracellular potentials of spinal motoneurones of the toad. Jap. J. Physiol. **7**, 42—50 (1957). [35, 160, 191]
— Excitability following antidromic activation in spinal motoneurones supplying red muscles. J. Physiol. (Lond.) **149**, 374—393 (1959). [178]
KUPFER, C., and G. B. KOELLE: A histochemical study of cholinesterase during formation of the motor end-plate of the albino rat. J. exp. Zool. **116**, 397—413 (1951). [240]
KUSANO, K., and S. HAGIWARA: On the integrative synaptic potentials of *Onchidium* nerve cell. Jap. J. Physiol. **11**, 96—101 (1961). [50, 77, 119]
LANDGREN, S., C. G. PHILLIPS and R. PORTER: Minimal synaptic actions of pyramidal impulses on some alpha motoneurones of the baboon's hand and forearm. J. Physiol. (Lond.) **161**, 91—111 (1962). [87, 208]
LANGLEY, J. N.: On the regeneration of preganglionic and of postganglionic visceral nerve fibres. J. Physiol. **22**, 215—230 (1897). [246]
—, and T. KATO: The physiological action of physostigmine and its action on denervated skeletal muscle. J. Physiol. (Lond.) **49**, 410—431 (1915). [127]
LAPORTE, Y., and D. P. C. LLOYD: Nature and significance of the reflex connections established by large afferent fibers of muscular origin. Amer. J. Physiol. **169**, 609—621 (1952). [6, 202]
—, and R. LORENTE DE NÓ: Potential changes evoked in a curarized sympathetic ganglion by presynaptic volleys of impulses. J. cell. comp. Physiol. **35**, Suppl. 2, 61—106 (1950). [83, 131, 134]
— A. LUNDBERG and O. OSCARSSON: Functional organization of the dorsal spino-cerebellar tract in the cat. II. Single fibre recording in the Fleschig's fasciculus on electrical stimulation of various peripheral nerves. Acta physiol. scand. **36**, 188—203 (1956). [119]
LARRABEE, M. G., and D. W. BRONK: Prolonged facilitation of synaptic excitation in sympathetic ganglia. J. Neurophysiol. **10**, 139—154 (1947). [83, 135]
LEKSELL, L.: The action potential and excitatory effects of the small ventral root fibres to skeletal muscle. Acta physiol. scand., Suppl. **31**, 1—84 (1945). [IV, 128]
LENHOSSÉK, M. v: Ursprung, Verlauf und Endigung der sensiblen Nervenfasern bei *Lumbricus*. Arch. mikr. Anat. **39**, 102—136 (1892). [1]

LENHOSSÉK, M. v.: Der feinere Bau des Nervensystems im Lichte neuester Forschungen. Berlin: Kornfeld 1893. [1]
— Das Ganglion ciliare der Vögel. Arch. mikr. Anat. **76**, 475—486 (1911). [25]
LEWIS, D. M.: The effects of denervation on the speeds of contraction of striated muscle. J. Physiol. (Lond.) **161**, 24 P (1962). [242]
LEWIS, P. R., and A. F. W. HUGHES: The cholinesterase of developing neurones in *Xenopus laevis* In: Metabolism of the nervous system, 511—514 pp. Ed. D. RICHTER. London: Pergamon Press 1957. [240]
LI, CHOH-LUH: Some properties of pyramidal neurones in motor cortex with particular reference to sensory stimulation. J. Neurophysiol. **22**, 385—394 (1959). [35]
— Cortical intracellular synaptic potentials. J. cell. comp. Physiol. **58**, 153—167 (1961). [18, 35, 46, 105]
—, and S. N. CHOU: Cortical intracellular synaptic potentials and direct cortical stimulation. J. cell. comp. Physiol. **60**, 1—16 (1962). [46, 161]
LIBET, B.: Slow synaptic responses in sympathetic ganglia. Fed. Proc. **21**, 345 (1962a). [131, 132, 133]
— Slow excitatory and inhibitory synaptic responses in sympathetic ganglia. Proc. XXII Int. Physiol. Congr. 1962(b), vol. II, p. 809. [131, 133]
LIDDELL, E. G. T.: The Discovery of Reflexes, 174 pp. Oxford: Clarendon Press 1960. [3]
—, and C. S. SHERRINGTON: Further observations on myotatic reflexes. Proc. roy. Soc. B **97**, 267—283 (1925). [231]
LILEY, A. W.: An investigation of spontaneous activity at the neuromuscular junction of the rat. J. Physiol. (Lond.) **132**, 650—666 (1956a). [29, 30, 95, 130]
— The quantal components of the mammalian end-plate potential. J. Physiol. (Lond.) **133**, 571—587 (1956b). [29, 75, 76, 87, 99, 100, 130]
— The effects of presynaptic polarization on the spontaneous activity at the mammalian neuromuscular junction. J. Physiol. (Lond.) **134**, 427—443 (1956c). [29, 30, 31, 33, 77, 79, 82, 228]
— Spontaneous release of transmitter substance in multiquantal units. J. Physiol. (Lond.) **136**, 595—605 (1957). [32]
—, and K. A. K. NORTH: An electrical investigation of effects of repetitive stimulation on mammalian neuromuscular junction. J. Neurophysiol. **16**, 509—527 (1953). [83, 87, 92]
LISSAK, K., E. ENDROCZI and E. VINCZE: Further observations concerning the inhibitory substance extracted from brain. In: Nervous inhibition, pp. 369—375, Ed. E. FLOREY. New York: Pergamon Press 1961. [192]
LLOYD, D. P. C.: A direct central inhibitory action of dromically conducted impulses. J. Neurophysiol. **4**, 184—190 (1941). [6, 202]
— Stimulation of peripheral nerve terminations by active muscle. J. Neurophysiol. **5**, 153—164 (1942).[IV, 128]
— Conduction and synaptic transmission of reflex response to stretch in spinal cats . J. Neurophysiol. **6**, 317—326 (1943). [4]
— Functional organization of the spinal cord. Physiol. Rev. **24**, 1—17 (1944). [39]
— Facilitation and inhibition of spinal motoneurons. J. Neurophysiol. **9**, 421—438 (1946a).[6, 102, 202]
— Integrative pattern of excitation and inhibition in two-neuron reflex arc. J. Neurophysiol. **9**, 439—444 (1946b). [202]
— Post-tetanic potentiation of response in monosynaptic reflex pathways of the spinal cord. J. gen. Physiol. **33**, 147—170 (1949). [99]
— Electrotonus in dorsal nerve roots. Cold Spr. Harb. Symp. quant. Biol. **17**, 203—219 (1952). [98, 230]
— Synaptic Mechanisms. In: Textbook of Physiology, Ed. by J. F. FULTON, 17th ed., pp. 69—90. Philadelphia and London: W. B. Saunders 1955. [39]
— Spinal mechanisms involved in somatic activities. In: Handbook of Physiology, Section 1. Neurophysiology, vol. II, chapt. XXXVI, pp. 929—949, Ed. J. FIELD. Washington: American Physiological Society 1960a.[39, 204]

LLOYD, D. P. C.: On the monosynaptic reflex interconnections of hind-limb muscles. In: Structure and function of the cerebral cortex, pp. 289—297, Ed. D. B. TOWER and J. P. SCHADÉ. Amsterdam: Elsevier Publ. Co. 1960b. [204]

— C. C. HUNT and A. K. McINTYRE: Transmission in fractionated monosynaptic spinal reflex systems. J. gen. Physiol. 38, 307—317 (1955). [103]

—, and A. K. McINTYRE, : Transmitter potentiality of homonymous and heteronymous monosynaptic reflex connections of individual motoneurones. J. gen. Physiol. 38, 789—799 (1955). [6, 103]

—, and V. J. WILSON: Functional organization in the terminal segments of the spinal cord with a consideration of central excitatory and inhibitory latencies in mono-synaptic reflex systems. J. gen. Physiol. 42, 1219—1231 (1959). [157, 204, 206]

LÖWENSTEIN, W. R.: The generation of electric activity in a nerve ending. Ann. N.Y. Acad. Sci. 81, 367—387 (1959). [106]

—, and R. RATHKAMP: The sites for mechano-electric conversion in a Pacinian corpuscle. J. gen. Physiol. 41, 1245—1265 (1958). [106]

LOEWI, O.: Über humorale Übertragbarkeit der Herznervenwirkung. Pflügers Arch. ges. Physiol. 189, 239—242 (1921). [8]

— Problems connected with the principle of humoral transmission of nervous impulses. Proc. roy. Soc. B 118, 299—316 (1933). [8]

— Aspects of the transmission of the nervous impulse. I. Mediation in the peripheral and central nervous system. J. Mt. Sinai Hospital 12, 803—816 (1945a). [8]

— Aspects of the transmission of the nervous impulse. II. Theoretical and clinical implications. J. Mt Sinai Hosp. 12, 851—865 (1945b). [8]

—, u. E. NAVRATIL: Über humorale Übertragbarkeit der Herznervenwirkung. X. Über das Schicksal des Vagusstoffes. Pflügers Arch. ges. Physiol. 214, 678—688 (1926). [8]

LONGO, V. G.: Spinal mechanisms involved in the convulsant action of 5, 7-diphenyl-1, 3-diazadamantan-6-ol (1757 S. I.). J. Pharmacol. exp. Ther. 132, 240—244 (1961). [191, 192, 231]

—, and S. CHIAVARELLI: Neuropharmacological analysis of strychnine-like drugs. In: Proceedings of the First Inter. Pharmacol. Meeting, vol. 8, p. 189—198, Ed. B. UVNÄS. New York: Pergamon Press 1962. [191]

— W. R. MARTIN and K. R. UNNA: A pharmacological study on the Renshaw cell. J. Pharmacol. exp. Ther. 129, 61—68 (1960). [67]

LORENTO DE N6, R.: Studies on the structure of the cerebral cortex. II. Continuation of the study of the ammonic system. J. Psychol. Neurol. (Lpz.) 46, 113—177 (1934). [17, 189, 210, 211, 212]

— The synaptic delay of motoneurons. Amer. J. Physiol. 111, 272—281 (1935). [4]

— Limits of variation of the synaptic delay of motoneurons. J. Neurophysiol. 1, 187—194 (1938a). [4]

— Synaptic stimulation of motoneurons as a local process. J. Neurophysiol. 1, 195—206 (1938b). [111]

— Transmission of impulses through cranial motor nuclei. J. Neurophysiol. 2, 402—464 (1939). [9]

— Action potential of the motoneurons of the hypoglossus nucleus. J. cell. comp. Physiol. 29, 207—288 (1947). [110, 123]

LUCAS, K.: The conduction of the nervous impulse. 102 pp. London: Longmans 1917. [5]

LUCO, J. V., and C. EYZAGUIRRE: Fibrillation and hypersensitivity to ACh in denervated muscle: effect of length of degenerating nerve fibers. J. Neurophysiol. 18, 65—73 (1955). [246]

LUNDBERG, A.: Adrenaline and transmission in the sympathetic ganglion of the cat. Acta. physiol. scand. 26, 252—263 (1952). [133]

—, and H. QUILISCH: Presynaptic potentiation and depression of neuro-muscular trans-mission in frog and rat. Acta physiol. scand. 30, Suppl. 111, 111—120 (1953a). [83, 87]

References

LUNDBERG, A., and H. QUILISCH: On the effect of calcium on presynaptic potentiation and depression at the neuromuscular junction. Acta physiol. scand. 30, Suppl. 111, 121—129 (1953b). [83, 87, 88]

LUSE, S. A.: Electron microscopic observations of the central nervous system. In: Inhibition in the nervous system and γ-aminobutyric acid, pp. 29—33, Ed. E. ROBERTS. New York: Pergamon Press 1960. [23]

LUX, H. D., u. M. R. KLEE: Intracelluläre Untersuchungen über den Einfluß hemmender Potentiale im motorischen Cortex. 1. Die Wirkung elektrischer Reizung unspezifischer Thalamuskerne. Arch. Psychiat. Nervenkr. 203, 648—666 (1962). [161, 162, 214]

MACHNE, X., E. FADIGA and J. M. BROOKHART: Antidromic and synaptic activation of frog motor neurons. J. Neurophysiol. 22, 483—503 (1959). [103, 104, 107]

MACINTOSH, F. C.: The distribution of acetylcholine in the peripheral and the central nervous system. J. Physiol. (Lond.) 99, 436—442 (1941). [9, 68, 70]

— Formation, storage and release of acetylcholine at nerve endings. Canad. J. Biochem. 37, 343—356 (1959). [33]

— Effect of HC-3 on acetylcholine turnover. Fed. Proc. 20, 562—568 (1961). [55, 60]

— R. I. BIRKS and P. B. SASTRY: Pharmacological inhibition of acetycholine synthesis. Nature (Lond.) 178, 1181 (1956). [55]

—, and P. E. OBORIN: Release of acetylcholine from intact cerebral cortex. Abst. XIX Int. Physiol. Congr. p. 580—581. 1953, [70]

MARRAZZI, A. S.: Adrenergic inhibition at sympathetic synapses. Amer. J. Physiol. 127, 738—744 (1939). [133]

—, and R. LORENTE DE NÓ: Interaction of neighbouring fibres in myelinated nerve. J. Neurophysiol. 7, 83—100 (1944). [8]

MARTIN, A. R.: A further study of the statistical composition of the end-plate potential. J. Physiol. (Lond.) 130, 114—122 (1955). [76]

—, and R. K. ORKAND: Postsynaptic effects of HC-3 at the neuromuscular junction of the frog. Canad. J. Biochem. 39, 343—349 (1961). [60]

—, and G. PILAR: Dual mode of synaptic transmission in the avian ciliary ganglion. J. Physiol. (Lond.) 168, 443—463 (1963a). [25, 28, 145, 146, 147]

— — Transmission through the ciliary ganglion of the chick. J. Physiol. (Lond.) 168, 464—475 (1963b). [25, 42, 44, 126, 145, 146]

MASLAND, R. L., and R. S. WIGTON: Nerve activity accompanying fasciculation produced by prostigmin. J. Neurophysiol. 3, 269—275 (1940). [127, 129, 130]

MATHEWSON, R., A. WACHTEL and H. GRUNDFEST: Fine structure of electoplaques. From "Bioelectrogenesis". Ed. C. CHAGAS and A. PAES DE CARVALHO, pp. 25—53. Amsterdam: Elsevier Publ. Co. 1961. [25]

MATURANA, H. R., J. Y. LETTVIN, W. S. McCULLOCH and W. H. PITTS: Evidence that cut optic nerve fibres in a frog regenerate to their proper places in the tectum. Science 130, 1709—1710 (1959). [247]

— — — — Anatomy and physiology of vision in the frog (Rana pipiens). J. gen. Physiol. 43, Suppl. 2, 129—175 (1960). [247]

MAYNARD, D. M.: Activity in a crustacean ganglion. II. Pattern and interaction in burst formation. Biol. Bull. 109, 420—436 (1955). [201]

McGEER, E. G., P. L. McGEER and H. McLENNAN: The inhibitory action of 3-hydroxy-tyramine, gamma-aminobutyric acid (Gaba) and some other compounds towards the crayfish stretch receptor neuron. J. Neurochem. 8, 36—49 (1961). [196]

McINTYRE, A. K.: Synaptic function and learning. Abst. 19th Int. Physiol. Congr. p. 107—114. 1953. [255]

— K. BRADLEY and L. G. BROCK: Responses of motoneurons undergoing chromatolysis. J. gen. Physiol. 42, 931—958 (1959). [111]

—, and R. F. MARK: Synaptic linkage between afferent fibres of the cat's hind limb and ascending fibres in the dorsolateral funiculus. J. Physiol. (Lond.) 153, 306—330 (1960). [119, 121]

McIntyre, A. K., R. F. Mark and J. Steiner: Multiple firing at central synapses. Nature (Lond.) **178**, 302—304 (1956). [45, 119]

—, and R. G. Robinson: Stability of spinal reflex synaptic pattern. Proc. Univ. Otago Med. School **36**, 25—26 (1958). [248]

McIsaac, R. J., and G. B. Koelle: Comparison of the effects of inhibition of external, internal and total acetylcholinesterase upon ganglionic transmission. J. Pharmacol. exp. Ther. **126**, 9—20 (1959). [57, 122]

McLardy, T.: Thalamic projection to frontal cortex in man. J. Neurol. Neurosurg Psychiat. **13**, 198—202 (1950). [215]

McLennan, H.: A comparison of some physiological properties of an inhibitory factor from brain (Factor I) and of γ-aminobutyric acid and related compounds. J. Physiol. (Lond.) **139**, 79—86 (1957). [196]

— The identification of one active component from brain extracts containing Factor I. J. Physiol. (Lond.) **146**, 358—368 (1959). [192]

— The fractionation and purification of Factor I. J. Physiol. (Lond.) **151**, 31—39 (1960). [192]

— Inhibitory transmitters — A review. In: Nervous inhibition, pp. 350—368, Ed. E. Florey, New York: Pergamon Press 1961. [192, 195]

— Inhibitory factors in the brain. In: Proceedings of the First Inter. Pharmacol. Meeting, vol. 8, p. 7—24. New York: Pergamon Press 1962. [192]

— Synaptic transmission, 134 pp. Philadelphia: W. B. Saunders Co. 1963. [IV, 54, 68, 192, 194, 195]

Miledi, R.: The acetylcholine sensitivity of frog muscle fibres after complete or partial denervation. J. Physiol. (Lond.) **151**, 1—23 (1960a). [62, 108, 243, 244]

— Junctional and extra-junctional acetylcholine receptors in skeletal muscle fibres. J. Physiol. (Lond.) **151**, 24—30 (1960b). [62, 64, 110, 244]

— Properties of regenerating neuromuscular synapses in the frog. J. Physiol. (Lond.) **154**, 190—205 (1960c). [244]

— Induced innervation of end-plate free muscle segments. Nature (Lond.) **193**, 281—282 (1962). [244]

—, and O. A. Trowell: Acetylcholine sensitivity of rat diaphragm maintained in organ culture. Nature (Lond.) **194**, 981—982 (1962). [244]

Minz, B.: The role of humoral agents in nervous activity. 230 pp. Springfield (Ill.): Ch. C. Thomas 1955. [8, 194]

Mitchell, J. F.: The spontaneous and evoked release of acetylcholine from the cerebral cortex. J. Physiol. (Lond.) **165**, 98—116 (1963). [70]

—, and J. W. Phillis: Cholinergic transmission in the frog spinal cord. Brit. J. Pharmacol. **19**, 534—543 (1962). [68, 145]

—, and A. Silver: The spontaneous release of acetylcholine from the denervated hemidiaphragm of the rat. J. Physiol. (Lond.) **165**, 117—129 (1963). [33, 59]

Monnier, A. M., et Z. M. Bacq: Recherches sur la physiologie et la pharmacologie du système nerveux autonome. XVI. Dualité du mécanisme de la transmission neuromusculaire de l'excitation chez le muscle lisse. Arch. int. Physiol. **40**, 485—510 (1935). [8]

Morrell, F.: Lasting changes in synaptic organization produced by continuous neuronal bombardment. In: Brain mechanisms and learning, pp. 375—392, Ed. J. F. Delafresnaye. Oxford: Blackwell Scientific Publ. 1961. [259]

Murray, J. G., and J. W. Thompson: The occurrence and function of collateral sprouting in the sympathetic nervous system of the cat. J. Physiol. **135**, 133—162 (1957). [137]

Nastuk, W. L.: The electrical activity of the muscle cell membrane at the neuro-muscular junction. J. cell. comp. Physiol. **42**, 249—272 (1953). [37, 62]

— Some ionic factors that influence the action of acetylcholine at the muscle end-plate membrane. Ann. N.Y. Acad. Sci. **81**, 317—327 (1959). [52, 62]

References

NASTUK, W. L., and J. T. ALEXANDER: The action of 3-hydroxy phenyldimethyl-ethyl-ammonium (Tensilon) on neuromuscular transmission in the frog. J. Pharmacol. exp. Ther. **111**, 302—328 (1954). [65]

NISHI, S., and K. KOKETSU: Electrical properties and activities of single sympathetic neurons in frogs. J. cell. comp. Physiol. **55**, 15—30 (1960). [35, 41, 42, 43, 49, 50, 73, 103, 105, 106, 107]

NONIDEZ, J. F.: The present status of the neurone theory. Biol. Rev. **19**, 30—40 (1944). [2]

OCHS, S., D. DALRYMPLE and G. RICHARDS: Axoplasmic flow in ventral root nerve fibers of the cat. Exp. Neurol. **5**, 349—363 (1962). [246]

OGATA, M., and E. B. WRIGHT: Intracellular recording of neuromuscular junction action potential in single isolated nerve-muscle fiber. J. Neurophysiol. **23**, 646—658 (1960). [106]

OOMURA, Y., and T. TOMITA: Some observations concerning the end-plate potential. Tohoku J. exp. Med. **73**, 398—415 (1961). [48]

OSCARSSON, O.: Functional organization of the ventral spino-cerebellar tract in the cat. II. Connections with muscle, joint, and skin nerve afferents and effects on adequate stimulation of various receptors. Acta physiol. scand. **42**, Suppl. 146, 1—107 (1957). [119]

OTANI, T.: Excitation and accommodation in toad's spinal motoneuron. From "Electrical activity of single cells". Igakushoin (Tokyo), pp. 133—143 (1960). [116]

—, and T. H. BULLOCK: Effects of presetting the membrane potential of the soma of spontaneous and integrating ganglion cells. Physiol. Zoöl. **32**, 104—114 (1959). [164, 201]

OTSUKA, M., M. ENDO and Y. NONOMURA: Presynaptic nature of neuro-muscular depression. Jap. J. Physiol. **12**, 573—584 (1962). [88, 89, 99]

PALADE, G. E., and S. L. PALAY: Electron microscope observations of interneuronal and neuromuscular synapses. Anat. Rec. **118**, 335 (1954). [3, 12, 15]

PALAY, S. L.: Synapses in the central nervous system. J. biophys. biochem. Cytol. **2**, 193—202 (1956). [3, 15, 16]

— The morphology of synapses in the central nervous system. Exp. Cell Res., Suppl. **5**, 275—293 (1958). [13, 14, 15, 16, 22, 92, 109]

— S. M. McGEE-RUSSELL, S. GORDON and M. A. GRILLO: Fixation of neural tissues for electron microscopy by perfusion with solutions of osmium tetroxide. J. cell. Biol. **12**, 385—410 (1962). [15, 17, 21]

—, and G. E. PALADE: The fine structure of neurons. J. biophys. biochem. Cytol. **1**, 69—88 (1955). [15]

PATON, W. D. M.: Central and synaptic transmission in the nervous system (Pharmacological aspects). Ann. Rev. Physiol. **20**, 431—470 (1958). [54, 68, 70]

PERRY, W. L. M.: Acetylcholine release in the cat's superior cervical ganglion. J. Physiol. (Lond.) **119**, 439—454 (1953). [55, 57, 92]

— Central and synaptic transmission (Pharmacological aspects). Ann. Rev. Physiol. **18**, 279—308 (1956). [68]

PHILLIPS, C. G.: Intracellular records from Betz cells in the cat. Quart. J. exp. Physiol. **41**, 58—69 (1956). [162]

— Actions of antidromic pyramidal volleys on single Betz cells in the cat. Quart. J. exp. Physiol. **44**, 1—25 (1959). [103, 111, 112, 162, 214]

— Some properties of pyramidal neurones of the motor cortex. In: Ciba Symp. "The nature of sleep", pp. 4—24, Ed. G. E. W. WOLSTENHOLME and M. O'CONNOR. London: J. & A. Churchill 1961. [46, 103, 105, 111, 112, 161, 162, 214]

POWELL, T. P. S.: Residual neurons in the human thalamus following hemidecortication. Brain **75**, 571—584 (1952). [215]

PRESTON, J. B., and D. G. WHITLOCK: Precentral facilitation and inhibition of spinal motoneurones. J. Neurophysiol. **23**, 154—170 (1960). [208]

— — Intracellular potentials recorded from motoneurons following precentral gyrus stimulation in primate. J. Neurophysiol. **24**, 91—100 (1961). [208]

PROSSER, C. L.: Acetylcholine and nervous inhibition in the heart of *Venus mercenaria*. Biol. Bull. **78**, 92—102 (1940). [200]

PURPURA, D. P., and B. COHEN: Intracellular recording from thalamic neurons during recruiting responses. J. Neurophysiol. **25**, 621—635 (1962). [161]

—, and H. GRUNDFEST: Nature of dendritic potentials and synaptic mechanisms in cerebral cortex of cat. J. Neurophysiol. **19**, 573—595 (1956). [110]

RALL, W.: Branching dendritic trees and motoneuron membrane resistivity. Exp. Neurol. **1**, 491—527 (1959). [44]

— Membrane potential transients and membrane time constant of motoneurons. Exp. Neurol. **2**, 503—532 (1960). [44]

RAMÓN y CAJAL, S.: Estructura de los centros nerviosos de las aves. Rev. trim. de Histologia normal y patológica. p. 1 (1888). [1]

— Sur les fibres nerveuses de la couche granuleuse du cervelet et sur l'évolution des élements cérébelleux. Int. Mschr. Anat. Physiol. **7**, 12—31 (1890a). [1, 2]

— Sur l'origine et les ramifications des fibres nerveuses de la moelle embryonnaire. Anat. Anz. **5**, 85—95 (1890b). [1]

— Repónse à Mr. GOLGI à propos des fibrilles collatérales de la moëlle épinière, et de la structure générale de la substance grise. Anat. Anz. **5**, 579—587 (1890c). [1]

— Les nouvelles idées sur la structure du système nerveux chez l'homme et chez les vertébrés. Paris: Reinwald 1895. [3]

— Un sencillo método de coloración selectiva del retículo protoplasmico y sus efectos en los diversos organos nerviosos. Trab. Lab. Invest. biol. Univ. Madr. **2**, 129—221 (1903). [2]

— Histologie du système nerveux de l'homme et des vertébrés, vol. 1, 986 pp. Paris: Maloine 1909 [2, 3]

— Histologie du système nerveux de l'homme et des vertébrés, vol. 2, 993 pp. Paris: Maloine 1911. [17, 18, 189, 210, 211, 213, 214, 255]

— Les preuves objectives de l'unité anatomique des cellules nerveuses. Trab. Lab. Invest. biol. Univ. Madr. **29**, 1—137 (1934). [2]

RASHEVSKY, N.: Mathematical biophysics. 669 pp. Chicago: Chicago University Press 1938. [255]

RASMUSSEN, G. L.: Further observations on the efferent cochlear bundle. J. comp. Neurol. **99**, 61—74 (1953). [191]

REGER, J. F.: The fine structure of neuromuscular synapses of gastrocnemii from mouse and frog. Anat. Rec. **130**, 7—24 (1958). [12]

REITZEL, N. L., and J. P. LONG: The neuromuscular blocking properties of α,α', dimethylethanolamino 4,4' biacetophenone (Hemicholinium). Arch. int. Pharmacodyn. **119**, 20—30 (1959). [60]

RENSHAW, B.: Activity in the simplest spinal reflex pathways. J. Neurophysiol. **3**, 373—387 (1940). [4]

— Influence of discharge of motoneurons upon excitation of neighbouring motoneurons. J. Neurophysiol. **4**, 167—183 (1941). [6, 160, 209]

— Reflex discharge in branches of the crural nerve. J. Neurophysiol. **5**, 487—498 (1942). [6, 202]

— Central effects of centripetal impulses in axons of spinal ventral roots. J. Neurophysiol. **9**, 191—204 (1946a). [45, 121, 160]

— Observations on interaction of nerve impulses in the gray matter and on the nature of central inhibition. Amer. J. Physiol. **146**, 443—448 (1946b). [6, 220]

— A. FORBES and B. R. MORISON: Activity of isocortex and hippocampus: electrical studies with micro-electrodes. J. Neurophysiol. **3**, 74—105 (1940). [123]

RETZLAFF, E.: Neurohistological basis for the functioning of paired half-centers. J. comp. Neurol. **101**, 407—446 (1954). [216]

RICHARDSON, K. C.: Electronmicroscopic observations on Auerbach's plexus in the rabbit, with special reference to the problem of smooth muscle innervation. Amer. J. Anat. **103**, 99—136 (1958). [61]

References

RIKER, W. F.: Excitatory and anti-curare properties of acetylcholine and related quaternary ammonium compounds at the neuromuscular junction. Pharmacol. Rev. **5**, 1—86 (1953). [8]

— G. WERNER, J. ROBERTS and A. KUPERMAN: The presynaptic element in neuromuscular transmission. Ann. N.Y. Acad. Sci. **81**, 328—344 (1959a). [129, 130]

— — — — Pharmacological evidence for the existence of a presynaptic event in neuromuscular transmission. J. Pharmacol. exp. Ther. **125**, 150—158 (1959b). [129, 130]

ROBBINS, J.: The excitation and inhibition of crustacean muscle by amino acids. J. Physiol. (Lond.) **148**, 39—50 (1959).[196]

—, and W. G. VAN DER KLOOT: The effect of picrotoxin on peripheral inhibition in the crayfish. J. Physiol. (Lond.) **143**, 541—552 (1958). [196, 197]

ROBERTSON, J. D.: Recent electron microscope observations on the ultrastructure of the crayfish median-to-motor giant synapse. Exp. Cell Res. **8**, 226—229 (1955). [149]

— The ultrastructure of a reptilian myoneural junction. J. biophys. biochem. Cytol. **2**, 381—394 (1956). [3, 12, 32]

— Electron microscopy of the motor end-plate and the neuromuscular spindle. Amer. J. phys. Med. **39**, 1—43 (1960). [12]

— Ultrastructure of excitable membranes and the crayfish median-giant synapse. Ann. N.Y. Acad. Sci. **94**, 339—389 (1961). [149]

ROMANES, G. J.: The motor cell columns of the lumbo-sacral spinal cord of the cat. J. comp. Neurol. **94**, 313—363 (1951). [249]

ROSENBLUETH, A.: The transmission of nerve impulses at neuroeffector junctions and peripheral synapses. 325 pp. New York: John Wiley and Sons 1950. [8, 194]

—, and J. V. LUCO: A study of denervated mammalian skeletal muscle. Amer. J. Physiol. **120**, 781—797 (1937). [242, 245]

ROSZKOWSKI, A. P.: An unusual type of sympathetic ganglionic stimulant. J. Pharmacol. exp. Ther. **132**, 156—170 (1961). [136]

ROZSOS, I.: The synapses of Burdach's nucleus. Acta morph. Acad. Sci. Hung. **8**, 105—109 (1958). [229]

RUSHTON, W. A. H.: Action potentials from the isolated nerve cord of the earthworm. Proc. roy. Soc. B **132**, 423—437 (1945). [138, 141]

SALMOIRAGHI, G. C., and F. A. STEINER: Acetylcholine-sensitivity of cat's medullary neurons. J. Neurophysiol. **26**, 581—598 (1963). [69]

SANDERS, F. K., and J. Z. YOUNG: The influence of peripheral connexion on the diameter of regenerating nerve fibres. J. exp. Biol. **22**, 203—212 (1946). [254]

SASAKI, K., and T. OTANI: Accommodation in spinal motoneurons of the cat. Jap. J. Physiol. **11**, 443—456 (1961). [114, 115, 116]

SCHADEWALD, M.: Effects of cutting the trochlear and abducens nerves on the end-bulbs about the cells of the corresponding nuclei. J. comp. Neurol. **74**, 239—246 (1941). [3]

— Transynaptic effect of neonatal axon section on bouton appearance about somatic motor cells. J. comp. Neurol. **77**, 739—746 (1942). [3]

SCHÄFER, E. A.: The nerve cell. In: Text-book of physiology, vol. 2, p. 592—615, Ed. E. A. SCHÄFER. London: Caxton 1900. [3]

SCHAEFER, H., u. P. HAASS: Über einen lokalen Erregungsstrom an der motorischen Endplatte. Pflügers Arch. ges. Physiol. **242**, 364—381 (1939). [37]

SCHEIBEL, M. E., and A. B. SCHEIBEL: The inferior olive. A Golgi study. J. comp. Neurol. **102**, 77—132 (1955). [22]

SCHIMERT, J.: Das Verhalten der Hinterwurzelkollateralen im Rückenmark. Z. Anat. Entwickl.-Gesch. **109**, 665—687 (1939). [2]

SCHMIDT, R. F.: Pharmacological studies on the primary afferent depolarization of the toad spinal cord. Pflügers Arch. ges. Physiol. **277**, 325—346 (1963). [213, 233]

—, and W. D. WILLIS: Intracellular recording from motoneurons of the cervical spinal cord of the cat. J. Neurophysiol. **26**, 28—43 (1963a). [233]

— — Depolarization of central terminals of afferent fibers in the cervical spinal cord of the cat. J. Neurophysiol. **26**, 44—60 (1963b). [233]

SEARS, T. A.: The properties and distribution of the synapses made by monosynaptic afferents in the intercostal nerves. (In course of publication) (1963). [86, 87]

SHEPS, J. G.: The nuclear configuration and cortical connections of the human thalamus. J. comp. Neurol. 83, 1—56 (1945). [215]

SHERRINGTON, C. S.: The central nervous system vol. 3. In: A Text-Book of Physiology, 7th ed., Ed. M. FOSTER. London: Macmillan 1897. [3]

— The spinal cord. In: Text book of physiology, vol. 2, p. 782—883, Ed. E. A. SCHÄFER. London: Caxton 1900. [3]

— Integrative action of the nervous system, 411 pp. New Haven and London: Yale University Press (1906). [3,4]

— Reciprocal innervation of antagonistic muscles. Thirteenth note. On the antagonism between reflex inhibition and reflex excitation. Proc. roy. Soc. B 80, 565—578 (1908). [4]

— Remarks on some aspects of reflex inhibition. Proc. roy. Soc. B 97, 519—545 (1925). [4, 5, 8]

— Inhibition as a co-ordinative factor. Nobel Lecture 1932. Stockholm: P. A. Norstedt 1932. [5]

SHIMBEL, A.: Contributions to the mathematical biophysics of the central nervous system with special reference to learning. Bull. Math. Biophys. 12, 241—275 (1950). [259]

SINGER, M.: The influence of the nerve in regeneration of the amphibian extremity. Quart. Rev. Biol. 27, 169—200 (1952). [241]

SPEHLMANN, R.: Acetylcholine and prostigmine electrophoresis at visual cortex neurons. J. Neurophysiol. 26, 127—139 (1963). [69]

—, u. H. KAPP: Die Wirkung lokaler Mikroelektrophorese von Acetylcholin auf einzelne Neurone des visuellen Cortex. Pflügers Arch. ges. Physiol. 274, 37—38 (1961). [69]

SPENCER, W. A., and E. R. KANDEL: Electrophysiology of hippocampal neurons. III. Firing level and time constant. J. Neurophysiol. 24, 260—271 (1961a). [103]

— — Electrophysiology of hippocampal neurones. IV. Fast prepotentials. J. Neurophysiol. 24, 272—285 (1961b). [112]

— — Hippocampal neuron responses to selective activation of recurrent collaterals of hippocampofugal axons. Exp. Neurol. 4, 149—161 (1961c). [161]

— — Hippocampal neuron responses in relation to normal and abnormal function. In: Physiologie de L'Hippocampe. Coll. int. centre national recherche sci. (Paris) 107, 71—103 (1962). [214]

SPERRY, R. W.: The functional results of muscle transposition in the hind-limb of the rat. J. comp. Neurol. 73, 379—404 (1940). [248]

— Transplantation of motor nerves and muscles in the forelimb of the rat. J. comp. Neurol. 76, 283—321 (1942). [248]

— The problem of central nervous reorganization after nerve regeneration and muscle transposition. Quart. Rev. Biol. 20, 311—369 (1945). [248]

— Effect of crossing nerves to antagonistic limb muscles in the monkey. Arch. Neurol. Psychiat. (Chic.) 58, 452—473 (1947). [248]

— Myotypic specificity in teleost motoneurones. J. comp. Neurol. 93, 277—287 (1950). [248]

— Mechanisms of neural maturation. In: Handbook of Experimental Psychology, Ed. S. S. STEVENS. New York: John Wiley and Sons 1951a. [247, 250, 252]

— Regulative factors in the orderly growth of neural circuits. Growth, Symposium, 10, 63—87 (1951b). [247, 248, 250, 252]

— Physiological plasticity and brain circuit theory. In: Biological and biochemical bases of behaviour, pp. 401—424, Ed. H. F. HARLOW and C. N. WOOLSEY. Madison: University Wisconsin Press 1958. [250, 252]

—, and N. DEUPREÉ: Functional recovery following alterations in nerve-muscle connections of fishes. J. comp. Neurol. 106, 143—161 (1956). [248]

SPYROPOULOS, C. S., and I. TASAKI: Nerve excitation and synaptic transmission. Ann. Rev. Physiol. 22, 407—432 (1960). [109]

STOUGH, H. B.: Giant nerve fibers of the earthworms. J. comp. Neurol. **40**, 409—463 (1926). [140, 141]

STRAUGHAN, D. W.: Release of acetylcholine from mammalian motor nerve endings. Brit. J. Pharmacol. **15**, 417—424 (1960). [33, 59]

STRAUS, W. L., and G. WEDDELL: Nature of first visible contractions of forelimb musculature in rat foetuses. J. Neurophysiol. **3**, 358—369 (1940). [239]

STRUMWASSER, F.: Post-synaptic inhibition and excitation produced by different branches of a single neuron and the common transmitter involved. XXII. Internat. Congr. Physiol. Sci. vol. 2, No 801, 1962. [199, 201]

SVAETICHIN, G.: Electrophysiological investigations on single ganglion cells. Acta physiol. scand. **24**, Suppl. 86, 1—57 (1951). [110]

— Component analysis of action potentials from single neurons. Exp. Cell Res., Suppl. **5**, 234—261 (1958). [110]

SZÉKELY, G.: Regulationstendenzen in der Ausbildung der „Funktionellen Spezifität" der Retinaanlage bei *Triturus vulgaris*. Wilhelm Roux' Arch. Entwickl.-Mech. Org. **150**, 48—60 (1957). [247]

—, and J. SZENTAGOTHAI: Reflex behaviour patterns elicited from implanted supernumerary limbs in the chick. J. Embryol. exp. Morph. **10**, 140—151 (1962). [253]

SZENTÁGOTHAI, J.: The anatomical basis of synaptic transmission of excitation and inhibition in motoneurones. Acta morph. Acad. Sci. hung. **8**, 287—309 (1958). [19]

— Anatomical aspects of inhibitory pathways and synapses. From: Nervous inhibition, Ed. E. FLOREY. London: Pergamon Press 1961. [19]

— Anatomical aspects of junctional transformation. In: Information processing in the nervous system, Ed. R. W. GERARD. Amsterdam: Excerpta Medica 1963a. [21]

— The structure of the synapse in the lateral geniculate body. Acta Anat. (Basel) (In press) (1963b). [233]

— The structure of the autonomic interneuronal synapse. Acta neuroveg. (Wien) (In press) (1963c). [23, 147]

—, and K. RAJKOVITS: Die Rückwirkung der spezifischen Funktion auf die Struktur der Nervenelemente. Acta morph. Acad. Sci. hung. **5**, 253—274 (1955). [92, 255]

—, and G. SZEKELY: Elementary nervous mechanisms underlying optokinetic responses, analyzed by contralateral eye grafts in Urodele larvae. Acta physiol. Acad. Sci. hung. **10**, 43—55 (1956). [247]

TAKESHIGE, C., and R. L. VOLLE: Bimodal response of sympathetic ganglia to acetylcholine following eserine or repetitive preganglionic stimulation. J. Pharmacol. exp. Ther. **138**, 66—73 (1962). [133, 134, 135, 136]

TAKEUCHI, A.: The long-lasting depression in neuromuscular transmission of frog. Jap. J. Physiol. **8**, 102—113 (1958). [83, 92]

— Neuromuscular transmission of fish skeletal muscles investigated with intracellular microelectrode. J. cell. comp. Physiol. **54**, 211—221 (1959). [34]

—, and N. TAKEUCHI: Active phase of frog's end-plate potential. J. Neurophysiol. **22**, 395—411 (1959). [47, 48, 50, 73, 83]

— — On the permeability of the end-plate membrane during the action of transmitter. J. Physiol. (Lond.) **154**, 52—67 (1960a). [29, 30, 53, 76]

— — Further analysis of relationship between end-plate potential and end-plate current. J. Neurophysiol. **23**, 397—402 (1960b). [47, 50, 51, 52, 53, 72]

— — Changes in potassium concentration around motor nerve terminals, produced by current flow, and their effects on neuromuscular transmission. J. Physiol. (Lond.) **155**, 46—58 (1961). [30, 31, 95]

— — Electrical changes in pre- and postsynaptic axons of the giant synapse of Loligo. J. gen. Physiol. **45**, 1181—1193 (1962). [36, 39, 78, 79, 83, 99, 124, 125]

— — Glutamate-induced depolarization in crustacean muscle. Nature (Lond.) **198**, 490—491 (1963). [63]

TAKEUCHI, N.: Some properties of conductance changes at the end-plate membrane during the action of acetylcholine. J. Physiol. (Lond.) **167**, 128—140 (1963). [52]

TANZI, E.: I fatti e la induzione nell' odierne istologia del sistema nervoso. Riv. sper. Freniat. **19**, 149 (1893). [255]

TAUC, L.: Étude de l'activité élémentaire des cellules du ganglion abdominal de L'Aplysie. J. Physiol. (Paris) **47**, 769—792 (1955). [37]

— Processus post-synaptique d'excitation et d'inhibition dans le soma neuronique de L'Aplysie et de L'Escargot. Arch. ital. Biol. **96**, 78—110 (1958). [36, 42, 43, 162, 186]

— Interaction non synaptique entre deux neurons adjacents du ganglion abdominal de l'Aplysie. C.R. Acad. Sci. (Paris) **248**, 1857—1859 (1959). [145]

— The site of origin of the efferent action potentials in the giant nerve cell of *Aplysia*. J. Physiol. (Lond.) **152**, 36P—37P (1960a). [106]

— Evidence of synaptic inhibitory actions not conveyed by inhibitory post-synaptic potentials. In: Inhibition in the nervous system and gamma-aminobutyric acid, pp. 85—89, Ed. E. ROBERTS. New York: Pergamon Press (1960b). [238]

— Site of origin and propagation of spike in the giant neuron of *Aplysia*. J. gen. Physiol. **45**, 1077—1097 (1962a). [43, 106, 110, 198, 199]

— Identification of active membrane areas in the giant neuron of *Aplysia*. J. gen. Physiol. **45**, 1099—1115 (1962b). [43, 106, 110, 198]

—, and J. BRUNER: "Desensitization" of cholinergic receptors by acetylcholine in molluscan central neurones. Nature (Lond.) **198**, 33—34 (1963). [65]

—, and H. M. GERSCHENFELD: Cholinergic transmission mechanisms for both excitation and inhibition in molluscan central synapses. Nature (Lond.) **192**, 366—367 (1961). [198, 199, 201]

— — A cholinergic mechanism of inhibitory synaptic transmission in a molluscan nervous system. J. Neurophysiol. **25**, 236—262 (1962). [74, 198, 199, 200]

TAXI, J.: Étude de l'ultrastructure des zones synaptiques dans les ganglions sympathiques de la Grenouille. C.R. Acad. Sci. (Paris) **252**, 174—176 (1961). [23]

— Étude au microscope électronique de synapses ganglionnaires chez quelques Vertébrés. From Proceedings IV. Inter. Congr. Neuropath., vol. II, p. 197—203, Ed. H. JACOB. Stuttgart: Georg Thieme 1962. [23, 25, 26]

TERZUOLO, C. A., and T. ARAKI: An analysis of intra- versus extracellular potential changes associated with activity of single spinal motoneurons. Ann. N.Y. Acad. Sci. **94**, 547—558 (1961). [104, 105, 109]

—, and T. H. BULLOCK: Acceleration and inhibition in crustacean ganglion cells. Arch. ital. Biol. **96**, 117—134 (1958). [164, 201]

THESLEFF, S.: The mode of neuromuscular block caused by acetylcholine, nicotine, decamethonium and succinylcholine. Acta physiol. scand. **34**, 218—231 (1955). [64, 65, 99]

— A study of the interaction between neuromuscular blocking agents and acetylcholine at the mammalian motor end plate. Acta anaesth. scand. **2**, 69—79 (1958). [62, 65, 191]

— Motor end-plate 'desensitization' by repetitive nerve stimuli. J. Physiol. (Lond.) **148**, 659—664 (1959). [87]

— Supersensitivity of skeletal muscle produced by botulinum toxin. J. Physiol. (Lond.) **151**, 598—607 (1960a). [30, 62, 191, 242, 243]

— Effects of motor innervation on the chemical sensitivity of skeletal muscle. Physiol. Rev. **40**, 734—752 (1960b). [244]

THIES, R. E., and V. B. BROOKS: Postsynaptic neuromuscular block produced by hemicholinium, No 3. Fed. Proc. **20**, 569—578 (1961). [60]

THORPE, W. H.: Learning and instinct in animals, pp. 493 London: Methuen 1956. [255]

TÖNNIES, J. F.: Die Erregungssteuerung im Zentralnervensystem. Arch. Psychiat. Nervenkr. **182**, 478—535 (1949). [255]

TOWER, S. S.: Function and structure in the chronically isolated lumbo-sacral spinal cord of the dog. J. comp. Neurol. **67**, 109—131 (1937a). [242, 254]

— Trophic control of non-nervous tissues by the nervous system: A study of muscle and bone innervated from an isolated and quiescent region of spinal cord. J. comp. Neurol. **67**, 241—267 (1937b). [242, 245, 254]

References

Tower, S. S.: Persistence of fibrillation in denervated skeletal muscle and its non-occurrence in muscle after tenotomy. Arch. Neurol. Psychiat. (Chic.) **42**, 219—223 (1939). [242]

— H. Howe, and D. Bodian: Fibrillation in skeletal muscle in relation to denervation and to inactivation without denervation. J. Neurophysiol. **5**, 398—401 (1941). [242]

Trautwein, W., u. J. Dudel: Zum Mechanismus der Membranwirkung des Acetylcholin an der Herzmuskelfaser. Pflügers Arch. ges. Physiol. **266**, 324—334 (1958). [187]

— S. W. Kuffler and C. Edwards: Changes in membrane characteristics of heart muscle during inhibition. J. gen. Physiol. **40**, 135—145 (1956). [187]

Vastola, E. F.: After-positivity in the lateral geniculate body. J. Neurophysiol. **22**, 258—272 (1959). [214]

Volle, R. L.: The actions of several ganglion blocking agents on the postganglionic discharge induced by diisopropyl phosphorofluoridate (DFP) in sympathetic ganglia. J. Pharmacol. exp. Ther. **135**, 45—53 (1962a). [133, 134, 137]

— Enhancement of postganglionic responses to stimulating agents following repetitive preganglionic stimulation. J. Pharmacol. exp. Ther. **136**, 68—74 (1962b). [134, 135]

—, and G. B. Koelle: The physiological role of acetylcholinesterase (AChE) in sympathetic ganglia. J. Pharmacol. exp. Ther. **133**, 223—240 (1961). [57, 133, 135, 136, 137]

Vrbová, G.: The effect of tenotomy on the speed of contraction of fast and slow mammalian muscles. J. Physiol. (Lond.) **161**, 25P—26P (1962). [242]

Waldeyer, H. W. G.: Über einige neuere Forschungen im Gebiete der Anatomie des Zentralnervensystems. Dtsch. med. Wschr. **17**, 1213—1218 (1891). [1]

Wall, P. D.: Excitability changes in afferent fibre terminations and their relation to slow potentials. J. Physiol. (Lond.) **142**, 1—21 (1958). [225, 233]

— Repetitive discharge of neurons. J. Neurophysiol. **22**, 305—320 (1959). [46, 119, 120]

—, and A. R. Johnson,: Changes associated with post-tetanic potentiation of a monosynaptic reflex. J. Neurophysiol. **21**, 149—158 (1958). [99]

Waser, P. G.: The cholinergic receptor. J. Pharm. Pharmacol. **12**, 577—594 (1960). [66]

— Investigations of receptors in the endplate with curarizing drugs. In: Bioelectrogenesis, Ed. Carlos Chagas and Antonio Paes de Carvalho, pp. 353—361. Amsterdam: Elsevier (1961). [66]

Washizu, Y.: Single spinal motoneurons excitable from two different antidromic pathways. Jap. J. Physiol. **10**, 121—131 (1960). [144, 145]

Watanabe, A.: The interaction of electrical activity among neurons of lobster cardiac ganglion. Jap. J. Physiol. **8**, 305—318 (1958). [142]

—, and T. H. Bullock: Modulation of activity of one neuron by subthreshold slow potentials in another in lobster cardiac ganglion. J. gen. Physiol. **43**, 1031—1045 (1960). [142, 143]

—, and H. Grundfest: Impulse propagation at the septal and commisural junctions of crayfish lateral giant axons. J. gen. Physiol. **45**, 267—308 (1961). [139, 140, 141]

Watanabe, Y.: Transmission of impulses through abdominal ganglia in the crayfish, *Cambarus clarkii*. J. Fac. Sci., Hokkaido Univ. **14**, 17—29 (1958). [119]

Weiss, P.: Selectivity controlling the central-peripheral relations in the nervous system. Biol. Rev. **11**, 494—531 (1936). [250]

— The problem of specificity in growth and development. Yale J. Biol. Med. **19**, 235—278 (1947). [250, 252]

— An introduction to genetic neurology. In: Genetic neurology, Ed. P. Weiss. Chicago: Chicago University Press 1950a. [250]

— The deplantation of fragments of nervous system in amphibians. I. Central reorganization and the formation of nerves. J. exp. Zool. **113**, 397—461 (1950b). [250]

— Central versus peripheral factors in the development of co-ordination. Res. Publ. Ass. nerv. ment. Dis. **30**, 3—23 (1952). [250]

WEISS, P.: The concept of perpetual neuronal growth and proximo-distal substance convection. From: Fourth Inter. Neurochem. Symp., pp. 220—242. Oxford: Pergamon Press 1960. [254]

— M. V. EDDS, and M. CAVANAUGH: The effect of terminal connections on the caliber of nerve fibers. Anat. Rec. **92**, 215—233 (1945). [254]

—, and H. B. HISCOE: Experiments on the mechanism of nerve growth. J. exp. Zool. **107**, 315—396 (1948). [246]

—, and A. HOAG: Competitive reinnervation of rat muscles by their own and foreign nerves. J. Neurophysiol. **9**, 413—418 (1946). [246]

WELSH, H. J., and M. MOORHEAD: The quantitative distribution of 5-hydroxy-tryptamine in the invertebrates especially in their nervous system. J. Neurochem. **6**, 146—169 (1960). [74]

—, and R. TAUB: The action of choline and related compounds on the heart of *Venus mercenaria*. Biol. Bull. **95**, 346—353 (1948). [200]

WERMAN, R.: Electrical inexcitability of the synaptic membrane in the frog skeletal muscle fibre. Nature (Lond.) **188**, 149—150 (1960). [108]

— Electrical inexcitability of the frog neuro-muscular synapse. J. gen. Physiol. **46**, 517—531 (1963). [108]

WERNER, G.: Generation of antidromic activity in motor nerves. J. Neurophysiol. **23**, 453—461 (1960a). [129]

— Neuromuscular facilitation and antidromic discharges in motor nerves: their relation to activity in motor nerve terminals. J. Neurophysiol. **23**, 171—187 (1960b). [128, 129]

— Antidromic activity in motor nerves and its relation to a generator event in nerve terminals. J. Neurophysiol. **24**, 401—413 (1961). [128, 129]

WHITTAKER, V. P.: The isolation and characterization of acetylcholine containing particles from brain. Biochem. J. **72**, 694—706 (1959). [70]

—, and E. G. GRAY: The synapse: Biology and morphology. Brit. med. Bull. **18**, 223—228 (1962). [15, 16, 17, 19, 26, 70]

WIERSMA, C. A. G.: Giant nerve fibre system of the crayfish. A contribution to comparative physiology of synapse. J. Neurophysiol. **10**, 23—38 (1947). [147]

—, and A. C. BOBBERT: Membrane potential changes on activation in crustacean muscle fibers. Acta physiol. pharmacol. neerl. **10**, 51—72 (1961). [90]

—, and A. VAN HARREVELD: On the nerve-muscle system of the hermit crab *(Eupagurus bernhardus)*. III. The action currents of the muscles of the claw in contraction and inhibition. Arch. néerl. Physiol. **20**, 89—102 (1935). [201]

WIESEL' T. N.: Intracellular recordings from retinal ganglion cells. In XXI. Inter. Congr. Physiol. Sci. Abstr. Comm. p. 296, 1959. [118]

WILSON, D. M.: The connections between the lateral giant fibers of earthworms. Comp. Biochem. Physiol. **3**, 274—284 (1961). [141]

WILSON, V. J.: Recurrent facilitation of spinal reflexes. J. gen. Physiol. **42**, 703—713 (1959). [209]

—, and P. R. BURGESS: Disinhibition in the cat spinal cord. J. Neurophysiol. **25**, 392—404 (1962a). [209]

— — Effects of antidromic conditioning on some motoneurons and interneurons. J. Neurophysiol. **25**, 636—650 (1962b). [209]

— F. P. J. DIECKE and W. H. TALBOT: Action of tetanus toxin on conditioning of spinal motoneurons. J. Neurophysiol. **23**, 659—666 (1960). [191, 209]

WINDLE, W. F., and S. L. CLARK: Observations on the histology of the synapse. J. comp. Neurol. **46**, 153—171 (1928). [2]

WOLFF, M.: Zur Kenntnis der Heldschen Nervenendfüße. J. Psychol. Neurol. (Lpz.) **4**, 144—157 (1905). [2]

WOODBURY, J. W., and H. D. PATTON: Electrical activity of single spinal cord elements. Cold Spr. Harb. Symp. quant. Biol. **17**, 185—188 (1952). [37]

References

WOOLSEY, C. N., and M. G. LARRABEE: Potential changes and prolonged reflex facilitation following stimulation of dorsal spinal roots. Amer. J. Physiol. **129**, P 501—P 502 (1940). [230]

WYCKOFF, R. W. G., and J. Z. YOUNG: The motoneuron surface. Proc. roy. Soc. B **144**, 440—450 (1956). [3, 15, 109, 111]

YAMAMOTO, T.: Electron microscopic investigation on the relationship between the smooth muscle cell of the proc. vermiformis and the autonomic peripheral nerves. Acta neuroveg. (Wien) **21**, 406—425 (1960). [61]

YOUNG, J. Z.: In: Evolution, pp. 179—204, Ed. G. R. DE BEER. Oxford 1938. [255]

— Essays on growth and form, pp. 41—94, Ed. W. E. LE GROS CLARK and P. B. MEDAWAR. Oxford: Clarendon Press 1945. [246]

— Effects of use and disuse on nerve and muscle. Lancet **2**, 109—113 (1946). [246]

— Growth and plasticity in the nervous system. Proc. roy. Soc. B **139**, 18—37 (1951). [255, 259]

ZAIMIS, E. J.: Motor end-plate differences as a determining factor in the mode of action of neuro-muscular blocking substances. J. Physiol. (Lond.) **122**, 238—251 (1953). [65]

ŽÁK, R.: Proteins in the denervated muscle, changes in their quantity, properties and metabolism. In: The denervated muscle. chapt. IX, pp. 273—340, Ed. E. GUTMANN. Prague: Czechoslovak Academy of Sciences 1962. [242]

ZELENÁ, J.: The morphogenetic influence of innervation on the ontogenetic development of muscles spindles. J. Embryol. exp. Morph. **5**, 283—292 (1957). [240]

— Effect of innervation on the development of skeletal muscle [in Czech with English and Russian summary]. (Babákova sbírka 12.) Praha: Státní zdravotnické nakladatelství 1959. [239, 240]

— The effect of denervation on muscle development. In: The denervated muscle, chapt. III, pp. 103—126, Ed. E. GUTMANN. Prague: Czechoslovak Academy of Sciences 1962. [239, 240, 241]

—, and P. HNÍK: Absence of spindles in muscles of rats reinnervated during development. Physiol. bohemoslov. **9**, 373—381 (1960). [240]

—, and L. LUBÍNSKA: Early changes of acetylcholinesterase activity near the lesion in crushed nerves. Physiol. bohemoslov. **11**, 261—268 (1962). [240, 254]

—, and J. SZENTÁGOTHAI: Verlagerung der Lokalisation spezifischer Cholinesterase während der Entwicklung der Muskelinnervation. Acta histochem. (Jena) **3**, 284—296 (1957). [240]

ŽUPANČIČ, A. O.: The mode of action of acetylcholine. Acta physiol. scand. **29**, 63—71 (1952). [65]

SUBJECT INDEX

Crustacean giant fibres:
   commissural bridge transmission, 142–
   145
   electrical transmission to motor fibres,
   147–150
   IPSPs of, 163–164, 196
   septal transmission 138–141
Crustacea — stretch receptor cells:
   initiation of impulse by, 106, 111
   IPSPs of, 162–167, 183–185, 195
Cuneate neurones:
   EPSPs, 46
   IPSPs, 161
   presynaptic inhibition of, 229, 233
Cutaneous impulses, 160, 229, 233
Cysteic acid, 71

Dale's principle, 199, 209
Decamethonium, 65–66
Dendrites:
   cortical pyramidal cells, 17, 109–112
   electrotonic linkage, 144–145
   fusion surface membranes, 144
   hippocampal pyramidal cells, 17, 112
   impulse initiation in, 109–112
   impulse propagation, 109–110
   motoneuronal, 44–45, 109
   spines of, 17
Depolarization
      (see endplate potentials; excitatory
      postsynaptic potentials; impulse ini-
      tiation)
Desmosomes, 16
Detonator action, 6
Development:
   neuromuscular synapses, 239–241
Dibenamine, 61, 132
Dibenyline, 61
Dihydro-β-erythroidine, 68, 131
Diisopropyl phosphofluoridate, 133, 135,
   137
Dimethyldiethanolammonium, 52
Disinhibition, 209
D-tubocurarine (dTC), 48, 60, 64, 68, 127,
   129, 131, 198–199
Dorsal root potential (DRP), 220, 226, 230,
   232:
   antidromically evoked, 68
   post-tetanic increase, 230

Edrophonium:
   applied electrophoretically, 65, 68
Electric coupling, 27–29, 263
      (see excitatory synapses, electrically
      transmitting)

Electric organs
      (see Electroplaques):
   Astroscopus, 108
   Narcine, 108
   Raia, 108
   synapses on, 25, 29, 50
   Torpedo, 108
Electric time constant membrane, 41, 44,
   47, 113, 153
Electrical inhibitory action, 216–219:
   anelectrotonus axon hillock, 218–219
   external hyperpolarizing potential
      (EHP), 216–218
   latent period of, 218
   mechanism of, 218–219
Electrical transmitting synapses
      (see Excitatory synapses, electrical
      transmitting)
Electrically inexcitable membranes, 29,
   107–113, 126, 147, 264
Electrochemical gradients, 50–53, 152, 155,
   173
Electrophoretic action on synaptic trans-
   mitters, 73–74, 230–231
Electrophoretic injection
      (see Ionic injection)
Electrophorus electricus, 66
Electroplaques:
   EPSPs of, 50
   synapses on, 25, 29
Electrotonic transmission:
   dorsal root potential, 220, 226, 230, 232
   electrical coupling, 27–29, 263
   electrical uncoupling, 28, 39, 263
   electrotonic decrement, 111
   EPSPs to ventral root, 37, 157–158
   IPSPs to ventral root, 157–158
Electrotonic transmission, intercellular,
   138–145, 157:
   Aplysia ganglion cells, 145
   dendrites, 144–145
   electromotor neurones, Mormyrid, 144
   lateral giant fibres annelids, 140
   lateral giant fibres crayfish, 138–140
   neurones, 142–147, 151
   septate axons, 138–140
   supramedullary neurones of Puffer fish,
      144
Endplate current (EPC), 47, 50:
   equilibrium potential of, 50–52
   ionic mechanism of, 49, 51–53
Endplate potential (EPP), 33–34, 37, 77,
   106:
   time course of, 39, 47
Ephaptic transmission, IV, 9

DATE DUE